Technology and the Worker

**Chandler Publications in
Anthropology and Sociology**
Leonard Broom, *General Editor*

Sociology
Charles M. Bonjean, *Editor*

TECHNOLOGY AND THE WORKER

Technical Demands and Social Processes in Industry

Martin Meissner

University of British Columbia

CHANDLER PUBLISHING COMPANY

124 Spear Street, San Francisco, California 94105

Science Research Associates, Inc., 259 East Erie Street, Chicago, Illinois 60611
A Subsidiary of IBM   Distributors

CONTENTS

TABLES

FIGURES

Preface

This piece of work pays attention to what production workers actually do, and to the machinery and technical processes that form the most obvious and often most demanding condition of eight hours of their working day. The stern demands of industrial technology were central to the analyses of the social organization of production in Europe by Karl Marx, Alain Touraine, and Heinrich Popitz, and I have learned much from their work. In close descriptions of work performance in steel production, Popitz particularly reminds one of the fact that factories exist in order to get work done. He did not want anything to do with the interest of American "plant sociology" in what workers do together at work—when they are not working, making the plant more livable in the process.

This book attempts to combine these two orientations, and it relies on the research evidence and analytical concerns of both. In the use of these sources, I was interested in two particular methodological questions: (1) What is the relationship between observations and the general statements that can be made from them? The result in this case has been a number of connected empirical generalizations. (2) What are the uses of available case studies for systematic analysis? I have tried here to demonstrate some possibilities in the secondary analysis of unquantified data.

I have spent much time working and observing in places where people work for a living. The experience gave substantive direction to this undertaking. It was also quite necessary in interpreting the data I have used.

To the men with whom I shared life at work, I owe a big part of my education. There is no return for the charm and generosity with which Robert Dubin has given me encouragement. For a time, Kaspar Naegele was an interested listener and commentator. My loving family has made things too easy for me, by enduring the hazards of a piece of work that would not end. Catherine Harrison did most of the actual work, typing down from the first giant-size draft. I have been aided substantially, with money, facilities, and willingness-to-wait, by the Institute of Industrial Relations of the University of British Columbia, and its director, Taite Montague. A special place is to be reserved in honor of the authors of case studies for supplying me unwittingly with data.

Part One

PROBLEMS AND CATEGORIES

Chapter I

PROBLEMS FOR ANALYSIS

This study is concerned with what industrial workers do when they are at work—how their behavior is socially organized and how the social order of their behavior is influenced by the technical conditions of production. One of the most comprehensive analyses of industrial organization has been provided by Karl Marx, in a curiously neglected section of *Das Kapital*. This analysis was preceded, however, by an expression of a fond, youthful dream of a "nonsociety" free of the debilitating constraints of the division of labor. In this vision,

> it is possible for me to do this today and that tomorrow, to hunt in the morning, to fish in the afternoon, to raise cattle in the evening, and also to criticize the dinner, just as the fancy strikes me, without ever becoming a hunter, a fisherman, or a shepherd or critic.[1]

From a romantic dream and the call for a final solution (following two years later in the *Manifesto*), Marx turned to a hard-nosed assessment of the conditions of work, not of shepherds or critics, but of boring-mill operators, bottle makers, and loom feeders. In the now irrelevant context of describing the production of surplus value, Marx demonstrated that certain forms of cooperation are dependent on the development of distinct combinations of technical innovations.[2]

1. The Technical Means of Production

Forms of cooperation and production techniques affect the makeup of a man's job and make demands on his performance. At the craft stage of production organization, a man made the complete product and chose from the full range of his tools; there was "simple cooperation," as between the craftsman and his few helpers. In manufacture the components of the craftsman's job were divided, and each man performed a small part over

---

[1] Karl Marx, "Die deutsche Ideologie (1845–46)," in *Die Frühschriften* (Stuttgart: Kröner, 1953), p. 361.
[2] Karl Marx, *Das Kapital* (1867) (Berlin: Dietz, 1947), Vol. I, Chapters 12 and 13, pp. 352–532.

and over again with a few specialized tools. He was tied to the process by the requirements of close attention to a repetitive job, immediate dependence on the work of others, temporal coordination, and spatial confinement. Jobs became invidiously ranked according to fine distinctions of skill. At the large-industry stage, machinery took over in a production process now independent from limitations of the human organism. Workers became machine feeders, skill distinctions were leveled, and cooperation became the technical coordination of machines and machine systems, dependent on the integrated availability of the double-acting steam engine, the fly wheel, transmission systems, and the slide rest.

The composition of work roles, the forms of cooperation, and the demands on working performance were central concerns in Marx's analysis, together with the influence of industrial technology. These interests reappear separately in two more recent investigations. From observations in automobile production, Touraine described the effects of three major stages of technical development on the distribution of work components in industrial jobs.[3] For the production of steel, Popitz analyzed the nature of cooperation and performance demands for different technical arrangements.[4]

2. Human Relations in Industry

About a half-century on the way from Marx to Touraine and Popitz, an entirely different development began in the sociology of industrial work, with the well-known Hawthorne studies. In the report of observations in the bank-wiring room, a distinction was made between the formal and informal organization of positions and behavior in industry.[5] Concessions were made to the formal organization grudgingly, perhaps in reaction to the extreme technical rationalism of the scientific-management movement whose representatives were very much alive at the time the Hawthorne experiments were conducted. Concessions made, the formal organization of production was virtually ignored. The researchers paid close attention to the unofficial conduct of workers. Their aim was to interpret the system of evaluations through which workers assessed each other's positions in the work group and to describe how these evaluations became expressed in their day-to-day relations. To be sure, they demonstrated that the processes of evaluation and interaction were tied to the particular tasks of these men. Yet, the technical nature of the work at hand was treated as an incidental referent for rules of conduct emerging from within the group. These rules were also fed by characteristics and expectations carried to work from the

---

[3] A. Touraine, *L'Évolution du travail ouvrier aux Usines Renault* (Paris: Centre National de la Recherche Scientifique, 1955).

[4] H. Popitz *et al.*, *Technik und Industriearbeit* (Tübingen: Mohr, 1957).

[5] F. J. Roethlisberger and W. J. Dickson, *Management and the Worker* (Cambridge: Harvard University Press, 1939), pp. 377–548.

surrounding community. Focusing, as they did, on a single case, these investigators could perhaps not recognize that the technical organization of production might constitute a systemic constraint on the possibilities for development of an elaborate internal group life.

The view of the nature of work organization that grew out of this study and many others of its orientation had the following major elements. Once men are together at work for whatever reasons, they will develop patterns of interaction much in excess of the requirements of the job imposed on them by management. Certain commonly important social characteristics, such as ethnic background, age, and personal style of behavior, together with selected features of their job—how dirty it is or how intricate, and how much skill it requires—become resources for evaluation. The system of relations that develops from interaction and evaluation is seen as bounded by authority, that is, by the demands transmitted through foremen and inspectors for getting work done efficiently. The internal system contains mutual obligations for recognition, help, and sociability, and these are to some extent incompatible with the demands of the external system. Thus develops an elaboration of behavior and evaluations which protects the boundaries. Sanctions are exercised which support the independent social life of the group and, at the same time, prevent excesses of sociability that would produce interference from the boss.

3. Two Approaches to Research

I have sketched the outlines of two approaches to social research in industry: one beginning with Marx; and the other with Mayo and the Hawthorne studies. What are the implications of these two approaches? What dimensions do they emphasize? What views do they imply of the social organization of production? The answers might begin with some rhetorical questions: Would the human-relations doctrine have got off the ground as it did if Mayo had first gone into a steel mill or an auto-assembly plant? And would researchers influenced by Marx have confined their interests to the harsh demands of technology and the formal properties of job composition and cooperative structure, if they had attended to production settings where workers had more opportunity to needle each other about their sexual prowess, to exchange jobs, to play games, or to heat a can of soup on the job?

The difference might best be demonstrated if we let a proponent of each of these approaches speak for himself. In his analysis of observations made in the Hawthorne studies, Homans argues:

The various attempts to show that [the group] is the mere creature of its surroundings have never been clinching, though they have helped social scientists to be tough-minded. The demands of the environment cannot be disregarded but they by no means wholly determine the constitution of the group. In fact, in the favorable instance, the group spontaneously evolves the behavior necessary to improve its standard of living in the environment.[6]

In the context of reviewing the arguments on technical determination and the workers' freedom, Popitz justifies his selection of research dimensions:

> The inclusion of informal association may be necessary for the whole of industrial sociology, but its importance must not be overestimated. I would even say that the import of formal contacts which derive necessarily from the production process have been largely overlooked as a result of the search for "informal groups." Although the mill provides wide latitude for informal association of all kinds, one must not forget that it is first of all a work place.[7]

In what kinds of industrial settings did research take place that followed these two orientations? The human-relations researchers went to places in which work was done on comparatively small work pieces, easily carried to a workbench by hand. The work consisted of either the assembly of small pieces or machining operations, both carried out independently on separate work stations. These assembly and machine shops were comparatively quiet, and workers could, at least to some extent, walk around from time to time. In short, human-relations men in search of Homans' "favorable instance" found what they were looking for. And so did the researchers intent on describing the formal technical demands of work and its consequences: They went to steel mills and automobile plants, where the massive array of integrated machinery is the most obvious and overwhelming fact of industrial life.

Common to both research interests were the observation and description of workers' behavior and of the elements of the situation in which that behavior took place. This fact offers the opportunity of looking afresh at studies of industrial work—to consider both technical conditions and behavior, formal and informal, for a greater range of possibilities than previous preoccupations have permitted.

4. Some Illustrative Cases

Let us look at a few widely different cases, leaving the analysis of all the available cases for later.[8]

---

[6] G. C. Homans, *The Human Group* (New York: Harcourt, Brace, 1950), pp. 87–88.
[7] Popitz *et al.*, *Technik und Industriearbeit*, p. 42.
[8] The following five sketches rely on reports to be used in the subsequent discussion, together with a larger number of others. In order, the references for these cases are C. R. Walker, *Steel* (Boston: Atlantic Monthly Press, 1922); A Zaleznik, *Worker Satisfaction and Development* (Boston: Harvard University Press, 1956); C. R. Walker and R. H. Guest, *The Man on the Assembly Line* (Cambridge: Harvard University Press, 1952); Popitz, *Technik und Industriearbeit*; W. F. Whyte, "Engineers and Workers," *Human Organization*, 14, No. 4 (Winter 1956), 3–12.

1. As part of the job of a maintenance gang in a steel plant, a number of men replace a defective cooler on a going blast furnace. One man takes off a nut with a wrench. Two men hold a curved bar, and a third knocks out some keys with a sledgehammer. A blowpipe, through which hot air is blown into the furnace, drops on the bar and is taken off quickly, as flames shoot from the hole left by the pipe. A hook at the end of a bar is set against the cooler—a cone-shaped water chamber around the blast pipe. Ropes are attached to a weight at the other end of the bar, and all the men available pull on the ropes in order to loosen the cooler. A new cooler is set into place, and four or five men bang a kind of ramrod with a square hammer end against the edge of the cooler. Once the cooler is seated, a man holds a shovel in front of the hole in order to protect another who is connecting the water pipes. On other parts of their job, these men go—two or three at a time—inside a still-hot firebox and loosen the glowing cinder with steel bars. The others pull the cinder out with a hoe, shovel it into a wheelbarrow, and then dump it over the edge of the platform. One or two at a time, they also clean out the inside of a stove with pick, shovel, bar, and sledgehammer, the tools being handed in through a small opening by the others. On many of their tasks, some of these men take time off to rest, chew tobacco, smoke, and talk, and then in turn take over from an exhausted man. While they work, they shout jokes and orders to each other, and in-between offer advice about the hazards of a certain task, tell stories, and grumble about the job. They stay together as they walk from job to job, carrying some of their tools with them.

2. There are fourteen men in the machine shop of a small-instrument manufacturer. Some of them are operators, wearing aprons; and some machinists, with long coats and toolboxes of their own. Each of the men has his work assigned to him by the foreman in small batches, and when he is done, he turns it in and starts the next job. Their work requires going to the tool crib and moving from machine to machine. Jobs include work on lathes, drill presses, milling machines, and soldering, honing, testing for water tightness, and grinding. Work pieces are comparatively small, although occasionally a man requires help in lifting a piece into a machine. In this job-shop machine shop, workers produce parts for instruments according to blueprints, and the parts are assembled elsewhere in the plant. The work done by each worker is independent of the work of the others, and there is no requirement built into the production process by which workers would have to work together and talk to one another. Yet they move around the shop a great deal and, in the course of their work, many opportunities arise for social interaction. They talk to each other, asking for advice on the interpretation of a blueprint or for help with setting up a difficult job or lifting a heavy work piece. There are conversations and kidding, and these do not interfere with the work.

3. Of the hundreds of men working on the main assembly line and the feeder operations of an automobile plant, a little less than half perform

only one or two operations. At any one time the line speed is fixed, and a man's job on one car takes somewhat less than 2 minutes. For most workers the assembly moves steadily on the line and they move with it for, say, 30 feet, either walking alongside, or crouching inside or riding on the conveyor with it. They work with files, hammers, welding guns and jigs, paint sprayers, hand polishers, clip guns, air-driven wrenches, drills, or screwdrivers. These are all hand tools, many of them connected to a suspended supply line, for electricity, air, paint, or water, and thus restricting movement by the reach of the line. The operations performed by a man vary from model to model. A man may put in the toe plates under the brake and clutch pedals on one model, and the shift lever on another. Except when working in pairs on larger pieces, as in the placing of a front seat, a man works independently of other men within a section. He might drill the holes for a molding which is actually installed only a half-mile farther down the line. Where the noise is not too great, a worker can have a short, half-shouting conversation with one of the few men in nearby positions. But having to look closely at the job under his hands, he might not notice that, in midsentence, the other man has moved on to the next assembly. In the clipped pace, with men sometimes trying to speed up a bit for a quick breathing spell between jobs, there is not much chance for giving a helping hand or telling a joke that takes more than a minute or two.

4. Three men convert ingots into blooms on the rolling mill of a large and integrated steel plant. Ingots are very large blocks of steel stripped of their molds after casting, and reheated in the soaking pit. From the soaking pit, they are delivered white-hot and in rapid succession to the mill. Blooms, still very hot, shoot down the roller conveyor away from the mill —rectangular in cross section, thinner, and much longer than the ingot, ready for further rolling into other shapes. The ingot is taken over by the rolling crew, at the point where it is set down on the intake conveyor by a fast overhead crane. The rolling mill consists of a large two-high reversible roll stand, powered roller conveyors in front and in back, and a canting machine over the front-end conveyor. The roll stand has six calibers, that is, six different widths between rolls for successive passes of the steel block from the widest to the narrowest, and is driven by steam. The canting device is used to shift the block sideways by remote control and to cant it, that is, to tip it around its longitudinal axis by ninety degrees after a back-and-forth pass through one caliber. The steering operator and the canter operator are positioned side by side on a glassed-in platform above the front-end conveyor. The position of the roll-stand operator is on one side of the roll stand. The steering operator regulates the speed and direction of the front-end conveyor and the distance between the two rolls of the roll stand. The canter operator controls the conveyor behind the roll stand and the canting machine. The roll-stand operator determines the

supply of steam to the rolls, and thus the direction and speed of rotation. In about 2 minutes the block might be reduced, for instance, from 23 inches square to 6 inches, in seventeen passes. While the steel block is being worked in the mill, each of the operators regulates part of its movement by several control levers. Each makes many instant, small, but crucial decisions adjusting the parts of the process under his control to the observed movements of work piece and equipment as affected by the other two men. The result is an intense flow of integrated movements, demanding close and nearly constant attention. Unless there is a break in the supply of ingots, there is little chance for conversation or banter. Even when there is a break, the two men on the platform could not talk directly with the third operator. Yet they are closely connected by dependence and cooperation in their every move. While they work, they communicate by observing the work piece they share and by feeling the movement of equipment in the vibrations transmitted to their control levers.

5. Three men work in the control room of a refinery producing aviation gasoline. The poly operator is responsible for the three operating units, especially for the coordination of the work of the hydro-stillman and the fractionator operator, both of whom share the control room with him. The engine room is connected with the control room by the technical process and a phone, and is manned by one lonely operator who comes into the control room for lunch. One wall of the control room is covered with charts and other automatic indicators of events in the remote and invisible production process. During routine operations the control-room operators are required to draw product samples every hour from various locations for testing, to make equipment checks, and to watch the charts. Constant adjustments on the controls are necessary when the process runs irregularly. Changes made by the hydro-stillman affect the process controlled by the fractionator operator. When an engine breaks down, the load on the other engines must be reduced quickly in order to avoid a larger and very costly breakdown. When everything goes well, the operators may sit in the control room and talk—with an eye on the charts—and have a bite to eat when they feel like it. Whenever something irregular appears on the indicators, they move into action. They are connected, not only by being near each other and being able to tell each other what is going on, but also by a large and integrated process. For appropriate action in unpredictable emergencies, they must comprehend the complexities of a process which ordinarily can take care of itself through monitoring control devices. Their relation to the engine-room operator is more indirect. They can see on their indicators what is going on with his engines, and they can talk to him on the phone when necessary.

These five cases implicitly convey the dimensions of a wide range of technical conditions and social behavior in industrial production organizations. They vary by the extent to which work components are performed by men or machines and by the demands made on workers by the production process. They also suggest large differences in the opportunities workers have to participate in a network of relationships of their own making. The steel-plant maintenance men supply the muscle, work with hand tools, and control among themselves all of the work process. On routine operations in the refinery, nearly all the work components are built into the process, from the power of the engines and the integrated design to the monitoring and feedback controls. In the machine shop and on the assembly line, major parts of the work are done by both machines and men. On the assembly line, the work piece is moved automatically and the work is done by hand and hand-controlled tools. In the machine shop, work pieces are moved by hand, but much of the conversion of materials takes place in the machines. The job of the blooming-mill operators is control and coordination; the massive machinery takes care of the movement and conversion of the work piece. These operators are confined to one position, with their hands on the controls. They communicate almost entirely through material objects, and cooperation is an unyielding technical demand. The auto assemblers move only with a short stretch of the line. Their possibilities for talking are quite limited. In the machine shop there is no technical necessity for cooperation, but plenty of occasion for the exchange of help and advice; on the assembly line there is neither. For the steel-plant maintenance gang and the refinery operators in the control room, technical necessity and voluntary cooperation appear merged. The maintenance men work together as a team. They communicate and coordinate their work directly. The refinery operators can talk to one another, but they are also linked and mutually influenced by the production process represented in the indicators on the wall. They have to keep an eye on the charts. Workers in the machine shop are technically independent. Their attention to the work is intermittent, but must be close. On the blooming mill, interdependence is high, and concentrated attention continuous. The work of an auto assembler is commonly independent of that of the next man, but they are both tied to the work flow on the line. The attention they must pay to the work is close but limited to the few repetitive bits of work assigned to them.

I have suggested before that the past literature has focused differentially either on production technology and its demands or on the social organization of workers and its emergent rules of conduct. The foregoing examples would suggest the importance of attempting to combine the two directions of inquiry. At the same time, it will be necessary to restrict its scope. For an extensive range of technical and social characteristics, data are not available for determining the properties of workers' positions, formal and informal, in the structure of the production organization.

Information is also too incomplete for outlining association patterns at the work place during nonwork time.

5. The Problem of This Study

The question to be answered in this book is twofold:

1. What is the nature of industrial technology and the demands it makes on the performance of its immediate users? More specifically: (a) Can the design of production operations be ordered analytically to distinguish stages of technical development in which components of work at one point performed by men are successively built into machines? (b) What do production workers have to do in order to make technical designs work?

2. Where does the social behavior of workers adapt to the constraints of technology and its demands? In particular, what analytically distinct differences can be observed under varying technical conditions in the characteristics of cooperation, influence, and communication among factory workers?

The problem is the formulation of empirical generalizations by inference from the data of published reports. These data will be analyzed independently of the expectations and conclusions of the reporting authors. The reports used contain all the accessible published data relevant to the problem and have not been selected for the purpose of illustration. They probably constitute most of the material for which published reports exist. The expected output of this study is descriptive categories of the technical culture and adaptive behavior found in industrial organizations, and of statements of relations among the dimensions described by these categories.

Only a few of the reports to be used have the focus of this study. They may consider problematic what will here be taken as given, and may take for granted what is to be considered problematic for the present purpose. In addition, the range of data made available in these reports, the methods used for collecting them, and the quality of observation and reporting vary greatly from report to report. Almost all of these reports are case studies. They were conducted in a variety of industries and countries and at different times during the past fifty years. In view of this diversity, the demand for rigor in classifying data will have to be modified. In the process of analysis, categories had to be changed and recombined in order to match the characteristics of the data. At the same time, occasional and more or less informed guesses were necessary in order to classify observations.

This would be an inappropriate procedure if we were to test already well-stated propositions. However, this study aims to contribute to the formulation of these propositions themselves. As long as the statements generated are understood to be meant for subsequent test and reformulation, there is less danger in this matching process. But the test itself is beyond the scope of this undertaking.

In the following chapter, schemes of descriptive categories will be set up for the ordering of data from case studies. That chapter forms the analytical base for the remainder of the book. In order to be viable in the application to a medley of data sources, Chapter II must necessarily be abstract, although some illustrations are used to clarify the characteristics of certain dimensions. A reader who prefers to begin closer to the ground, with empirical descriptions, may wish to proceed directly to Chapter III and refer to Chapter II for occasional guidance.

In the chapters of Part Two observations reported in the case-study sources will be presented in detail insofar as they are required for the coding of cases by the characteristics of technology and the technical constraints which affect workers' activities. Greatest emphasis will be given to the details of case descriptions and their classification in these chapters (IV to IX) because it is this area which has received least attention in past research in industrial sociology. Chapter X contains a summary of the empirical regularities accumulated in Part Two. It shows the distribution of the constraints of space, function, time, and perception over the types of conversion and transfer technology.

In Part Three the reported social behaviors of workers will be ordered and then related to the differences in technical conditions distinguished in Part Two. The classes of behavior dealt with are cooperation and influence (in Chapter XI) and communication (in Chapter XII). Each of these classes will be differentiated as being either technically required or technically permitted (but not required). We thus return, with a closer focus, to the earlier distinction of formal and informal conduct, and specify the conditions for their incidence.

A summary of findings will be provided in the final chapter (XIII). The study will be put into context by comparing its results with those of the major reports in the research literature.

Chapter II

CATEGORIES OF ANALYSIS

The purpose of this chapter is to describe categories and relations between categories. Defined categories will be useful according to their capacity to differentiate observed phenomena with the degree of determinacy necessary for making sense of data from divergent sources.

To deal at this point with the relationships between categories means taking, in part, a step ahead of what is planned for later chapters. But the purpose of those chapters is to fill the categories here defined with observations collected from various research reports. Categorization is meaningful insofar as it takes its place in a scheme of descriptive dimensions. In this chapter the discussion of relations will be abstract and concerned with relations between categories. In later chapters, these categories will be given life, as it were, and become phenomena, and the relations between them operative: the abstract model is set in motion.

The expected output of this sequence of arguments is empirical generalizations induced from available data. That output seems possible, however, only when the data are ordered first; and for that initial order a tentative, interrelated system of categories seems indispensable. The tautological characteristic of this procedure is no defect as long as the end product is a set of statements (1) made meaningful through some interplay between abstractions and the empirical data to match them, and (2) set forth for the purpose of testing and in a manner which makes testing feasible.

1. Technology

We are concerned with variations in the technical conditions of work and with the differences in worker behavior associated with those variations. Let us call the technical conditions of work *technology* and say that the technology of a work place consists of its tools, machines, parts, and materials; the equipment used to move these parts and materials from place to place; and the buildings and parts of buildings which house all these things and the people working with them. But to go only this far in our definition would mean that we would only speak of the material characteristics of the work environment. We would say that the technology of a work place consists of pieces of steel, stone, and wood in certain shapes. But that is not what is meant. When we speak of technical conditions of work—of the technology of work places—we refer to the fact that these material things (their presence, shapes, and interconnections) are the product of designs, the manifestation of the ideas of those who planned a process and the means of facilitating it.[1] These ideas were guided by distinct objectives. Probably these objectives appear first; then the technical means of reaching them are planned and designed; and finally, the means are constructed and put into operation.

Ordinarily, when a man enters a processing or manufacturing plant, he finds all these steps completed. All he can perceive is the physical setup in operation. At least part of the material things he sees become meaningful as the movement of things in operation reveals the design and its objectives. Added to the meaning already obtained when he sees physical parts in motion is his perception of men working and the knowledge about technical designs and processes he brings with him. When our hypothetical man has been employed to perform a certain task in a particular work space and with the use of certain tools, machines, or controls, he will also learn about operating instructions, safety regulations, production schedules, and perhaps engineering drawings. All these add meaning to what he perceives. In many situations he will be trained for the job. The training requires and enables him to acquire knowledge and experience which make meaningful at least the part of the process directly related to his own task.

People who work with tools and on machines are not men from Mars. The technical meaning of work-place technologies is accessible to them, at least to the extent to which they can learn to play their part in a technical process. It can be described as follows: This tool, machine, plant, or process is so designed that, in order to attain the specific result a, certain events q, p, and o must first occur in sequence z. We might call this the teleology of production.

The question of whether a man, whose performance is fitted in with the technology of his work place, has an interest in the specific result—in the immediate end-in-view of the process—will not be considered problematic in this study. A man who begins to make pans in a place designed to make teakettles is not likely to continue making pans for very long. Being not likely even to have the means of making pans in the first place, he will either make teakettles or leave the work place. In this study we are

---

[1] ". . . nearly all engineers are vitally concerned with materials and processes as regards the opportunities they provide for, and the limitations they impose on, the translation of ideas into reality." E. P. Degarmo, *Materials and Processes in Manufacturing* (New York: Macmillan, 1957), p. vii.

concerned only with those who are in fact working at any given work place. The choices men make when taking a job, and the reasons for their coming to work, too, are not our problem. Our problem is the choices men have while at work and, particularly, the restraints or limitations which the technology of the work place imposes on these choices. With the technology of a work place, or the technical conditions of work, we mean the physical characteristics of the work environment so far as they are meaningful expressions of the designer's ideas and of the means to attain predetermined ends. We also mean the rules, whether implicit in the design or expressed in instruction, which make known the requirements for making the design work and for attaining planned ends.

The objection may be raised that the confinement to the focus just suggested implies uncritical acceptance of the goals and values of managers and engineers. It should be noted, however, that we are taking the *immediate* end for granted and that we remain entirely unconcerned with goals which are further removed, such goals as profit or the maintenance of managerial or professional prerogatives. We are also unconcerned with variation in the interests or more extended goals of workers.

The technical reasoning built into machines appears, in fact, to be comparatively independent of cultural differences. Independently of their beliefs and of the ritual requirements of their communities, the nonliterate Indian worker in a weaving mill in Ecuador,[2] the Catholic working at the Usines Renault,[3] and the Communist at his job in a piston plant in the Soviet Union[4] can learn to perform their machine-tending tasks. Regardless of their image of the good life, their preferences about the distribution of power in their social environment, their obligations to associates and kin, or their "joy in work," they are likely to understand, once they have come to work, that in order to make a roll of cloth, a connection between two automobile seat springs, or a hole into a piston rod, they must perform certain acts.

That does not mean that the acts required to change the shape or consistency of materials are entirely fixed. Variations are possible and can be observed, but certain minimal numbers and kinds of acts are necessary and must remain within certain limits of variation. Under certain conditions these minimal acts are not performed and technical limits to variation are exceeded. Nonconformance with the rules designed into a technol-

---

[2] B. R. Salz, "The Human Element in Industrialization: A Hypothetical Case Study of Ecuadorean Indians," *Economic Development and Cultural Change*, 4, No. 1, Part 2 (October 1955).

[3] A. Touraine, *L'Évolution du travail ouvrier aux Usines Renault* (Paris: Centre National de la Recherche Scientifique, 1955).

[4] A. Erivansky, *The Soviet Automatic Plant* (Moscow: Foreign Language Publishing House, 1955).

ogy becomes the object of industrial policing, of conflict, and of negotiation. By and large, however, work organizations turn out the products for which they were designed. The focus of this study is the behavior variation associated with technological differences, and not the difference between compliance and noncompliance with technical requirements of one, or any, technological setting.

The technology of a work place is characterized by the phrase "in order to," and its boundaries are specified by the description of the immediate end product, attainment of which follows that phrase. It consists of physical objects which constitute the stage on which workers play their parts and which set the boundaries for the range of their performances. It provides the very means of putting on the show without which the performance, as we see it, could not be staged.

Differences among work-place technologies will be measured by technical distinctions. The characteristics of parts of the means of producing a material product are specified in the following four categories:

1. The central part of producing material goods consists of changing the properties of materials—of *conversion* from one state to another. We shall call the tools, machines, and apparatus which change the properties of materials *conversion equipment*.

2. In order to change their properties, materials must be brought together with the conversion equipment. Materials or conversion equipment, or both, must be moved. The means of moving, or transportation, we shall call *transfer equipment*.

3. Most conversion takes place at several stages, and conversion stages are separated in space and time. The part of conversion which constitutes a stage takes place at a work *station*, and the part of the conversion which is performed at a station is a *conversion operation*.

4. The movements of materials or equipment, or both, between stations involves the use of transfer equipment which performs a *transfer operation*.

Conversion Operations

Our distinctions between different kinds of conversion equipment will follow a dual line. The history of technical development can be seen as a sequence of innovations, in which some new combination of techniques and designs has been added to those already in use. At the same time, each step in that sequence seems to have changed the relation between man and machine by progressively conferring more of man's qualities upon machines, by allocating to machines actions previously performed by men.

Nearly all the kinds of activities of men for which machine equivalents have been designed and put to use are still performed by men. It is therefore possible to view the sequence of historical events also as a set of contemporary differences between types of machines.[5] The criterion for distinguishing these differences is the number of work functions accumulated in machines. As kinds of work functions shift from activities of men to the movements of machines, the contact between the man and the converted product and the control of the man over operations become increasingly remote.

In order to distinguish between different types of conversion operations, a tentative listing of small work components was made, as well as a list of a number of case descriptions from the data sources. The two lists were then both ordered, in relation to each other, with the aim of producing a scale. It was possible to obtain a rough correspondence between the two lists by recognizing groupings of cases where the breaking point between the operation parts performed by men and those performed by machines was approximately the same. Proceeding in order from case to case, more work components performed by equipment were found *in addition* to those already performed by machines in the preceding cases. Similarly, in going from work component to work component in the ordered list, increasingly more cases were added where components are performed by machines instead of men.

We have taken these groupings of cases as the basis of our classification of conversion operations. The names finally given to these categories describe the kinds of equipment generally found in the corresponding cases. Two categories (3 and 6) are mixtures of equipment named in the two adjacent categories, where certain work components are performed by both men and machines, making for a qualitatively different technical situation. The result of this procedure is Table 1.

Transfer Operations

A similar procedure was followed for transfer operations. But in this case only three characteristics of transfer operations were used. The resulting classification (Table 2) consists of all possible cases, where "possible" means less than the full range of logical combinations. The aim is again to attain a scale. By reference to what one can think of as technically possible and existing, one pair of classes is allowed where a reversal in scale sequence occurs. The order of these two categories within the whole set can be suggested by reference to one of the dimensions, the "choice of routes," a dimension which separates all categories into two parts according to whether a fixed line of transfer is present or not.

---

[5] For evidence of the simultaneous presence of equipment from different stages of technical development, see Touraine, *L'Évolution du travail ouvrier aux Usines Renault;* H. Popitz *et al., Technik und Industriearbeit* (Tübingen: Mohr, 1957); and M. Hammer, *Vergleichende Morphologie der Arbeit in der europäischen Automobilindustrie* (Basel: Kyklos-Verlag; and Tübingen: Mohr, 1959).

TABLE 1. CATEGORIES OF CONVERSION OPERATIONS

Elements of Conversion Operations	Scale Points[a]						
	1	2	3	4	5	6	7
Energy supply (supply and transmit power)	---	O[b]	O-E[b]	E[b]	E	E	E
Tool and work-piece manipulation during operation (hold, move, and direct tool or work piece)	---	O	O-E	E	E	E	E
Feeding, loading, assembling (move tool to work piece, or work piece to tool, and bring work-piece parts together)	---	O	O	O	E	E	E
Control over cycles (stop and start, coordinate tool and work-piece movements, correct for speed variation)	---	O	O	O	O	O-E	E
Planning (know planned outcomes and steps to outcomes, translate plans into movements, compare outcomes with plans, feedback)	---	O	O	O	O	O-E	E?

[a]Scale:
1. No conversion.
2. Hand tools.
3. Hand and machine tools.
4. Machine tools.
5. Steered automatics.
6. Steered and self-regulating automatics.
7. Self-regulating automatics.

[b]O = Performed by operator.
E = Performed by equipment.
O-E = Performed by both operator and equipment.

TABLE 2. CATEGORIES OF TRANSFER OPERATIONS

Elements of Transfer Operations	Scale Points[a]				
	1	2	3	4	5
Energy supply	O[b]	E[b]	O	E	E
Choice of routes (equivalent to manipulation, feeding, and planning in conversion operations)	O	O	E	$\frac{E}{O-E}$[b]	E
Control over cycles	O	O	O	O	E

[a]Scale:
1. Hand transfer (hand, hand trucks).
2. Automotive transfer (motorized trucks).
3. Dead line (dead rolls, connecting benches, hand-pushed rail cars).
4. Steered line (locomotives, remote-controlled conveyors, cranes).
5. Live line (overhead conveyors, belts, chains, transfer machines; with continuous movement).

[b]O = Performed by operator.
E = Performed by equipment.
O-E = Performed by both operator and equipment.

By putting the scales of categories for conversion and transfer operations together, we obtain a matrix of types of technical conditions, with thirty-five possible combinations (Table 3). It appears, however, that a number of types are unlikely to occur. This typology constitutes our first order of distinctions, and we can attempt to place all cases from our reservoir of reports into this first framework.

There are two limitations to the generalizing use of this scheme. In some of the reported cases, information is insufficient for accurate distinction. But inferences can be made from available information by supplementing it with other sources of knowledge about the technical design of particular processes and from the probability that the technology of the reported work situation has certain characteristics. The second limitation lies in the fact that a sufficient number of case studies is not available to fill all the categories of our scheme. This restriction cannot be made good in this study, and our generalizations will be confined to those types of technical conditions about which research has been reported. In Part Two the manner of locating cases in the matrix will be demonstrated in detail.

TABLE 3. TYPES OF WORK-PLACE TECHNOLOGY

	Transfer				
Conversion	C1 Hand Transfer	C2 Auto Transfer	C3 Dead Line	C4 Steered Line	C5 Live Line
R1 No conversion	R1-C1	R1-C2	R1-C3	R1-C4	R1-C5
R2 Hand tools	R2-C1	R2-C2	R2-C3	R2-C4	R2-C5
R3 Hand and machine tools	R3-C1	R3-C2	R3-C3	R3-C4	R3-C5
R4 Machine tools	R4-C1	R4-C2	R4-C3	R4-C4	R4-C5
R5 Steered automatics	R5-C1	R5-C2	R5-C3	R5-C4	R5-C5
R6 Steered and self-regulating automatics	R6-C1	R6-C2	R6-C3	R6-C4	R6-C5
R7 Self-regulating automatics	R7-C1	R7-C2	R7-C3	R7-C4	R7-C5

2. Technical Constraints

Our distinctions among types of technology implied an historical process of technical development in which work components are "taken away" from men and "given to" machines. At each stage a reduced number of work components is left in the hands of men, and a greater number is built into machines. What is left in the hands of men is not built into machines. Both parts must be performed, however, for the accomplishment of technical ends, and thus the part left in the hands of men is left out of machine design: it is "spared out." What is spared out must have a distinct relation to what is built into machines in order to attain designed-for outcomes. The spared-out components must be matched with built-in components: human performance must be "fitted in" with equipment performance.

We will subsequently attempt to classify the social behavior of workers which is a part of the fitted-in performance, together with social behavior which occurs in addition to the requirements of fitting in. In order to link social behavior and types of technology, we will attempt to describe how behavior is matched with technology through a number of technical constraints.

Spatial constraints describe how workers are located in relation to their own work stations and to the work stations of other workers. *Functional constraints* indicate the relations of a worker's station to the work stations of other workers in the production process. *Temporal and perceptual constraints* regulate the coordination of body (and primarily hand) movement with perception of technical events, in relation to the time regimen of operation cycles.

Space

Production workers are assigned to certain positions in a production operation. The distance of a worker's position at a work station from the positions of other workers is modified by perceptual barriers. This perceptually modified distance is of interest here only in relation to the communicative possibilities it offers. We will estimate distances between work stations as differences between (1) *talking distance,* (2) *shouting distance,* (3) *seeing distance,* and (4) *beyond seeing distance.*

Distances also become modified by the extent to which workers change their positions in relation to others. A worker's location relative to work stations on which he works can be *open;* that is, during actual working time, workers move beyond the boundaries of one particular work station to other stations. A worker may be *confined* to a particular place, even though that "place" may move under some circumstances. These dimensions of spatial constraints are combined in Table 4.

Function

The relationships among work stations are defined by the characteristics of the production process of which they are a part. As workers are assigned to work stations, their relations are likely to be affected by the technical connections between stations. The *flow* of work may pass by successive stations, or work may flow to and away from each station separately. Tasks may be *dependent* on one another in the sense that the second operation can be performed only if the first is performed. Functional dependence is modified by the *exclusiveness* with which tasks are performed. We can distin-

TABLE 4. SPATIAL CONSTRAINTS

Location of Workers in Relation to Work Stations	Distance between Work Stations			
	Talking	Shouting	Seeing	Beyond Seeing
Open	1	2	3	4
Confined to fixed place	5	6	7	8
Confined to mobile place	9	10	11	12

guish situations in which (1) all tasks are undifferentiated; (2) several tasks are differentiated, but each is shared by several workers; (3) several tasks are differentiated, and some are performed exclusively and some are shared; and (4) all tasks are differentiated. The three dimensions of functional constraints are combined in Table 5.

Time and Perception

So far we have indicated differences in the way in which workers and their work stations are located spatially and functionally. We will now attempt to classify the dimensions of constraints by which the acts of individual workers are matched with the requirements of the operation on which they work. Different operations make it necessary for workers to *focus visually* on different parts of their environment. Workers may be required to focus (1) on their hands and the tools and work pieces manipulated, and not on other work stations; (2) on the larger production process and other work stations; or (3) on indicators of a remote production process. These three possibilities also suggest an increasing remoteness from the actual conversion or transfer operation.

The critical parts of work performance usually reside in the movements of a worker's hands, and occasionally feet. These movements display varying degrees of *habituation*, indicated by the regularity, uniformity, and temporal extension of patterned sequences. Visual focus and habituation of movements are related to the *level of cognitive involvement* in the work process. Some production operations could not be performed and fit into the process if a worker thought the process through every time it occurred. In other kinds of work, thinking-through of the process is necessary.

TABLE 5. FUNCTIONAL CONSTRAINTS

Differentiation Pattern	Work Flow and Dependence			
	No Work Flow		Work Flow	
	Indepen-dent	Depen-dent	Indepen-dent	Depen-dent
All tasks undifferent-iated	1	5	9	13
Several tasks differ-entiated, but each shared by several workers	2	6	10	14
Several tasks differ-entiated; some per-formed exclusively and some shared	3	7	11	15
All tasks different-iated	4	8	12	16

The distribution of work activities over time is regulated by the characteristics of *operation cycles*. Operation cycles may be comparatively short and repetitive when their content is constant and the sequence of the components unchanging. They may be comparatively long and repetitive when the content is unchanging, but the greater length of the cycle may permit variation in sequence, and makes for intermittency in the demands of different components. Cycle length may be variable, or there may be no recognizable cycle, when both content and sequence of components change frequently.

For subsequent analysis it is not necessary to work out systematically the relationships among these dimensions. Instead, we will construct from these components a simple set of categories by combining variants that are likely to occur most commonly in combination. We will call the combination of these dimensions *attention requirements*. The classification is shown in Table 6. Attention requirements are *low* when workers focus loosely on their hands, the tools and work pieces they manipulate, and on the work performed by other men nearby. Their movements are partly

TABLE 6. TEMPORAL AND PERCEPTUAL CONSTRAINTS (ATTENTION REQUIREMENTS)

Hand Movements	Operation Cycles	Cognitive Involvement and Visual Focus				
		Low Involvement		High Involvement		
		Focus on Hands	Focus on Process	Focus on Hands	Focus on Process	Focus on Indicators
Habituated	Repetitive and short	2 surface			4 external focus	
	Repetitive and long					
Partly habituated	Repetitive and short	1 low				
	Repetitive and long				3 detailed	
Not habituated	Not repetitive, and variable or absent					5 watching

habituated in the sense that subsidiary movements are relatively automatic, as it were, and more inclusive movement patterns, or whole sequences, are not. There is little necessity for thinking-through of the work process regularly. There may be no operation cycles, or they may be variable or long, so that variation in sequence or in sequence and content would be possible.

We will say that *surface* attention[6] is required when workers focus visually on their hands; when hand movements are habituated; when

---

[6] C. R. Walker and R. H. Guest, *The Man on the Assembly Line* (Cambridge: Harvard University Press, 1952), pp. 12–14.

thinking-through of the work process is not necessary (and often not possible); and when short cycles contain an unchanging content and sequence of components. When *detailed* attention is necessary, workers focus on the work immediately under their hands; hand movements are only partly habituated; a high level of cognitive involvement in the work process is required; cycles are predominantly variable and commonly make intermittent demands on close attention.

We say that required attention is *externally focused* when workers must observe the production process and be aware of events at other work stations. Hand movements are habituated; cognitive involvement in the process is high; operation cycles have a constant content and may be either comparatively long or short. The attention requirements of *watching* occur when workers focus on indicators of remote production processes. Movements are not habituated and there are no relevant work cycles. Workers must comprehend events in a larger and integrated production process which is inaccessible to direct perception.

3. Behavioral Adaptations

In the first section of this chapter, we have presented a typology of work places, distinguished according to differences of the means employed for the production of material goods. In the design of a production operation, the performance of its components is assigned in varying amounts to equipment. Components which are not so assigned are "spared out" for human operators to perform.[7]

In the second section, we have attempted to specify further characteristics of work-place technologies. These characteristics describe constraints on the behavior of operators. They regulate the "fitting in" of operator performance with equipment performance. They constitute conditions for the attainment of outcomes for which the operation was designed.

In this section we will attempt to classify actual social behaviors of workers. To begin with, we will distinguish behaviors which are technically required from those which are not so required but possible within technical limitations. When we describe behaviors as *required* by the technology, on the one hand, and as *permitted* by the technology, on the other, we imply (and assume without test) an order of determination. This order is defined

---

[7] We are taking here the characteristics of the equipment at any one work place as given and constant, in the sense that we are not concerned with the behavioral conditions preceding a technical change. We will compare given technical designs in order to observe the variations in behavioral consequences that may or may not be associated with different technical conditions. But it is not only a matter of our scheme of comparison that the technology of work places is taken as an initial, given condition. The behavior of production workers is at the center of our concern here. From their point of view the technical conditions of work are given elements in their day-to-day working lives, and not subject to immediate change by their decision.

by certain consequences of behavior variation. Noncompliance with rules designed into technical processes is likely to be followed by nonattainment of technical objectives. Organizational means of preventing this kind of noncompliance are likely to be more severe and immediate in their effects on operators than would be control of behavior variation which does not affect technical requirements but is technically possible. For that part of operator behavior which we call technically permitted, rules may or may not be present; but if they are present, they are not directly related to the technical design and may be the product of interaction among peers or of authority relations between workers and supervisors.

In the subsections to follow, we will speak about cooperation and communication as technically required and technically permitted. We will then consider influence relations, and distinguish among them those that are technically determined from those that are not.

Technically Required Cooperation

We have by now introduced several categories by which we wish to distinguish connections between work stations and relationships between *operating functions* which set the conditions for spared-out human work behavior. We will now turn to the relationships among *men* which are required to make the technical design work.

Earlier, we have simply asked whether products move from a particular station to another station, and whether the work done to the product at the first station is a requisite for the work to be done at the second. We have also asked whether a task was performed exclusively by one person or by several persons. These distinctions implied nothing about the relationship between the behavior of two operators who both perform the same task (within a given unit of observation) or about the relationship between two operators who work at stations which may be connected by proximity, work flow, or functional dependence.

The term *cooperation* (like its opposite, conflict) describes a relationship between two or more parties where the parties share certain properties of their environment and their behavior displays certain arrangements which regulate the distribution of whatever is shared.

We propose now that what is shared in *technically required cooperation* are certain combinations of time, task, work piece, and equipment.

When we say *the same task,* we mean identical or nearly identical operations of conversion or transfer. The drilling of a hole of a certain size into a certain location of an engine block is the same task as the drilling of a hole of the same size at the same spot of another engine block. The moving of an engine block from machine A to machine B is the same task as the moving of the next engine block from machine A to machine B. Where there are two sets of machines A and B, and where machine A' and machine A'' perform identical tasks, and machines B' and B'' perform identical tasks, and where the move between A' and B' is identical to the move from A'' to B'', then the moving of an engine block from A' to B' is the same task as the moving of an engine block from A'' to B''.

When we say *the same equipment*, we mean the use, by two or more operators, of at least a part of the very same piece of equipment. Several smelter workers, jointly opening a blast furnace to allow metal to flow out, work with the same equipment so far as they work on the same blast furnace, even though they may work with different tools. Whenever any part of the equipment is used or worked on by several operators, the same equipment is involved; and only when no part of the equipment is so used, do we not use the term.

By the expression *the same work piece*, we mean any of the materials, parts, or products which are converted or moved, and we refer not to work pieces of the same kind but to the very same piece. It should be noted that *work piece* refers to any material that is worked on and may not have the discreteness implied by the term (for example, petroleum flowing through a cracking plant or coal moving on a belt).

Cooperation is *not technically required* (1) when only time and task are shared, that is, when the same task is performed at the same time, but when work is done on different work pieces and with different parts of equipment; (2) when work is done on the same work piece and with the same parts of equipment, but at different times and involving different tasks; (3) when the same task is performed with the same equipment but at different times and on different work pieces; (4) when only one of the four factors is shared. By our definition, it is not possible for the same task to be performed on the same work piece at different times, either with the same or different equipment.

Technically required cooperation is present (1) when time and work piece are shared, that is, when two or more operators work on the same work piece at the same time, but perform different tasks with different equipment; (2) when two or more operators use the same equipment at the same time, but for different tasks on different work pieces; (3) when time is shared and there is any paired combination of work piece, equipment, and task; (4) when all four factors are shared.

These distinctions are summarized in Table 7. There it can be seen that shared time is common to all conditions for technically required cooperation. Shared task only appears in combination with two other conditions (time, equipment; time, work piece), which alone were sufficient for the presence of technically required cooperation.

We can now attempt to define the kinds of behavior which constitute technically required cooperation and to distinguish the ways in which they vary. We have suggested before that the technology of a work place is a design of operations for the production of specific material outcomes. We

TABLE 7. CONDITIONS FOR TECHNICALLY REQUIRED COOPERATION

	Shared Time	Shared Part of Equipment	Shared Work Piece
Shared task	∷∷∷∷∷	∷∷∷∷∷	- - - - -
Shared work piece	* * * * *	∷∷∷∷∷	
Shared part of equipment	* * * * *		
Shared task and shared part of equipment	* * * * *		- - - - -
Shared work piece and shared task	* * * * *		
Shared part of equipment and shared work piece	* * * * *		

* * * * *
* * * * *   Technically required cooperation
* * * * *

∷∷∷∷∷
∷∷∷∷∷   No technically required cooperation
∷∷∷∷∷

- - - - -
- - - - -   Impossible by definition
- - - - -

will say that the behaviors of two or more operators are in a relationship of *technically required cooperation* (1) when these operators share any of the sets of factors which we have just specified as conditions for the presence of technically required cooperation and (2) when these operators perform acts necessary for the attainment of technical ends and constituting those parts of the technical design "spared out" for human performance.

When operators share work pieces or equipment at the same time and when they perform acts for the attainment of a specific common outcome, the acts of one must be related to the acts of the other in such a way that the sum of their acts results in that end. Thus, when the behavior of one varies, the behavior of the other has to "make up" for that variation. The making up of variation can be sequential, simultaneous, or anticipatory; and it can consist of *taking up* of a change of the other's behavior by a change in one's own behavior, or of *taking over* a part or all of the required behavior of the other in addition to one's own. "Taking up" is a characteristic of *sequential cooperation;* and "taking over," of *simultaneous cooperation.* Anticipatory behavior changes can be a characteristic of both types of cooperation. It can be observed only when it occurs mistakenly,[8] and most of our data fall short of this refinement. The acts comprising simultaneous or sequential cooperation are confined by operation cycles. When cycles are absent, but when the possibility of sequential cooperation is indicated by a time lag between related behaviors, cooperation may occur which we will call *sporadic.* It is characterized by its comparatively rare and irregular incidence. The classification of technically required cooperation is given in Table 8.

Technically Permitted Cooperation

Technical requirements specify lines of action for operators, indicating for them to do *this* rather than *that* and to follow a certain sequence of steps. Technical limitations allow a wider range of behaviors than that which is technically demanded and constitute boundaries within which operators can make choices. Our main concern here is to determine variation of these limitations as related to technology. We are less concerned with the "determinants" of behavior choices made within these limitations.

But the behavioral scientist cannot make mere possibilities the object of his deliberations. In fact, our data are descriptions of actual behaviors observed or reported. The question then remains: To what extent have the workers observed in these studies "taken advantage" of the opportunities for extratechnical behavior provided by their work-place technology? We propose to solve this problem by introducing an assumption which we do

---

[8] For a discussion of "the rule of anticipated reactions," see H. A. Simon, *Models of Man* (New York: Wiley, 1957), pp. 67–68.

not intend to test explicitly. The assumption is that human beings are much more likely to elaborate behavior patterns beyond the immediately necessary than to perform only the acts necessary to attain certain objectives. Much of the research literature concerned with human relations in industry has focused almost entirely on behavioral elaborations beyond required work activity, to the neglect of work activity itself. On a broader plane, sociologists have long recognized that an understanding of human behavior by means of a rationalist-utilitarian model of man is limited and often impossible. Ideally, we would require for this study a law that human behavior will always be so elaborate as to fill the space provided by the environment over which men, in their immediate time and place, have little control.

Since, fortunately, we do not live in a social scientist's utopia, we will be content with a more limited assumption. We will compare observations of work behaviors. The technical environment of some of these behaviors is more restricting than that of others. We will assume at best that behavior

TABLE 8. TECHNICALLY REQUIRED COOPERATION

1. No technically required cooperation
2. Simultaneous taking over[a]
3. Sequential taking up[a]
4. Sporadic taking up

[a]Distribution of cooperative acts:

Temporal Relationship between Behaviors of Cooperators	Means of Redistribution of Behaviors of Cooperators for Fixed-Sum Outcomes	
	Taking Over	Taking Up
Simultaneous	••••••••••••• ••••••••••••• ••••••••••••• •••••••••••••	
Sequential		••••••••••••• ••••••••••••• ••••••••••••• •••••••••••••

patterns in the less restricting environment are likely to be elaborated beyond those occurring in the more restricting environment. At least we will assume that elaboration is greater in the first case than in the last.

Taken by itself, this statement could be tautological, since it might imply that we would measure variation of technical limitation by variation in relative elaborateness of behavior patterns. This problem can be readily solved once our statements are made to sound less deterministic, albeit more bland. We have already undertaken to say what behaviors are technically required by given technologies. If we then find behaviors in excess of technical demands, we "know" that these are elaborations.

First we distinguish two classes of elaborations beyond the behaviors which make the technical design work. We can look again at operator relationships as they are technically required and ask whether these relationships have meanings beyond the fulfillment of technical objectives. Cooperation might provide for a total sum of activities required for the completion of an operation, but the actions performed can also be interpreted in the light of felt obligations of operators to one another.

This first class of elaborations consists of behaviors interpreted both as technically permitted and as technically demanded, where the same actual behavior contains both elements. The second class of elaborations consists of behaviors which themselves do not find a place in those parts of the technical operation spared out for human performance, but are still delimited by the technical setting of the work place. In the presence of some technological conditions, the difference between technically demanded behavior with a meaning exceeding technical demands, on the one hand, and technically permitted behavior not demanded by the technology, on the other, will be relatively indeterminate. Under what conditions this is the case will be demonstrated with the data.

We have suggested before that cooperation is a technically demanded form of interaction when certain properties of the work situation are shared by two or more operators. Whenever a particular work piece or equipment part, or both, must be shared by operators at the same time, cooperation is a technical requirement. We have also spoken of technically required cooperation when the behaviors of several operators add up to a sum of performance necessary to attain technical outcomes. The relative distribution of acts among the operators is regulated by the demand for the attainment of technical ends.

We will now speak of *technically permitted cooperation* when a distribution of behaviors among operators is regulated by mutual obligation. Mutual obligation describes the rules of an exchange and means that when one operator varies his behavior to make up for another's behavior variation, he expects the other to do the same in reverse at another time. This form of cooperation might occur when work piece or equipment parts are shared at the same time (a condition for technically required cooperation), but also when other combinations of sharing are present which were not specified as conditions for technically required cooperation. It could occur both when behaviors add up to a constant sum and when they do not.

We can now refer to Table 7 (p. 28) and suggest under what combination of conditions technically permitted behavior can occur:

1. When operators A and B perform the same task, with the same equipment, on different work pieces, at different times, A might exchange work pieces with B; A might do the work on B's work piece in addition to doing the work on his own work piece, one after the other, while B would do the same at some other time; or A might do the work on B's work piece now, while B does the work on A's work piece immediately before or after A performs the operation.

2. When operators A and B perform different tasks at different times, on the same work piece, with the same equipment, A might exchange tasks with B. A might perform B's task on the same work piece, in addition to performing his own task, while B would do the same on some other work piece; or A might perform B's task, while B would perform A's task, on the same work piece.

3. When operators A and B perform the same task at the same time, on different work pieces, with different equipment, A might exchange with B either work pieces or equipment, or both.

We would determine the presence of technically permitted cooperation by observing (1) whether A takes over a component of the work of B, and (2) whether B reciprocates. "Taking over" in this case may mean the performance of all or part of another man's task. Giving advice or information can be regarded as the performance of part of another man's task, when the possession and use of knowledge is part of that task. It may also mean the use of another man's technical resources: work pieces and equipment. When knowledge is considered a technical resource, its "taking over" is the receipt of advice and information. A man can reciprocate for the use of another man's technical resources by making his resources available to the other. These resources for reciprocation may be technical or social. Resources are usually exchanged in combination.

Thus, A may lend a tool to B and offer him advice as to its use. B may reciprocate by helping A to lift a work piece onto a bench and by displaying deference toward A. A may actually do B's job on B's work piece with B's equipment, and B may do the same for A in reverse, or praise A in the presence of a third person, or both.

When an operation can be completed as technically designed only when one operator varies his behavior to make up for the variation of another's behavior, we speak about technically required cooperation. *Permitted cooperation* occurs (1) when an operation can be completed as technically designed in the absence of this relationship of behavior variations of two operators; (2) when operators still vary their behavior in relation to behavior variations of others; and (3) when this relationship possesses the characteristics of an exchange. Suggested categories are shown in Table 9.

TABLE 9. TECHNICALLY PERMITTED COOPERATION

Cooperative Activity	Permitted Behavior Part of Required Behavior	Permitted Behavior Independent of Required Behavior
Taking over part of another man's task: Use of work piece and equipment	1	2
Taking over part of another man's task: Giving advice and information	3	4
Taking over all of another man's task	5	6
No taking over	7	

Technically Required Communication

When sociologists speak about interaction, they most commonly refer to acts of communication and to *verbal* communication as the dominant form. Previously, we discussed a form of human relationship which, taken by itself, is not considered communicative interaction. Technically required cooperation may, or may not, be possible without direct, person-to-person communication. The distribution of behaviors among cooperators may under some conditions be accomplished by means of direct communication. But it may also be mediated through the operators' perception of the behavior of work pieces or equipment. The term *mediated* implies that, in this case, work pieces or equipment parts become means of communication.[9]

Technically required cooperation, then, may involve technically me-

---

[9] The concept of "technically mediated cooperation" appears in Popitz *et al.*, *Technik und Industriearbeit*, esp. p. 65.

diated communication, or it may be accompanied and made possible by other forms of technically required communication. Technical means other than work pieces or equipment parts may facilitate communication: signal lights, horns and whistles, public-address systems, transcribers. Finally, the operators themselves may supply the means of communication: voice, hand signals, facial expressions, and other body movements.

Technically required communication is the conveying of information by one operator and the receiving of that same information by another, where the transmission of information enables the receiver to change his operating behavior in order to achieve technical ends. We have so far classified technically required communication by the means facilitating it. Necessary information may be conveyed (1) through the material things of conversion or transfer operations, that is, through work pieces or equipment parts; (2) by way of installations specifically designed for technically required communication; and (3) through sound or sight signals emitted and directly received by human organisms.

We use the expression *communication by words* to indicate transmission of verbal messages without intervening technical resources directly exchanged between workers. The term *communication by objects* indicates the sending and receiving of cues perceived, and reacted to, by observing or feeling movements in the technical objects on which workers work. We add *communication by signs* where cues are *not* transmitted through and mediated by work pieces or equipment parts, or sent directly from worker to worker. Signs constitute movements of hands and arms, sometimes supplemented by whistling. These signs are still transmitted directly from an operator's body and follow the rules of a shared sign language, where different postures of hands and arms have meanings which can be translated by the receiver into information usable for changing his own behavior. Finally, we will use the term *communication by signals* to indicate the sending of messages by way of technical transmission installations, such as dials, armature boards, indicators, horns, and lights which receive electrical or mechanical impulses causing them to produce a message read or heard by a receiver. Signals might be transmitted directly through technical channels from sender to receiver, as when one man pushes a button and a light turns green at another man's work station. But signals might also be transmitted from one man to a production process, and changes in the process are then "reported" through similar channels to indicators at the work station of another man, who then reads them as signals. These different means of communication may be found singly or in combination.

These categories are presented diagrammatically in Table 10. We will attempt further distinctions not shown in that table. We will ask with what frequency and regularity communications are technically required, and expect that these are related to operation cycles. We will also attempt

TABLE 10. TECHNICALLY REQUIRED COMMUNICATION

	Sensory Means of Perception		
Means of Transmission	Touch	Hearing	Sight
Human organism		words[a]	signs[a]
Technical resources	objects	objects	objects
Technical transmitters		signals	signals

[a]Cues emitted from a human organism and received by hearing can consist of something other than words; for instance, whistling or hand-clapping. Similarly, cues emitted from a human organism and received by sight can consist of something other than signs given by hands, arms, or head movement; for example, writing words with a piece of chalk. Among production workers, cues provided by hearing or sight seem predominantly differentiated by their literacy; that is, cues perceived by hearing are primarily parts of common language, and those seen tend to be part of a special repertory of signs.
A combination of words and signs (as defined narrowly) appears not very probable in technical communication. Where words are possible, signs become unnecessary. Similarly, when both signs and signals are possible for the same purpose, signs would probably be preferred over signals.

to describe the characteristics of the networks of communication through which operators under different technical conditions are linked. What kind of network is observed is likely to depend on the combination of types of communication means in use and on the characteristics of work flow and required cooperation.

Technically Permitted Communication

We distinguish technically required communication from technically permitted communication by reference to the achievement of technical ends. Transmission of information which does not enable the receiver to change his performance to achieve technical ends is *technically permitted communication*. We must add, however, that communicative behavior which is not technically demanded may have consequences for technical performance. We will still classify it as technically permitted.

TABLE 11. TECHNICALLY PERMITTED COMMUNICATION

A. Culturally Defined Sufficiency of Means of Expression

A Count of Available Means		Sufficiency
Gesture	1. None	
	2. Any one	
Facework	3. Any two	Low
Literacy	4. Any three	
Completion of discourse	5. Any four	
	6. All five	High
Choice of partners		

B. Regulation of Frequency by Operation Cycles

1. Cycle-free, continuous
2. Governed by cycles, intermittent

C. Determinacy of Boundaries of Communication Network

	Definition of Boundaries		
Choice of Partners	Closed	Floating	Open
No choice	1	4	7
Choice restricted by proximity	2	5	8
Unrestricted choice	3	6	9

Information transmitted in technically required communication consists of cues which are directly translatable into an operator's moves as part of technical performance and which have meaning with a technical reference. Technically permitted communication is not immediately translatable into changes of operating behavior without reference to nontechnical interpretations of the situation. Technical meaning lies in the rules implied in the technical design and in designed outcomes. The technical meaning of communication interprets the relationship of operators to the technology, that is, to equipment, work pieces, tasks, and relations among operators insofar as they constitute a part of the technology. Nontechnical meaning of communication refers to rules which are a product of that part of the social organization of production workers and of their environment which is not, or only indirectly, related to the technology of the work place under observation.

In technically permitted communication, information may be transmitted which enables the receiver to change his behavior toward others with the end of satisfying individual or social demands of the situation. "Others" may be peers, bosses, outsiders, or the communicator himself. Communication may also be an end in itself, as an expression of the quality of relationships among participants.

Technically permitted communication will be classified by *amount*; by the extent to which it fits definitions of *expressive sufficiency* prevalent in the nontechnical culture of the work place and its environment; by type of *linkage system* and *choice of participants*; and by the extent to which its possibility is *governed by operation cycles*. Amount is classified by presence or absence and by continuity or intermittency. The extent to which technically permitted communication fulfills cultural demands refers to the following characteristics of human communication: literacy; the simultaneous presence of speech, facial expression, and gesture, and their perceptibility by a receiver; completion of a culturally defined unit of (uninterrupted) discourse; choice of communication partners and exclusion of unwanted receivers. Table 11 is a summary of these analytical distinctions.

Influence

In their discussion of social power, Thibaut and Kelley[10] speak of the control which a person A exercises over the behavior (and fate) of a person B. A controls B's behavior by varying B's outcomes, or payoffs.

In March's definition, influence "induces behavior on the part of the individual at time t_1 different from that which might be predicted on the basis of a knowledge of the individual organism at time t_0. By behavior is meant any change in the state of the organism."[11]

Simon's definition "involves an asymmetrical relation between influencer and influencee." He suggests that "to determine the influence of A

[10] J. W. Thibaut and H. H. Kelley, *The Social Psychology of Groups* (New York: Wiley, 1959), p. 101.

[11] J. G. March, "An Introduction to the Theory and Measurement of Influence," *American Political Science Review*, 49 (1955), 438.

upon B, we simply observe a number of situations in which the behavior of A varies, and note what is the concomitant variation in B's behavior."[12]

But there is the problem of feedback from influencee to influencer. A possible solution to this problem lies in the recognition that "processes of influence take time,"[13] so that the "influence-related activities of the individuals are partitioned into mutually-exclusive sets in such a way that within each set asymmetry holds.[14]

Dahl proposes that a description of a power relation should include references to the "base," "means," "amount," and "scope" of power.[15]

We have assembled the main components of the notion of influence that seem relevant for our purposes. We will now attempt to put these components together in such a way that they become useful analytical tools for distinguishing behaviors in technical settings.

Influence "base" refers to the resources available to A. The use of these resources is his "means" of influence and affects B's payoffs. Variation in payoff is affected by the kind of resources used.

We will distinguish technical resources from resources produced by nontechnical behavior systems. By the use of shared *technical resources*, A implicitly invokes the teleology of production design: Production equipment is designed for the attainment of a specific output. B's immediate payoff for compliance with the requirements of technical design lies in the attainment or nonattainment of that output. When the designed-for output is not produced and, for instance, "the mill breaks down," a congregation of supervisors, engineers, and inspectors might be the result. This is something to be assiduously avoided. An extended payoff could be the maintenance or loss of pay and employment.

The use of *nontechnical resources* invokes the rules of the social systems of which influencer and influencee are members. Compliance or noncompliance with these rules can have payoffs related to technical or nontechnical requirements. A may use his "informal leadership position" as a resource and help B with his work. The help he extends influences B's technical performance. A may use his skills as a mimic as a resource and "influence" B's nontechnical behavior by making him laugh.

Where the use of technical resources influences technical performance, we will speak of *technical influence*. Where the use of nontechnical resources influences technical performance, we will speak of *semitechnical influence*. The term *extratechnical influence* will refer to the effect on nontechnical behavior of the use of nontechnical resources. The fourth

---

[12] Simon, *Models of Man*, p. 66.
[13] *Ibid.*
[14] March, "An Introduction to the Theory and Measurement of Influence," p. 436.
[15] R. A. Dahl, "The Concept of Power," *Behavioral Science*, 2 (1957), 203.

possibility, where nontechnical behavior is influenced through the use of technical resources, will be excluded from our discussion for lack of data. For purposes of gross distinction, we use the term *nontechnical influence* as a residual category in contrast to *technical influence* as defined above.

We will now attempt to put the three types of influence relations into a rank order. The reason for this attempt is twofold: In our analysis, we will emphasize technical influence, and further categories for distinctions within this type will be added presently. In contrast, the measurement of the two types of nontechnical influence will be confined to the determination of presence or absence. In addition to a justification of our preferred emphasis, the following argument is meant to show why payoffs can be seen to be more compelling in relations of technical influence than in those of nontechnical influence.

We assume that in the definition of the situation of most people at work, the work place is first a place where work is to be done, and then a place to do other things. It seems plausible that, at least in industrial work situations, the continued nonattainment of technical ends precludes the attainment of other ends. For example, when work is persistently not done as designed, the chances for continuing to enjoy the company of friends during breaks or for continuing to engage in the processing of grievances are likely to decline radically. Thus, a "break" is a break from another dominant activity; if there is nothing to have a break from, there is no break. We assume, then, that among production workers and those in their immediate environment, the attainment of technical ends is ranked first in order of importance. Although at any one time, this may not hold and other behavior consequences may be ranked higher, it will be sufficient to assume that it is more likely to hold over extended periods than would other rankings. We can then treat importance as a payoff in itself, and differences in importance as equivalent to differences in the value of penalties and rewards.

We can now return to the question of symmetry in influence relations, as suggested by Simon and March. Instead of making an effort to keep behavior sequences with opposite directions separate at all cost, we will treat symmetry as a variable. In order to do so, we require a notion of the "state" of the relationship with regard to which there is symmetry or asymmetry. As suggested, influence takes time. The technically relevant "state of time" is the operation cycle. The boundaries of a state of the relationship are the beginning and the end of an operation cycle. We will ask whether the direction of influence can change within an operation cycle.

We will use the term *reversible* influence to refer to a relationship of technical influence in which the direction of influence changes within an operation cycle. *Irreversible* influence is the term for technical-influence

TABLE 12. INFLUENCE

	Behavior Influenced	
Influence Base	Nontechnical Behavior	Technical Performance
Social resources	Extratechnical influence	Semitechnical influence
Technical resources		Technical influence Reversible[a] Irreversible[a]

[a]By symmetry within operation cycle.

relations in which the direction does not change during a cycle. Variation of amount of influence is then at least partly determined by the incidence of operation cycles: their length, frequency, and regularity. The presence of technical influence requires a technically determined relationship between operators' performances. Technically required cooperation is a condition for technical influence. Table 12 sets out the types of influence relations.

4. Dimensions of Industrial Work

In this chapter, we have defined the terms for a number of analytical categories. Each of these categories has been given a place in an attempted descriptive scheme. For each we have proposed subcategories for the description of variation, thus translating categories into variables. The scheme has three major classes of variables:

First, there is the technology of work places. Technology has two dimensions: conversion operations and transfer operations. Variation of each is seen as a progression of technical change: at each stage an additional component of work is performed by machines rather than by men. A matrix of types of technologies is produced when the progressive scales of the two dimensions are put together.

Second, we have distinguished the following categories of technical constraints on the behavior of industrial workers: space, function, time, and perception. Variation of these constraints is described by a composite of several combined dimensions.

Finally, we have categories for the social behavior of workers. Sharing of combinations of technical resources is noted as a defining condition of cooperation. By reference to the outcomes for which technical processes are designed, both cooperation and communication are distinguished as being either technically required or technically permitted. Our first interest is whether required and permitted cooperation occur alone or in combination. Variation of required cooperation is further distinguished by the distribution of cooperative acts over time. Differences in communication are analyzed in terms of varying combinations of communication means and linkage networks. Technical and nontechnical resources as bases of control of technical performance and nontechnical behavior are the characteristics of types of influence. The symmetry of technical-influence relations is treated as a variable when the direction of influence is seen as reversible or irreversible within the limits of an operation cycle.

Of the three major parts of our descriptive scheme, technology is an independent variable, and the three main types of behavior are dependent variables. Technical constraints are linked with both technology and behavior. Certain categories of technical constraints in combination are expected to provide more complete explanations for the relationships between technology and behavior. Some behavior variation might be better explained by reference to joint effects of technology and technical constraints.

Chapter I suggested that this study attempts to cope with two analytical problems: (1) the nature of industrial technology and its constraints, and (2) the behavioral adaptations of industrial workers to technology and technical constraints. The first problem will be dealt with in Part Two. The chapters of Part Three will be concerned with the second analytical problem. At the same time, an attempt will be made in Part Three to translate categories and analyzed data into the kind of explanatory statements just suggested.

TECHNOLOGY AND ITS DEMANDS

Chapter III

SOURCES OF DATA

The preceding chapter presented a number of interrelated categories in the abstract. These categories are meant for the coding and ordering of data in the following analysis of material from various research reports. These data have been reported primarily in narrative form. They are often mixed with the comments and speculations of the authors. Our data-gathering procedure consisted of a page-by-page search for records of actual observations. As much as possible an attempt has been made to distinguish reported observation from speculation. However, at certain times observations were found within a speculative or summarizing context. Such information has also been used unless it appeared in other places, in the report of the authors, designated specifically as reports of observation. Often the data consisted of long stories of particular events. While an attempt will be made to keep as close to the data as possible, it will be necessary to summarize lengthy stories for the sake of lucidity and economy.

In Chapter II, observable phenomena of work-place technology and worker behavior have been kept analytically distinct. In our sources of data, however, these phenomena appear in different contexts and are often mixed one with another. Also there is no report which concerns itself with all our categories. Where required data are missing in the description of the technical design of the work operation, some cautious and limited inferences will be made in order to complete the description of technical features. Where data are missing with regard to worker behavior, some reports will have to be left out from the analysis from time to time. If observations are reported on a number of different phenomena which we wish to treat separately at different places, these data might be repeated later or a reference might be made to a previous discussion.

In this part, an attempt will be made to introduce data for the first two major categories introduced in Chapter II: (1) the work-place technology of conversion and transfer operations, and (2) the technical constraints which channel human work performance. Viewed independently from Part Three, this analysis will be a description of the nature of industrial technology and its demands on the behavior of workers. For use in Part Three, the phenomena analyzed here will be the conditions to which workers' behaviors adapt. They will be the variables used for the explanation of behavior differences.

In addition to marshaling and coding data for the first two sets of categories, we will record the general characteristics of the research studies from which these data are drawn. So far as given by the authors, we will note when, where, by what methods, and with what purpose the study was conducted. The quality of the generalizations which this analysis is expected to produce rests on the data from published reports. Therefore, it seems important to describe variations in the characteristics of the data sources, immediately before the data themselves are presented.

Coding of data will be in accord with the following procedure. The reported observations will be given. Where this material appears insufficient for placing the case into any given category, an inferential argument might be made by which the case can still be coded. Then the case will be assigned to categories.

The unit of our analysis is the work place as defined by the original researchers. At this point no attempt will be made to define in general terms the criteria for determining the boundaries of each unit. What these boundaries are will be revealed when the data are presented. In most cases the work place as our unit of analysis is a unit of the formal organization. Substantial differences will be found, however, in the extent to which this unit also coincides with an interaction system as the unit, or with a unit defined by physical or technical boundaries.

Each report on which we have drawn does not necessarily coincide with a unit of analysis. Thus, one book which we have used may deal with more than one work place. In a few cases a generalized work place will be used as a unit, on the basis of information drawn from several reports. Furthermore, some of the references on which we draw may present only small pieces of information and these may be used in addition to information provided by other, larger reports. Finally, information about one given research project may have been available in a number of different publications. In summary, information about several work places or units may have come from one research report, or information about one work place may have been found in several reports.[1]

The thirty-four publications used have yielded thirty-two cases. These

---

[1] The following system of notations will be used. Material describing a certain work place will be called Case 13, for example, followed by a brief description of the case. Presentation of data will be followed by the author's last name and the page number in parentheses. When several publications by the same author are used as sources of data, the author's name will be followed by the year of publication. When more than one publication by the same author have appeared in the same year, the year will be followed by a lower-case letter to distinguish different publications. The appendix, "Data Sources by Case Number," will give the short designation together with the full reference. Associated case numbers will be listed alongside. References not considered data for purposes of this report will be treated in the conventional footnote form.

cases were initially put into a preliminary order of similarity of technical characteristics and industry, and numbered in that order. Each case was then systematically coded and given a place in our typology of work-place technologies. In order to obtain a manageable division, the cases were assigned to clusters. Each cluster was called a "type" of technology and was given a number. The type numbers follow the sequence of technical development implied in the original typology. This sequence is not wholly determinate, since the typology has two dimensions and it is possible to go both to the right and down in the matrix when following a line of development represented by cases. Each of the following six chapters deals with one or two of these types in sequence.

In the process of coding, it became necessary to divide six of the cases into two parts. Each of these two parts has distinguishable technical characteristics requiring assignment to different types. For major sections of Part Three, these two parts are treated as separate cases. They are identified by their original number, followed by a letter. In these six cases, one part is considered to have the dominant technical characteristics, namely, the part involving the regular production operations. Since the material used for coding in Part Two is not readily separable into our two parts, these six cases will be discussed in the chapter relevant for their dominant technical characteristics.

The analysis began with thirty-five undivided cases to which numbers were given according to a preliminary order. Three cases were dropped because the data were too incomplete. The original numbering was retained, and Cases 2, 12, and 30 do not appear in our discussion. Of the remaining cases, six were divided and a letter designation added to their number. As a result, we are dealing with thirty-eight cases divided into a number of types. Case numbers do not necessarily coincide with the sequence in which cases are now presented.

It was proposed earlier that the categories presented in Chapter II were meant to facilitate the search for data and that they should be viewed as relatively flexible in the matter of the coding of data. With the given diversity of sources, it is likely that categories will have to be modified, extended, or recombined in order to match the characteristics of the information available. The main aim here is to produce statements of relationship, not an exhaustive set of categories.

Each of the following chapters in Part Two will be followed by a summary showing the distribution of cases in our categories. In the last chapter of this part, this distribution is shown in full, and categories are recombined in preparation for subsequent analysis. Additional tables will show the relationships of these categories with variation in technology.

Chapter IV

HANDLING:
Manual Moving of Heavy Materials

Case 1—Steel-Plant Maintenance

For one summer in 1919 Charles Walker worked in a Pittsburgh steel mill and kept a diary.[1] Taken from the diary, this case is concerned with a gang of maintenance men working around a blast furnace. Although vivid, the case material is limited for the purposes of our analysis. It is included here as an example of technically undifferentiated crew work. Three elements of the work of this crew are described: (1) the routine cleaning of a firebox of a stove which feeds heated air to the blast furnace; (2) repairs on the cooling system of the blast furnace; and (3) the cleaning-out of the inside of the stove.

1. Two or three men work inside the firebox and loosen the glowing cinder with steel bars, aiming at a crack, thrusting hard, and with all the weight at the end of the bar moving it up and down until the cinder breaks off. With a hoe one man pulls out the cinder and puts it into a wheelbarrow. Another dumps the load over the edge of a platform. When he goes "for a chew," a fifth or sixth man takes over. Clearing-out of one firebox takes 15 minutes, and the crew does five in a row, climbing steps to the next level and carrying the wheelbarrow along. The men change jobs from one time to the next. They skip one stove which is "on." Should they try to open it, the blast would probably kill them, thrusting a man 40 yards. There is a lull after the five jobs, and the men roll cigarettes or add to a chew in their cheeks. (Walker 1922, 84–85)

2. A tuyere, a sort of outside cooler on the blast furnace, goes bad every other day. A cooler, a cone-shaped water chamber around the blast pipe, may require replacement only once every three months. A tuyere has to be removed for work on a cooler. Several men go through a series of operations, working rapidly. One man takes off a nut with a wrench, two men hold a curved bar, while a third knocks out some keys with a sledgeham-

---

[1] C. R. Walker, *Steel: The Diary of a Furnace Worker* (Boston: Atlantic Monthly Press, 1922).

mer. The blowpipe falls on the bar and is taken off quickly, as flames shoot out of the hole from which the pipe has been removed. Then the tuyere is knocked loose with a bar.

A hook at the end of a pull bar is set against the edge of the cooler. There is a weight at the other end of the bar, to which ropes are attached. Men are recruited from all around to pull on these ropes, in order to loosen the cooler. When the new cooler is in place, four or five men carry a kind of ramrod, with a square hammer end, to the cooler, and ram it against the edge of the cooler, the jar going through the men's hands. Once the cooler is seated, a man connects the waterpipes, while another holds a shovel in front of the hole to protect the first man from the flames. (Walker 1922, 107–110)

3. In order to enter a stove for cleaning, the gas in the combustion chamber is turned off overnight, and the stove allowed to cool for several hours. With wooden sandals over their shoes, jackets and caps tightened, one or two men crawl through a 14-inch opening into the hot and gaseous chamber, taking pick and shovel with them. The combustion chamber is at most 4 × 8 feet large and partly filled with cooling cinder. Remaining inside for as long as an hour at a time, the men work individually with pick and shovel, and jointly with bar and sledgehammer, under the light of an electric bulb shoved in through the hot-blast valve. Men outside hand in tools.

Clearing out cinder takes 3 hours. Moving to the other side, a crew of five or six shovels flue dust 1 or 2 feet high from the brick arches to the entrance from where it is hoed out by other men. The next day, these men poke out flue dust from the brick checkerwork which retains heat when the stove is in use. One man climbs down a ladder to a platform and, with a steel bar, pokes out three holes with all his might, and then comes out again, to be replaced by the next man. The inside is extremely hot, and the men have to be careful not to fall down the shaft of the combustion chamber next to the checkerwork. (Walker 1922, 129–134)

The work of this crew includes virtually no conversion of materials and a comparatively small amount of transfer operations. The case is, in a sense, a zero point for our analysis. What is moved here are not the products of the production process, but the cinder which has to be broken loose from the blast-furnace heating equipment and the waterpipes around the blast furnace which are to be exchanged. This is clearly work performed with hands and hand tools: hoes, wheelbarrows, steel bars, ropes, and shovels. (Code T3:R1-C1)[2]

---

[2] These code numbers have the following reference. T refers to Table, and the number following it to the table number of Chapter II. The numbers following the colon refer to the code numbers in these tables. Ordinarily, there will be only one code number for each table. In the case of Table 3, two dimensions are combined: the C refers to the column, and the R refers to the rows of the matrix of types of technology.

The three examples of the work of this gang indicate a variety of jobs. Men move around in their large work area, changing positions freely. They tend to stay close together and can talk to each other. There is a semblance of work flow when several men loosen the cinder, others pull it into a wheelbarrow, and the next man dumps the wheelbarrow load. By and large, however, there is no persistent movement of material from work station to work station. While the work of these men is not commonly linked by work flow, each man's job is dependent on that of the others. This gang performs many different operations, and the division of work is limited, rather temporary, and fluid. These men have to look at the work directly before them and to take account of what the other men are doing. The work is not intricate, does not require very close coordination of perception and hand movement, and entails little thinking about the work process. Certain movements, as in shoveling, would be habitual, but each job as a whole is not repetitive enough to involve a habituated pattern.

There are certain more or less pronounced cycles within each job and in the distribution of jobs over time. Fireboxes are cleaned on five stoves successively. Each cleaning contains approximately the same work content and is separated from the next by moving from one level to another. At the end of five cleanings there is a lull. Repair of the cooling system follows a distinct sequence of steps, and two parts of this operation are repeated over different times: tuyeres every other day, and coolers once in three months or so. In cleaning out the brickwork, men take turns for 3 minutes of work inside and a period of rest outside. There are, then, fairly distinct cycles, but cycles that vary from each other in length and in the distribution of activities within a cycle. These conditions, taken together, signify a "low" attention requirement. (Code T4:1; T5:5; T6:1)

Case 3—Smelting

This case is one of a total of nine from one large research project. The general characteristics of the research will be given here for all of the nine cases. The research took place for nearly two years in 1953 and 1954 in a number of steel plants in western Germany. The project consisted of two parts and was published in two separate volumes. The purpose of the first part was to describe the effects of steel-industry technology on the social organization of work among rank-and-file production workers. It contains an analysis of cooperation, workers' perception of the work situation, and performance demands. The second part deals with the workers' views of the class structure of their society. The material for the second part was obtained entirely through interviews. For the first part, direct observations were supplemented by detailed work descriptions from interviewed workers. The study is not much concerned with so-called informal association.

This exclusion is discussed together with the presumed nontransferability of the results of American research and its overemphasis of a "romanticism of group formation."[3]

The present case of work on blast furnaces and Thomas converters is a combination of several components. The observations on blast furnaces were made in two different plants, in each of which there was a battery of blast furnaces. Observations on Thomas converters were made in one plant. Our case will be confined to the work of men at the output end of these operations. We will look mainly at the work of the four smeltermen on the blast furnace and supplement the case with information about similar processes on the converter.

The smelting crew on the blast furnace consists of the first, second, third, and fourth smeltermen. Only the first smelterman is concerned with the whole blast-furnace process, and the second might substitute for him. The work of this crew proceeds through a number of steps: the cleaning and rebuilding of the runners through which the slag and molten metal run from the tap hole to the slag and pig-iron cars; the opening of the tap hole; the pouring of the metal; and the closing of the tap hole. The runners are long, interconnected troughs built of a special sand. Some runners are used to draw off slag; and others, metal. (See Figure 1.) What these men do will be described in sequence. We will then focus on two of its main components and subsequently treat these as separate subcases.

After the tap, and when the tap hole is closed, the cycle of work begins with the cleaning-out of the runners. In cleaning and rebuilding, each man has his own section, but one man helps another with a wrecking bar in order to remove a heavy lump of slag. The runners are rebuilt with a number of hand tools and an air hammer with which the sand is tamped down firmly. When one man has finished, he will go and help another man, and they all finish and have their break together before the next tap. The working space of these men consists of a large platform on which they move around freely. When blast air is "on" and the men are dispersed over the platform, they can see each other but one man can talk to another only by walking over to him. On work in preparation for the tap, the tasks of the smeltermen are functionally independent and are not linked by work flow. With the exception of some components of the work of the first smelterman, we can say that the four men perform the same undifferentiated tasks. The full working cycle extends over about 4 hours, permitting a great deal of discretion in the distribution of work components within. Discretion is limited only by the requirement for tapping which is controlled by the blast-furnace process. Short sequences of hand movements are likely to be habituated, but longer sequences would be less so, as the

[3] H. Popitz *et al.*, *Technik und Industriearbeit* (Tübingen: Mohr, 1957); H. Popitz *et al.*, *Das Gesellschaftsbild des Arbeiters* (Tübingen: Mohr, 1957).

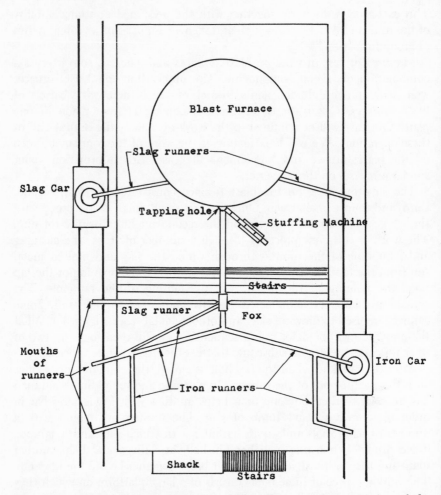

FIGURE 1. **Case 3—Tapping Platform of Blast Furnace** (By permission of the publisher and authors from H. Popitz, H. P. Bahrdt, E. A. Jüres, and H. Kesting, *Technik und Industriearbeit*, Tübingen: Mohr, 1957, p. 53. Redrawn for this book.)

condition of runners to be rebuilt varies from time to time and from section to section. It is necessary to look at the movement of hands and tools and at the sand worked on. Specific thinking-through of the work process every time would seem to be unnecessary. (Popitz 1957a, 52–54, 114–115, 180)

In order to permit slag and metal to flow out, the hardened clay in the opening must be broken. In our case, this is accomplished with a tapping hammer driven by compressed air. The hammer is suspended on a wheel running along an overhead track. Two smeltermen, one on each side, grasp a bar which protrudes from the hammer, pushing it in the right direction. Another bar is inserted into the hammer and is driven with rapid blows into the tapping hole. When the hole is completed, the hammer is reversed and the smeltermen pull back on the handlebars. When the iron flows too rapidly, the hammer is taken off the bar and pulled back quickly, and the bar melts in the flow of metal. The men then watch the metal in the runners and redirect it from time to time. When a runner threatens to overflow, quick action is necessary to redirect the metal. This may require disregarding safety rules and jumping across filled runners. (Popitz 1957a, 115, 155) Following the tap, the first smelterman shoots clay into the tap hole with a stuffing machine, which is moved back once the stuffing compound has hardened. (Popitz 1957a, 115–116, 153) At this point the cycle is completed.

Popitz also provides a brief description of the tap on a converter which occurs about every 20 minutes. The converter is mechanically tilted, permitting metal to run out of its top. One of the four men takes a sample, adds manganese and other additives, and keeps the mouth of the converter clear and lime from flowing out. The second man runs a long steel bar through the flowing slag so that the converter operator can see when steel begins to flow. Once the slag is tapped, the remaining two men throw lime into it with the help of the first two men. The steel tap completed, all four throw fly slag into the steel remaining in the converter in order to cool the steel and stop the flow. Jobs are rotated from tap to tap. (Popitz 1957a, 39–40)

We will now classify the second component, the tapping, in this operation and assign codes to both the first and the second part at the same time. The work in preparation for the tap will be called Case 3a, and the tap itself Case 3b. Air hammers are used both for tamping the runners and for opening the tap hole. Although the blow of such a hammer is produced by compressed air, the hammer is directed and manipulated as if it were a heavy hand tool. These men are involved in moving materials—sand for the runners and the flowing slag and metal. The actual conversion is not part of their job. For both subcases, then, there is no conversion, and transfer of material is accomplished with hand tools. (Code T3:R1-C1) This does not mean that the work of these operators is not affected by the conversion process in the large apparatus, to the extent that it determines the temporal boundaries of the operation and creates occasional emergencies. In the second phase of the work, these men are close enough to one another to communicate by shouting. Only during the opening of the tap hole are they specifically confined to a certain position, but otherwise are still relatively free to move about. As in the first part, the tasks of these four men are not connected by work flow, but they are now functionally interdependent. Attention requirements are now more intense, though still comparatively low, as the time dimensions of the tapping operation permit less discretion. (Case 3a: Code T4:3; T5:1; T6:1) (Case 3b: Code T4:2; T5:5; T6:1)

Case 4—Docks

The fragments of information for this case were taken from a study conducted by the Department of Social Science at Liverpool University.[4] The study was carried out in the port of Manchester from 1950 to 1951. It consisted of a number of preliminary discussions with senior officials of the company, the dock labor board, and the union, and of interviews with 305 of the 2,400 dock workers and with the supervisors. The purpose of the research was a description of working conditions at the Manchester docks, of labor-management relations, of the relations of dock workers to the unions, of their earnings, and of strike activity. Data used for our purposes were only ancillary to this report. The case will be useful, however, in comparison with other cases for some information concerning the types of cooperation found among dock workers.

Work on the docks consists of three segments: work in the hold of a ship, the operation of a crane, and work on the dockside and its warehouses and railroad cars. We have here no information on the operation of the crane and thus face a problem similar to that of the last case. While the work of the men aboard ship and on the dockside is very much affected by the operation of the crane, we can specifically focus only on the work of the crews on each of the two ends of the process and describe the characteristics and relationships of the tasks of the workers within these subunits. Ordinarily, crews of eight men load and crews of six men discharge goods aboard ship. In the hold of the ship, pairs of men usually "work a corner" and such pairing often involves close and lasting relationships between the two men.

The report indicates that there are no forklift trucks or conveyor belts, and a large amount of the work is manual and heavy. Types of cargo mentioned are copper, newsprint, timber, bagged goods, cotton, general cargo, and ore. Newsprint packed in large cylinders is transferred by crane, and the men in the sheds merely undo the sling and kick or push the newsprint to get it rolling into place. In contrast, shoveling ore into skips is very hard work, especially when it is encountered together with protective sacking in the hold. (Liverpool, 62–63, 76, 191–192, 196) There is no conversion operation, and the work of these gangs consists of transfer operations by hand. (Code T3:R1-C1)

These men can move around in their work area and are within talking

---

distance of one another. Within each crew there is usually no linkage by work flow and no differentiation of tasks. The work of one man is dependent on the work of others. The temporal and perceptual characteristics of work are very similar to those in the preceding cases. (Code T4:1; T5:5; T6:1) There is presumably a loose cycling of the operation determined by the work of the crane. The length of cycles and their working content would be quite variable, however.

Case 5—Blast-Furnace Batching I

This case is derived from the study by Popitz and his associates discussed in Case 3. Cases 5, 6, and 7 are all concerned with the operation of bringing together, moving up to, and feeding into the blast furnace the materials required for the smelting operation. Observations were made in two different plants, one of which had an older installation of blast-furnace batching and feeding equipment, built around 1900. The installation in the second plant was built just before World War II and was of more advanced design. The total process at the back of the furnace consists of the following operations: the dropping of materials such as ore, coke, lime, and additives from the bunkers into transport vehicles; the weighing of materials; the moving of materials by elevator to the top of the blast furnace; and finally the dumping of materials into the blast furnace.

We will separate this operation into work-place units for purposes of analysis as follows. Case 5 will be concerned only with the older blast-furnace installation and will end at the point at which two men take over the materials carriages to move them into the elevator. Case 6 will again be confined to the older installation and comprise the remainder of the process from the bottom of the elevator to the dumping of materials into the blast furnace. We will call this the feeding of the blast furnace. (See Figures 2 and 3.) Case 7 will contain both the batching and feeding operations in one case, this time for the newer, more mechanized installation. Cases 6 and 7 will be discussed in a later section. Case 6 will be subdivided into two parts, of which one part will then be classified with the cases in the present section.

Twelve men work on each shift in the batching section of blast furnace I. Each of six men pushes an empty wagon under a bunker, fills it with ore, and pushes it back to the scales. Each of two men move wagons of coke in the same fashion, and two men operate scales. Two setters move filled carriages from the scales into the elevator and move empty ones out of the elevator. These two men will later be considered part of Case 6. One "load" consists of 14 coke wagons, 12 ore wagons, and 3 wagons with lime or other additives. Coke wagons are not weighed since their weight is known. (An empty wagon weighs about 1,300 pounds, and a filled wagon about one ton.) On each of the two scales 6 ore wagons are weighed

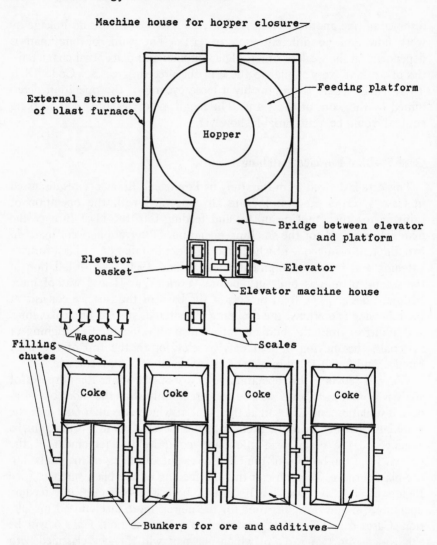

Figure 2. Cases 5 and 6—Batching and Feeding Plant of Blast Furnace I (By permission of the publisher and authors from H. Popitz, H. P. Bahrdt, E. A. Jüres, and H. Kesting, *Technik und Industriearbeit*, Tübingen: Mohr, 1957, p. 48. Redrawn for this book.)

together. The wagons have three wheels and are hand-pushed by one man. Under the bunkers they run on tracks. The six ore men are assigned to different kinds of ore and additives. This assignment is changed from week to week in order to equalize the variations in distance, dust, and difficulty in getting materials to run out of the bunkers. While the coke for one load is moved up, each ore man is required to haul two wagons. The wagons

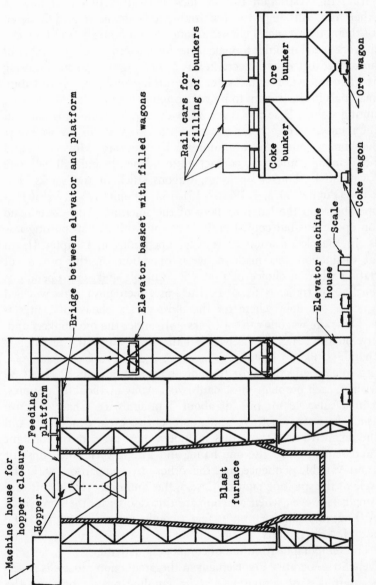

FIGURE 3. Cases 5 and 6—Batching and Feeding Plant of Blast Furnace I (By permission of the publisher and authors from H. Popitz, H. P. Bahrdt, E. A. Jüres, and H. Kesting, *Technik und Industriearbeit*, Tübingen: Mohr, 1957, p. 75. Redrawn for this book.)

must be ready when the loading of coke is completed in order to avoid delay in blast-furnace feeding.

The six ore men are jointly responsible for having the load ready on time. Within this restriction the ore men have discretion over how to arrange their run. Although the type of material to be hauled is determined for them, they can still choose among several bunkers, and they can vary their work speed in order to make time for longer breaks. A number of knacks make the work easier: a certain way of holding the wagon and using its inertia when it leaves the tracks, for easy turning; and properly distributing the materials in the wagon, to prevent tipping. From 30 to 40 loads are moved during a shift. Base pay is for 20 loads, and a premium is paid for more. The men can see each other except when they are in the walkways under the bunkers and can communicate by shouting. Moving around freely, the men come into close contact quite frequently and will help one another with sticky bunker openings, wagons stuck in the tracks, and spilled loads. (Popitz 1957a, 47–51, 62, 151–152) (Popitz 1957b, 34–36)

The operations on the batching floor of the smelting plant contain no conversion operations but consist entirely of the work of transporting raw materials. In the classification of transfer operations in Chapter II, an important distinction was made between operations in the process of transportation where a choice of routes is available and such operations where the line of traffic is fixed. In this case, men push three-wheeled carriages across the floor where for the most part a choice of routes is available. These ore wagons run on tracks only under the ore bunkers and, apparently, on the scales themselves. All the work up to the elevator is done by hand. (Code T3:R1-C1)

If we assume an effective shift time of about 420 minutes at about 30 loads per shift, each ore man must haul two wagons in about 14 minutes, resulting in a subcycle for him of about 7 minutes. In Chapter II we distinguished between repetitive and nonrepetitive cycle conditions, and among the repetitive ones those that include a short cycle and a constant content and sequence, on the one hand, and a long cycle and constant content and variable sequence, on the other. In comparison with the 4-hour cycle of the smelting crew of Case 3, the 7-minute cycle of this case is quite small. However, when we compare this case with others in which cycles are 1 minute long or only a few seconds, we can argue that the 7-minute cycle still permits a fair amount of discretion in varying the sequence and temporal distribution of component activities.

Relatively little cognitive involvement in the production process is necessary. The usefulness of various knacks in handling ore wagons and the variability of conditions from run to run indicate partial habituation. Workers must focus on their wagon and on the space ahead of them. They would be little concerned with the bunkers, except when they need help from above to have materials pushed through the opening. They must

TABLE 13. CODING SUMMARY: TECHNOLOGY TYPE I

Technology: Type I (R1-C1) No Conversion - Hand Transfer

Case 1 Steel-Plant Maintenance. Case 3a Smelting (Building Runners). Case 3b Smelting (Tapping). Case 4 Docks. Case 5 Blast-Furnace Batching I.

T4: SPATIAL CONSTRAINTS

Relation of Workers to Work Stations	Talking Distance	Shouting Distance	Seeing Distance	Beyond Seeing
Open	1,4	3b,5	3a	
Confined to fixed place				
Confined to mobile place				

T5: FUNCTIONAL CONSTRAINTS

Differentiation Pattern	No Work Flow		Work Flow	
	Independent	Dependent	Independent	Dependent
All tasks undifferentiated	3a	1,3b,4		
Each differentiated task shared	5			
Some exclusive and some shared tasks				
All tasks performed exclusively				

TABLE 13. CODING SUMMARY: TECHNOLOGY TYPE I (continued)

T6: TEMPORAL AND PERCEPTUAL CONSTRAINTS

Attention Requirements		Operation Cycles	
Low	1,3a,3b,4,5	Variable	1,4
Surface		4 hours	3a,3b
Detailed		7 minutes	5
External focus			
Watching			

recognize which bunkers contain the material they are expected to haul. Events at the scales and the elevator must be perceived for the appropriate timing of work. These are the conditions for what we have called "low" attention requirements.

The ore handlers as a whole are part of a larger work-flow sequence, but there is no work flow between them. They are not technically dependent on each other, except in the sense that the coke handlers' timing must fit into a certain part of the process and that the scale men are functionally connected with the ore men on one side and the setters who load the elevator on the other. There are several different tasks, but each is shared by several workers. Workers can move around freely in an open work space and are within shouting distance of one another. (Code T4:2; T5:2; T6:1)

Summary

Hard manual labor in moving materials and heavy equipment is common to the cases described in this chapter. Backbreaking work of this sort seems to be disappearing rapidly from the modern industrial scene, but is by no means extinct. All of these cases are components of larger production processes which possess more advanced technical characteristics, and the work of these men is—at least in its loose temporal boundaries—affected by these larger processes. Within the operations described, no conversion takes place and materials are moved by hand and with hand-operated tools and equipment. There is little specialization: no job in any of these cases is performed exclusively by one man. The work of these men is not linked by work flow, although in all cases but one the whole team occupies a position in a work-flow sequence. Temporal and perceptual demands are loosely defined, and thus attention requirements are "low." In all these cases, men move freely in the large work space. In the one case where they are not perceptually close enough to one another even for shouting, one man can easily enough walk over to the next and talk to him. In Table 13 the classification of these cases is summarized. The technological characteristics of these cases are labeled Type I. Parts of four more cases from later chapters will also be assigned to this type.

Chapter V

HAND WORK:
Changing and Moving Work Pieces by Hand

Case 10—Coal Mining I

This is one of three cases on coal mining. Information about the studies
from which the data were taken is given here for all three cases, of which
two will be discussed in subsequent chapters. The three cases differ from
most of the other cases in some respects. They are concerned with an
extractive industry, rather than a manufacturing industry. They are a
composite of information from four studies because each study does not
offer enough information for our purposes. The characteristics of each
study will be briefly outlined first.

The earliest study, by Trist and Bamforth,[1] was conducted over a period
of two years and published in 1951. It took place in the British coal-mining
industry, and no specific location is reported. The purpose of the study, in
line with many of the research activities of the Tavistock Institute, was
social therapy. A concern is expressed repeatedly for the loss of intimate
relationships among miners at work resulting from the mechanized longwall method of coal mining. Data were gathered for two years by interviews
and discussions with 20 key informants representing various coal-face
occupations, and with managers and psychiatrists. (Trist, 5)

The second study, by Jantke,[2] was carried out in coal mines in the
northern Ruhr district during 1950. The purpose of the study was to report
miners' opinions and objectively observed characteristics of wage-payment
systems, supervisors, works council and trade union, and accidents and
welfare. Our data come predominantly from the section on different
wage-payment systems. In the first system, miners choose their own mates
and make a group contract with the company. Wages are related to
production by the ton. In the second system, miners make individual
contracts and production is measured by the depths of the cuts into the

---

[1] E. L. Trist and K. W. Bamforth, "Some Social and Psychological Consequences
of the Longwall Method of Coal-Getting," *Human Relations*, 4 (1951), 3–38.
[2] C. Jantke, *Bergmann und Zeche: Die sozialen Arbeitsverhältnisse einer Schachtanlage des nördlichen Ruhrgebietes in der Sicht der Bergleute* (Tübingen: Mohr, 1953).

coal seam. Data were gathered by interviews and direct observations in the mines, dormitories, and homes.

The study by Dennis, Henriques, and Slaughter[3] is a community study of an English coal-mining town. How the authors went about gathering their data is not mentioned. They describe the relationships among work, leisure, family, and trade unionism in the coal-mining community. Work underground is described in detail. Published in 1959, the study by Goldthorpe[4] was also conducted in British coal mining but not with reference to a specific mine. The use of documents and the report of interviews with 45 coal-mine deputies are the basis for the information presented. The study attempts to show the effects of change in mining technology on the relationships of miners to their supervisors.

Central to the work operations described by Trist, Jantke, and Dennis is the so-called longwall method of coal-getting. Goldthorpe suggests, however, that the presence of a long coal face does not by itself indicate the stage of technological development to which Trist and Bamforth refer in using the term. What is important is the combination of a long coal face with the mechanization of certain operations. All four reports refer to the hand-got system which precedes the mechanized longwall method. Goldthorpe describes very briefly a later technical development of further mechanization. Only Goldthorpe, in fact, systematically follows through these three stages.

We will use each of the first two stages as the basis for one case. Within the case concerned with the mechanized longwall method, an additional distinction will be necessary among the technical characteristics of certain discrete parts of the whole underground operation. (See Figure 4.) The present case is concerned with the hand-got system of coal mining.

At the time of these studies, hand-got mining was apparently still found in Britain, often alongside the more mechanized methods. Small crews of two's and three's, sometimes extended to seven or eight, make piece-rate contracts and form self-contained units performing all the operations of underground work. The small teams ordinarily consist of two colliers, a hewer and his mate, assisted by a trammer (a boy or an old man), who moves the filled tubs away from the face and supplies the teams with empty tubs. Tubs run on rails and are pulled by ponies. Coal is obtained by pick and is shoveled by hand into tubs for transportation to the pit head. Blasting is sometimes used, but less often than under the more mechanized coal-mining methods. These self-contained teams might have a division of labor within the group but not between groups. Trammers are

[3] N. Dennis, F. Henriques, and C. Slaughter, *Coal Is Our Life: An Analysis of a Yorkshire Mining Community* (London: Eyre and Spottiswoode, 1956).

[4] J. H. Goldthorpe, "Technical Organization as a Factor in Supervisor-Worker Conflict: Some Preliminary Observations on a Study Made in the Mining Industry," *British Journal of Sociology*, 10 (1959), 213–230.

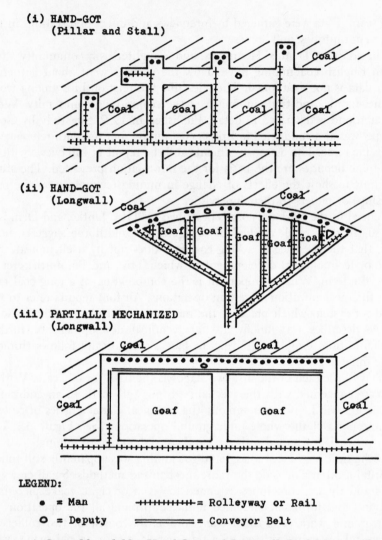

(i) HAND-GOT
(Pillar and Stall)

(ii) HAND-GOT
(Longwall)

(iii) PARTIALLY MECHANIZED
(Longwall)

LEGEND:

• = Man   ++++++++++++ = Rolleyway or Rail

O = Deputy   ============ = Conveyor Belt

FIGURE 4. Cases 10 and 11—Hand-Got and Longwall Coal Mining (By permission of the publisher, Routledge and Kegan Paul, Ltd., from J. H. Goldthorpe, "Technical Organization as a Factor in Supervisor-Worker Conflict," *British Journal of Sociology*, vol. 10, 1959, p. 229. Redrawn for this book.)

boys learning the trade or men who had once been colliers. The deputy is responsible for seeing to it that colliers are adequately supplied with tubs, and thus is in control over the trammers. There is no such supervision for the colliers. Face workers are craftsmen, with skills taught by their fathers and not by the employer. They provide their own tools and even powder. Face workers, in contrast to the trammers, possess the full range of coal-face skills and can substitute for one another. Recruitment is through mutual choice of prospective members who usually know each other and have worked together for years. The independence of these small teams allows an uneven advance of work where geological conditions vary, and teams determine their own pace. Ordinarily, teams work in individual stalls, although the hand-got system is also used on the longwall. Individual teams are widely dispersed in their stalls, isolated from one another both by work assignment and by darkness. At the end of a shift, work can be stopped at whatever point has been reached. The work performed by the team consists of occasional blasting, hewing out of coal, shoveling coal into tubs, removing the tubs, and setting up pillars. (Trist, 6–9; Jantke, 37, 242; Dennis, 55, 57; Goldthorpe, 214–217)

In this case we can speak of conversion operations in the sense that the solid coal face is converted into lumps of coal, but most of the work consists of the moving of materials. At the coal face itself, moving is performed by hand and along open lines, while movement away from the face follows the fixed line of the tracks on which the tubs are pulled by ponies. Our main concern will be with the work at the face itself, where face workers are not connected with one another by fixed lines of transfer. (Code T3:R2-C1)

The attention requirements of hand-got coal mining appear very similar to those of the preceding cases. However, variations in rock and coal are so great that there must be a continuous concern over the possibility of a collapse in roof or face. A very close focus on the work seems unlikely when the material is relatively coarse and the place is illuminated only by small hand lamps. Work content is constant, in the sense that colliers do the same kind of thing all the time, but work activities are not distributed over time in such a way that separable and regularly repeated phases can be observed. The connection between time and activity varies with geological conditions and team-determined pacing. Although work is likely to be divided up by the irregular timing of blasting and by the arrival and departure of tubs, time seems better described as mere duration rather than as cycle.

Taking the pair of colliers as an example, we can say that the men in this case are functionally interdependent, both in hewing and shoveling and in securing the roof, and there is no work flow between them. Each face worker possesses all the skill and experience required for getting coal. His is the job of a craftsman, learned only over the years. All the relevant jobs are performed by these men and include the routine getting of coal as well as the securing of the roof. For any short time span, presumably a different work function is performed by each man. While interchangeability is high, at times crews are expanded to larger units comprised of several hewers and their mates together with their attendant trammers. In the absence of much more detailed description, we will say at least that each of the possibly differentiated tasks is shared. Within the confinements of a work space often only 3 feet high, workers can move at their discretion. Taking a small contract crew at the face as our unit, including the face workers and the trammers at the time they are at the face, we find men in close proximity, able to talk to one another. (Code T4:1; T5:6; T6:1)

Case 13—Relay Assembly

The studies on which the following three cases are based were all conducted by human-relations research groups of the Harvard Business School. From early 1927 to the middle of 1932, five relay assemblers, young women, together with a supply worker were put in an experimental room and their behavior observed and in part recorded. This was the first of the well-known Hawthorne experiments, thoroughly described and analyzed by Whitehead.[5] This study is the source of our Case 13. As part of the same research project, sixteen male workers were transferred into the bank-wiring observation room, again supplied with raw materials by an additional man. Observations of their behavior were reported by Roethlisberger and Dickson and are the source of data for our Case 14.[6]

Since the general characteristics, aims, and procedures of these research undertakings are well known, it will not be necessary to describe them here in detail. We might only note that in the relay-assembly observation, the assumption was made that variations in social behaviors of the assembly workers could be held constant in order to study the effects of experimentally introduced external changes on the productivity of individual workers. In addition to records of productivity and changes in experimental conditions, observations about the social organization of these workers were recorded when there appeared to be, in the eyes of the observer, undue variation. The latter records were not kept systematically, but contain long and detailed diary accounts of conversation and "social" events.

Case 15 is based on a study reported by Zaleznik, Christensen, and Roethlisberger,[7] as is Case 16, which is discussed in a later chapter. This study was conducted from 1954 to 1956 in one department of an equipment-manufacturing company in the United States. It was designed to test a number of specific hypotheses worked out in collaboration with G. C. Homans. Data consisted of the following: two sets of interviews with all workers of this department and with staff and line personnel; so-called clinical observations in the department; company records on productivity;

---

[5] T. N. Whitehead, *The Industrial Worker: A Statistical Study of Human Relations in a Group of Manual Workers.* 2 vols. (Cambridge: Harvard University Press, 1938).

[6] F. J. Roethlisberger and W. J. Dickson, *Management and the Worker* (Cambridge: Harvard University Press, 1939), Part IV: "Social Organization of Employees."

[7] A. Zaleznik, C. R. Christensen, and F. J. Roethlisberger, *The Motivation, Productivity, and Satisfaction of Workers: A Prediction Study* (Boston: Division of Research, Graduate School of Business Administration, Harvard University, 1958).

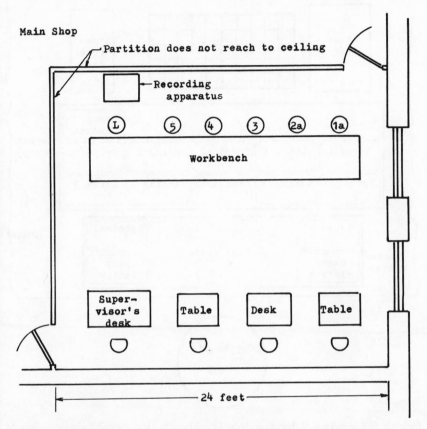

Main Shop

FIGURE 5. **Case 13—Relay-Assembly Room** (Reprinted by permission of the publishers from T. N. Whitehead, *The Industrial Worker*, Cambridge, Mass.: Harvard University Press, Copyright, 1938, by the President and Fellows of Harvard College, vol. II, p. A-2. Redrawn for this book.)

and individual characteristics of workers found in personnel records. The department studied consisted of four subunits: two assembly shops and two machine shops. Each of the two machine shops supplied parts to one of the two assembly shops. Case 15 will be concerned with the two assembly shops; Case 16 with the two machine shops (to be dealt with later).

In the relay-assembly room (Case 13), five girls sit side by side at a long workbench. (See Figures 5 and 6.) Immediately in front of each operator is a fixture designed to hold the parts of the relay together during the assembly. Around this fixture are a number of boxes containing the various assembly parts, and on the right is a hole through which completed assemblies are dropped onto a chute and from the chute into a box.

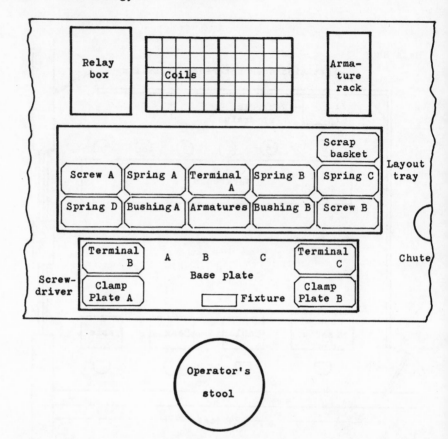

FIGURE 6. **Case 13—Relay-Assembly Workbench** (Reprinted by permission of the publishers from T. N. Whitehead, *The Industrial Worker*, Cambridge, Mass.: Harvard University Press, Copyright, 1938, by the President and Fellows of Harvard College, vol. II, p. A-3. Redrawn for this book.)

Assembly parts are delivered to each position by a sixth woman, the layout operator. The only tool used is an automatic screwdriver on which the blade rotates when the handle is pushed against a screw. These workers are paid by a piece-rate arrangement. They inspect their own work and repair faults, and time for this part of the work is lost toward piece-rate earnings. Each operator would complete between 450 and 500 standard relays in a day. Each assembly requires more than thirty different operations by each hand. Various parts are slipped over pins, and this pile-up of pieces has to be held together while the worker reaches for other parts. At the end, screws are put in place of the pins and fastened.

Performed at the rate of about 1 minute per assembly, this task requires remembering the relative position and sequence of assembly and coordinating hand movements which are often not symmetrical for both hands. The work requires the development of a near-automatic pattern of quick movements. Mistakes in sequence or loss of pattern result in faulty assembly, broken parts, upset pile-ups, stripped screw threads, and burred heads. (Whitehead, 17–19, 23–24, 235)

Both the conversion and transfer operations in this case are clearly performed by hand. The only tool observed is a screwdriver. Parts and completed assemblies are manually moved by the operators and carried in boxes to and from the work place by other employees. (Code T3:R2-C1) We find here what we have called "surface" attention. This means short cycles and highly repetitive and habituated movements where full thinking-through of the process would not make it possible to work at the expected rate. What the hands do is not deliberate action in which the movements are part of the worker's awareness. At the same time, the eyes can never be diverted from the work being performed and must persistently recognize the small variations occurring in the putting together of a small assembly consisting of many parts. Changes in assembly type do happen, quite frequently for one operator in particular, but there is a fairly persistent general pattern in the temporal distribution of activities over the short cycle.

Assembly parts are moved to the assembly room, where they are distributed by the layout operator to the assemblers' bench; completed assemblies are moved away from the room. However, since work pieces are in storage before and after the operation, this work is not a temporal part of a work-flow sequence. All five assemblers perform the same task. These tasks are performed independently and are not linked by work flow. Sitting fairly close to one another, side by side on their stools in front of their work stations, operators are confined to a fixed place and are within talking distance. (Code T4:5; T5:1; T6:2)

Case 14—Bank Wiring

Working in the bank-wiring room were nine wiremen, three soldermen, and two inspectors. In addition, a trucker occasionally came into the room to deliver raw materials on a hand truck and to take finished products out. As in the relay-assembly room of Case 13, an observer was sitting at his desk.

Work is done on a number of long benches, and the work of each wireman occupies two-thirds of a bench. A wireman's bench space has two positions, on each of which he works alternately, permitting a solderman and an inspector to work on the other. The work of a wireman begins when he places a fixture on his bench. The fixture is a wooden board, 8 inches wide and 6 feet long, which has eleven pairs of pins projecting upwards. A number of banks are slipped over these pins. Projecting from each bank are

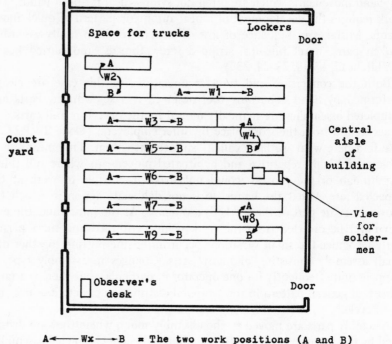

A◄──── Wx ────►B = The two work positions (A and B)
of Wireman x

FIGURE 7. **Case 14—Bank-Wiring Room** (Reprinted by permission of the publishers from F. J. Roethlisberger and W. J. Dickson, *Management and the Worker*, Cambridge, Mass.: Harvard University Press, Copyright, 1939, by the President and Fellows of Harvard College, p. 403. Redrawn for this book.)

either 100 or 200 terminals. Wire with insulation stripped at regular intervals is wound off a spool by the wireman, who then winds a blank section of wire once around a terminal on the first bank, connects the wire to the equivalent terminal on the next bank, and so forth to the end of a row of ten or eleven banks. He then cuts the wire and starts again on the second terminal on the first bank. Once all the terminals of a row of banks have been wired, the wireman moves to his other position and performs the same task there. Meanwhile, a solderman, with an electric soldering iron, solders each wire connection to a terminal. Wiremen prefer to work on banks with 100 terminals because there is more space between terminals. Soldermen like the 200-point bank better because on these the terminals are so close together that they can slide the soldering iron from point to point without interruption.

Once one row of banks has been wired and soldered, fibre insulators are placed over it, and a second level of banks is put on for wiring and soldering. A completed equipment has either two or three such levels.

When one level has been soldered, an inspector tests whether circuits between terminals are completed. He attaches a test set to an equipment, and a buzzer sounds when contact is made with a connected terminal. Faulty connections are checked out visually and may lie in reversed wiring, broken wire, or solder spanning the gap between two terminals. (Roethlisberger, 392–397, 403–404, 432, 467–468, 498)

Conversion and transfer operations are performed by hand and with hand tools, including pliers, soldering irons, and a hand truck. (Code T3:R2-C1) As part of their work, it is necessary for these fourteen operators to walk to various places in the room. Wiremen pick up fresh wire spools and banks from a place near the door and move between their two working positions. Soldermen cover the working area of three wiremen and go to a vise on one of the benches to file their soldering tips several times a day. The two inspectors divide the work between them and thus move through various parts of the work area. The men are within talking distance of one another. Each of the three tasks is shared by several men.

Wiremen could prevent the soldermen or inspectors from keeping up with them by, for instance, all finishing a level at the same time and thus gaining time on the successive worker. A wireman could also, toward the end of the day, connect wires in irregular and incomplete fashion on several levels. He would thus prevent a solderman and an inspector from working on his equipment until, next morning, he would quickly complete the connection and suddenly have several levels completed. The performance of the second and third operations, then, is dependent on the performance of the preceding one. The wiremen, who are first in line, are themselves dependent on the completion of the subsequent operation in order to continue their own work. However, we should note that men within each of these three task categories are functionally independent of one another. In addition, work pieces are not actually moving from operator to operator, and the actual transfer of work from one task to the next is very infrequent. Taking about 6,000 connections as a day's work and either 1,000 or 2,000 connections per level, we can say that a wireman's rate of shifting from one position to another and thus having work ready for a solderman would be between about 80 and 160 minutes.

With a view to the infrequency of "work flow" between tasks and to the fact that only workers with different classifications are linked by this flow, we will classify this case as having no work flow, and the tasks as being functionally independent. In subsequent analysis we will note when the connections between work stations that do exist are relevant. This work requires a close focus on hands and work piece but, at the rate of about fifteen terminals a minute for wiremen and three times that number for soldermen, the level of cognitive involvement in the work process would be low, and hand movements highly habituated. The use of the term "cycle" is barely applicable for this very short-range repetition. Other forms of relatively loose and variable cycling might be seen in the completion of one row of connections across ten or eleven banks of one level, or even completion of a whole equipment about twice a day. Assuming a repetitive, short cycle and constant work content and sequence, we have the conditions of surface attention. (Code T4:1; T5:2; T6:2)

Case 15—Equipment-Assembly Shop

Both Case 15 and Case 16 are based on a study of a department having four subsystems. Machining on rotating equipment takes place in Subsystem III, and machined parts are assembled in Subsystem I into finished rotating units. This equipment is made into two basic sizes, with variations in gear trains. Parts for utility equipment are machined in Subsystem II, and part assemblies are made in Subsystem IV. Case 15 is concerned with the two assembly subsystems, I and IV. Figure 8 shows the distribution of the subsystems in the department, and Figure 9 shows the arrangement for the two assembly subsystems. With the meager information in the report of what these assemblers actually do, our data and their classification must be rather tentative.

Working in Subsystem I are a group leader, a paint sprayer, six assemblers, and two inspectors; four of these ten workers are women. In Subsystem IV there are a group leader, a drill-press operator, and five assemblers; there are three women among the seven workers. Workers are grouped around three workbenches in Subsystem I, and around one large bench in Subsystem IV. Work in this department is done on job orders. Workers are assigned batches of work by their group leader, and they return a batch of work to a local storage area. (Zaleznik 1958, 90–101, 108–113)

With the exception of the drill press in Subsystem IV, it would appear that the work of putting together parts is done by hand and with hand tools and that work pieces are moved by hand. (Code T3:R2-C1) Workers are probably confined to a particular place at the bench and are within talking distance of one another. Several tasks are likely to be shared, and a few are exclusive. There is no work flow between these workers, and tasks are performed independently. They do light assembly work in batches, and most of their pay categories indicate that the job is set up for them. This would suggest that surface-attention requirements might best describe the temporal and perceptual constraints of this case. (Code T4:5; T5:3; T6:2)

Case 21—Auto Assembly I

The data for this case and Case 22 are based on studies of the technology project of the Yale Labor and Management Center. Research began in 1949 in the assembly plant of a major American automobile manufacturer, in the course of which a stratified sample of 180 workers was interviewed in

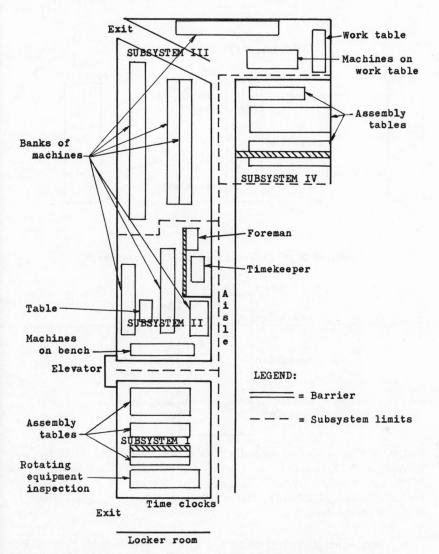

Exit

SUBSYSTEM III

Work table

Machines on
work table

Assembly
tables

Banks of
machines

SUBSYSTEM IV

Foreman

Timekeeper

A
i
s
l
e

Table

Machines
on bench

SUBSYSTEM II

Elevator

LEGEND:

= Barrier

= Subsystem limits

Assembly
tables

SUBSYSTEM I

Rotating
equipment
inspection

Time clocks

Exit

Locker room

FIGURE 8. **Cases 15 and 16—Equipment Machining and Assembly Shops** (By permission of the publisher from A. Zaleznik, C. R. Christensen, and F. J. Roethlisberger, *The Motivation, Productivity, and Satisfaction of Workers: A Prediction Study*, Boston: Division of Research, Harvard Business School, 1958, p. 91. Redrawn for this book.)

SUBSYSTEM I [Assembly of rotating equipment]

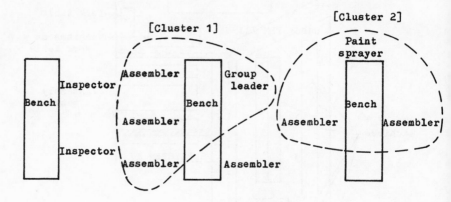

SUBSYSTEM IV [Assembly of utility equipment]

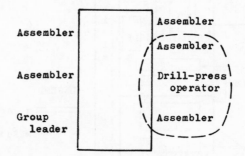

Figure 9. Case 15—Two Assembly Subsystems (By permission of the publisher from A. Zaleznik, C. R. Christensen, and F. J. Roethlisberger, *The Motivation, Productivity, and Satisfaction of Workers: A Prediction Study*, Boston: Division of Research, Harvard Business School, 1958, pp. 109, 112. Redrawn for this book.)

their homes. This study was concerned with the satisfactions that workers derive from their jobs.[8] The research was then continued with a study of the same plant, in which the actions of a number of assembly-line foremen were observed over eight-hour periods and recorded in detail.[9] Subsequently the studies were repeated in a second plant of the automobile company, called Plant Y in contrast to Plant X of the first set of studies.

[8] C. R. Walker and R. H. Guest, *The Man on the Assembly Line* (Cambridge: Harvard University Press, 1952); Robert H. Guest, "Men and Machines: An Assembly-Line Worker Looks at His Job," *Personnel*, 31 (1954–1955), 496–503.

[9] C. R. Walker, R. H. Guest, and A. N. Turner, *The Foreman on the Assembly Line* (Cambridge: Harvard University Press, 1956).

We rely on a further publication based on the studies in both of these plants.[10]

Like other mass-production assembly operations, automobile assembly has at its center the continuously moving assembly line on which an automobile is put together and worked on in a long sequence of highly segmented operations. Automobile parts which eventually become components of the completed product are supplied by feeder plants at other locations away from the assembly plant. But before many of these parts reach the main assembly line, additional preparatory work and the making of subassemblies take place at work stations which are near the assembly line but not a direct part of it and which form the tributaries of the main stream. These preparatory operations may be performed at individual work stations from which parts are delivered to the main line; they may be performed at a number of interconnected work stations which themselves form minor, moving assembly lines; or they may take place at work stations just off the line at which several operators jointly preassemble larger parts. This joint putting together of large parts, which in some cases might also take place on the main line itself, is the kind of operation on which we will focus in Case 21. Case 22 will follow in a subsequent chapter and will focus on workers on the main line and on the tributary, smaller assembly lines. Isolated workers at separate work stations off the line will be disregarded.

About 21 per cent of the men in the sample are classified as working on subassembly off the moving belt. (Walker 1952, 51, 76) Two or three and as many as fifteen men might work on subassembly in a team. Two men might cooperate as partners, for instance, in spot-welding work on rear-quarter panels. One man spot-welds together two sheet-metal pieces which his partner holds in place on a jig. On the line itself, two men together put large instrument panels in place and attach them to supports. Hanging cloth to the ceiling of the car involves the same kind of partnership.

Larger teams are found where front fenders, grilles, and radiators are assembled into a unit on stationary bucks. The large parts are moved into the area by overhead conveyors, and the completed unit is put on a conveyor and moved to the main line. (Walker 1952, 21, 74–75) Several of the same work stations with partial assemblies on bucks are set up side by side with several men working on them. These men jointly put on the larger parts of this partial assembly and fasten them with the use of hand-controlled power tools.

This case, as well as two other cases to follow later, suggests an addition to our categories of transfer operations. Many of the work pieces used here are moved to the work station by overhead conveyors and leave it again by

---

[10] F. J. Jasinski, "Technological Delimitation of Reciprocal Relationships: A Study of Interaction Patterns in Industry," *Human Organization*, 15, No. 2 (Summer 1956), 24–28.

moving conveyors in such a way that the right subassembly meets the right car at the right point on the main assembly line. We should note that almost every car on the line differs from the preceding one in many possible respects—model, color, or the addition of different accessories. We have characterized our fifth category of transfer operations, labeled "live line," as one in which power supply, choice of routes, and control over cycles are external to workers and lie in the production equipment. While all these characteristics are present for this case, work pieces are temporarily taken off the line, and the distribution of time within a work cycle is independent of line speed. The cycle here is a multiple of the average 1½ minutes on the main line, and several work stations are used for the same operation. We can compare this situation with that in other cases in which some of the characteristics of work pacing are similar. The smelter and converter men in Case 3 performed work within the framework of the timing requirements of the blast furnace or converter, but had a choice in the disposition of their time within that cycle.

The work of these crews just off the main line is built into a work flow carried by overhead conveyors. But once the work pieces have been taken off the conveyor, transfer operations are performed by hand. Hand-manipulated tools are used in the conversion operation of subassembly work. (Code T3:R2-C1)

Men in these teams are within talking distance, unless the noise of conveying machinery and powered hand tools extend the distance perceptually to shouting distance. Their work location is relatively open. The tasks within the team are not linked by work flow but are interdependent. Tasks are highly segmented and, at least in the larger teams, are likely to be shared by several men. Although there is no positive information on the matter, the length of operation cycles is probably several times the basic cycle of the main line. In the assembly of front ends of car bodies on bucks, we might assume, for instance, that there would be four such work stations and that the cycle would be approximately 6 minutes. Such a cycle might permit some variation in sequence, to which the variation in models and makes of cars is added. Where bulky work pieces are handled repetitively, hand movements would be partly habituated. With an operation fitted into the larger temporal sequence and with coordination being necessary among several men in fitting pieces together, attention focus would be divided between the work under a man's hands and the larger production process. There would be little necessity for thinking about the work process. These are the conditions for what we have called low attention requirements. (Code T4:1; T5:6; T6:1)

Summary

Table 14 shows the distribution of these five cases among our categories. In all of these cases, work in the conversion and movement of materials is

TABLE 14. CODING SUMMARY: TECHNOLOGY TYPE II

Technology: Type II (R2-C1) Hand Tools - Hand Transfer

Case 10 Coal Mining I. Case 13 Relay Assembly. Case 14 Bank
Wiring. Case 15 Equipment-Assembly Shop. Case 21 Auto
Assembly I.

T4: SPATIAL CONSTRAINTS

Relation of Workers to Work Stations	Talking Distance	Shouting Distance	Seeing Distance	Beyond Seeing
Open	10,14,21			
Confined to fixed place	13,15			
Confined to mobile place				

T5: FUNCTIONAL CONSTRAINTS

Differentiation Pattern	No Work Flow		Work Flow	
	Independent	Dependent	Independent	Dependent
All tasks undifferentiated	13			
Each differentiated task shared	14	10,21		
Some exclusive and some shared tasks	15			
All tasks performed exclusively				

TABLE 14.   CODING SUMMARY: TECHNOLOGY TYPE II (continued)

T6: TEMPORAL AND PERCEPTUAL CONSTRAINTS

Attention Requirements		Operation Cycles	
Low	10,21	No cycles	10
Surface	13,14,15	6 minutes	21
Detailed		? minutes	15
External focus		1 minute	13
Watching		4 and 12 seconds	14

performed by hand and with hand tools. In spite of this uniformity, however, we find two sets of conditions when we look at variation in technical constraints. There are no recognizable cycles in the hand-got coal mining of Case 10, and there are relatively long cycles in the off-line auto assembly of Case 21. The remaining three cases have shorter cycles. We have described all five cases as having no work-flow connection between tasks, although Case 21 is built into a larger work-flow sequence and Cases 10 and 14 have a work-flow component which we have considered of comparatively small importance. In Cases 10 and 21, however, we have indicated functional dependence and low attention requirements; while in the remaining cases, work is done independently and surface attention is required.

The people in all these cases are within talking distance, and the workers' relation to their work station is relatively open in Cases 10 and 21, as well as in Case 14. In the assembly operations of Cases 13 and 15, workers are confined to a fixed position. In subsequent analysis we will find that the general difference between Cases 10 and 21 and the remainder and between the cases with open work positions and those with confined positions does indeed make a difference.

Chapter VI

MACHINE WORK:
Work-Piece Conversion on Separate Machines

Case 11—Coal Mining II

The coal-getting method observed in this case is called the longwall method by Trist, and the partially mechanized or conventional system by Goldthorpe. Information for this case has been derived from the same four studies used for Case 10. In contrast to the hand-got system, the coal is undercut by a coal cutter, shot firing is regularly used, and coal is moved to the main road of the mine by a continuously moving conveyor. The task of "filling off," however, remains the same; the fillers work with pick and shovel on the coal which has been loosened by blasting, and shovel the coal onto the moving conveyor. They also use an air hammer to break up the coal further.

The tasks which were all previously performed by one team during one shift are now distributed over three different shifts and among men performing specialized functions. In the presence of more machinery, additional operations are performed which were not found in the hand-got system. The distribution and combination of tasks performed varies slightly among our four sources of data, but most of the described characteristics are very similar. The layout of the work area is illustrated in Figures 10 and 11.

In this case, coal is no longer obtained in small stalls, but along an extended coal face of approximately 200 yards in length. The coal face is connected with the mining road by two side gates extending from the road to each end of the face and by a main gate extending from the road to the center of the face. The space immediately in front of the coal face is about 6 feet wide and 3 feet high. The roof is held by props spaced 3 feet apart in each direction. The gates are roadways from 7 to 9 feet high, built up permanently, which provide space for coal conveyors and access both for men and for air. The coal seam is commonly about 3 feet high, sometimes higher, and is cut out to a depth of 6 feet each day. Operations are

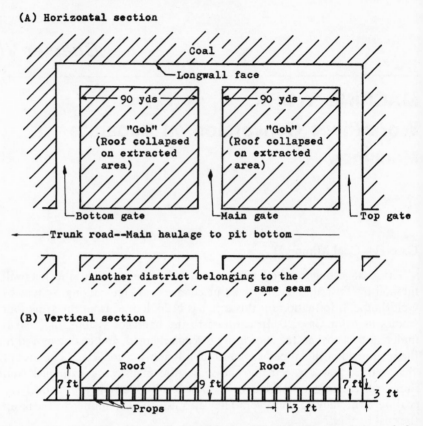

(A) Horizontal section

(B) Vertical section

FIGURE 10. **Case 11—Longwall Coal-Mining District** (By permission of the publisher, the authors, and the Tavistock Institute of Human Relations, from E. L. Trist and K. W. Bamforth, "Some Social and Psychological Consequences of the Longwall Method of Coal-Getting," *Human Relations*, vol. 4, 1951, p. 12. Redrawn for this book.)

performed over three shifts: two for face preparation, and the third shift for filling off. Each shift is dependent on the completion of work during the preceding shift, while operations performed during one shift are generally independent of one another. An approximate sequence of operations is given below.[1]

Holes, spread over the entire face, are drilled to the depth of the cut by a pair of borers. Two cutters operate the cutting machine which cuts out a few inches of the coal seam, usually at the bottom. The holes drilled by the borers are later filled with explosives, and the undercut made by the cutters

---

[1] This information is most systematically reported by Trist, and we will follow that report most closely. But the data are corroborated by the other reports, and page references are given for all four.

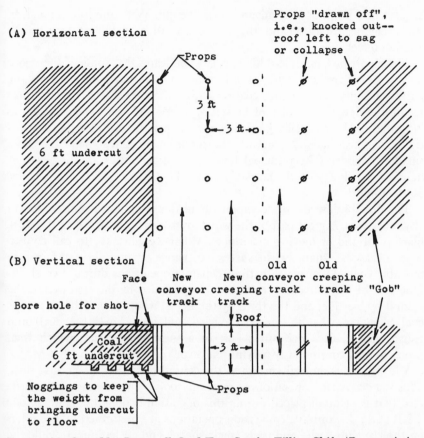

FIGURE 11. Case 11—Longwall Coal Face Set for Filling Shift (By permission of the publisher, the authors, and the Tavistock Institute of Human Relations, from E. L. Trist and K. W. Bamforth, "Some Social and Psychological Consequences of the Longwall Method of Coal-Getting," *Human Relations*, vol. 4, 1951, p. 13. Redrawn for this book.)

allows the coal to drop and break up during the shot firing. The cutters are followed by the four gummers, who remove coal from the cut made by the coal cutter in order to allow a clear drop of coal during the shot firing. The gummers also place supports in the cut to keep the coal from shifting before blasting. Two belt breakers disassemble the conveyor belt and move it forward by two lines of props. On the second shift, the two belt builders reassemble the belt directly in front of the coal face. Approximately eight rippers extend the main and side gates to greater height and build it up permanently. Usually, shots are fired at the end of this shift. During the third shift, some twenty fillers are evenly distributed over the length of the coal face. They break up the coal and shovel it onto the conveyor. They also set new props as they advance into the cut. With the following shift, the cycle begins anew and the whole operation is moved forward by another 6 feet.

The report by Dennis and his associates indicates that some of these jobs may be distributed differently. For instance, a crew may jointly operate the cutting machine and remove coal dust from the cut. A separate crew may secure the new stretch of roof by setting props and stone pillars. Also, as indicated in the report by Jantke, conveyors may be of different construction. Coal faces may be somewhat shorter or longer, and some of the crews smaller or larger. The principal technical characteristics are, however, as here given. (Trist, 10–26; Jantke, 22–24, 217–218, 232, 239, 242; Dennis, 38–48; Goldthorpe, 217–221)

The distribution of work components in this operation is unlike that in any other case. A great part of the work consists of reconstructing the work place itself and of moving machinery. What we will have to call conversion in this case—namely, the successive change of the solid coal face into movable coal—takes place in three separate operations during two shifts. One part of the conversion operation is performed by the coal cutter; the second by blasting; and the third by the fillers, who not only break up the coal further so that it can be shoveled, but also shovel the coal onto conveyors and thus perform a part of a transfer operation which then proceeds on a continuously moving conveyor.

We will focus on coal cutting as the central operation of the first shift. This is a conversion operation by machine tools.[2] The moving of the little coal that is being displaced during this operation is done by hand. (Code T3:R4-C1) In contrast, conversion operations are performed by the fillers on the last shift with hand tools (pick, shovel, and air hammer), while the bulk of the moving takes place on a continuously moving and fixed line. (Code T3:R2-C5) The present Case 11, then, will be divided into two parts which we will subsequently call Case 11a and 11b. We do not completely separate these two parts because, as Trist emphasizes very strongly, coal-cutting work and filling work are functionally interdependent, although they are separated by shifts and the men working in these operations never see each other. Case 11b—Coal Mining II (Filling) will be coded in this chapter, together with Case 11a—Coal Mining II (Cutting). In the summary for this chapter, Case 11b will be omitted. It will be included in the summary of the next chapter together with other cases of the same type of technology.

The cutting machine operates on electricity and occasionally compressed

---

[2] It should be noted that the use of the term "machine tool" as a category in our types of technologies does not have the narrow meaning of common usage, which refers to machine-shop equipment. Instead, as discussed in Chapter II, it is the name given to a stage in technical development in which work components performed by men are successively conferred on machines.

air. It cuts from 4 to 6 feet into the coal face by means of a long jib. Cuts 2 or 3 inches deep are made at either the bottom, the top, or the middle of the seam. The machine weighs "many hundredweight," uses a great deal of electric power, and produces vibrations in the coal face, the roof, and the floor. Maneuvering such a heavy machine in the limited space available is difficult and hazardous, and requires skill, strength, and close cooperation. (Dennis, 38–39) The cutting machine is operated by two men. Two men bore holes, and the requirements of their work would be similar to those of cutting. Although we have classified this case as involving the use of machine tools, it will become apparent later that the case is more similar to others in which heavy objects are handled manually.

In the dark and narrow tunnel alongside the coal face, only the pairs of operators are within talking distance when machines are not running and within shouting distance when the machines are running. Work locations are open, and workers move along the entire face during their work. During the two preparation shifts, there is no work flow to speak of. Tasks within the pair teams are interdependent. Each of the several differentiated tasks is shared by at least two men. Workers focus their attention on the work directly before them and—as always underground—on the potentially shifting conditions of the face and the ceiling. Certain component steps in their performance will be habituated, but the whole pattern involving the shifting and directing of the machine is probably not. Where a heavy machine must be moved and operated under difficult conditions— that is, in a confined space and accompanied by persistent danger and changing geological conditions—a great deal of variation would be expected, even in an operation that otherwise would be routine. Work on the cutting shift constitutes a part of a 24-hour cycle. Within this partial operation, the work runs continuously throughout the shift from one end of the face to the other, divided into irregular parts by the moving of the machine and the difficulties encountered with the cut. Thinking-through of the steps of the process is probably necessary with every cut. These are the conditions for detailed attention requirements. (Case 11a—Coal Cutting: Code T4:2; T5:6; T6:3)

The fillers work on "stints" of from 8 to 10 yards, spread along the coal face. Each filler must clear the depth of the cut for his stint on his own. With shovel, pick, and hammer, he works in a "hammer-and-tongs rhythm" throughout the shift, interrupted by a 20-minute break taken at an agreed time. Fillers wear shorts, boots, kneepads, and a cap with a lamp, and spend the entire shift on their knees. They must constantly be aware of the potential danger of the roof or face falling in. (Dennis, 40)

Fillers are at best within shouting distance of one another, the distance between them extended by the conveyor noise and the darkness. At times a man is likely to be only a few feet away from the next man and can call over to him. There is a work flow away from the fillers to the conveyor and down the conveyor, but the performance of the task of one filler is independent of that of the next. Within the filling crew, all tasks are undifferentiated. Hand movements are habituated, no intensive thinking-through of the work process is necessary, and workers focus on the work of their hands before them. The hammer-and-tongs rhythm implies a short, repetitive cycle of perhaps a few seconds. We will classify the case as requiring surface attention, although it does not involve the intricacies of jobs with surface attention described later, and is mixed with "low" attention requirements. (Case 11b—Filling: Code T4:2; T5:9; T6:2)

Case 16—Machine Shop

In this case we continue with information from the source of Case 15. We are now dealing with the two machine-shop subsystems of the department. The seven workers in Subsystem II are all machine operators and turn out parts for utility equipment. The nineteen workers in Subsystem III also operate machines for work on rotating equipment parts. (See Figures 12 and 13.) Work is assigned by the group leader to each worker individually, and work pieces are taken out of storage by each operator and returned to storage. The pieces of equipment used are machine tools, and materials are moved by hand. (Code T3:R4-C1) Among the machines used are lathes, milling machines, grinders, and drill presses. We know that production is in job-lot batches and by individual assignment. We will assume, then, that these are general-purpose machine tools rather than highly specialized ones. Kinds of work pieces turned out are likely to vary greatly in their characteristics. Following the indication from the original report that workers of a pay grade of four and lower have their work set up for them, we find five workers in Subsystem III who would not set up their own work, and five in Subsystem II.

Work on general-purpose machine tools permits only subsidiary habituation of hand movements. It requires closely focused visual discrimination and high cognitive involvement. Under conditions of changing job assignments, both the work cycles and the content are variable. Cycles are likely to be very pronounced for work on machine tools where time is regularly divided by activities associated with setting up, placing work pieces into machine fixtures, and the actual metal-removing operations. This means that the relatively high level of detailed attention is required only intermittently. For instance, during a cutting sequence on a lathe, demands on the operator are temporarily reduced. Workers are required to move through the work area in order to pick up and return a batch of work and to work on different machines. Work stations are within talking distance. Work is done independently, is not connected by work flow, and each of the specialized tasks is shared by several workers. (Code T4:1; T5:2; T6:3)

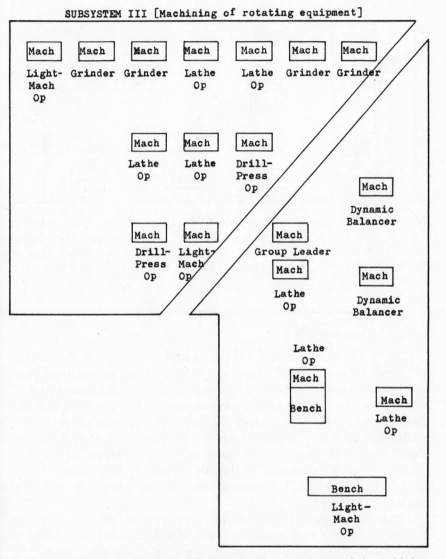

FIGURE 12. **Case 16—Machining Subsystem** (By permission of the publisher from A. Zaleznik, C. R. Christensen, and F. J. Roethlisberger, *The Motivation, Productivity, and Satisfaction of Workers: A Prediction Study,* Boston: Division of Research, Harvard Business School, 1958, p. 116. Redrawn for this book.)

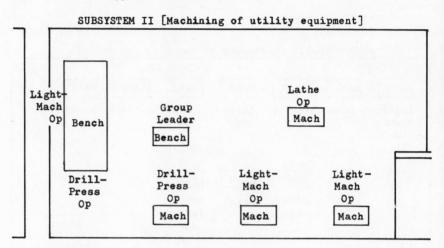

FIGURE 13. Case 16—Machining Subsystem (By permission of the publisher from A. Zaleznik, C. R. Christensen, and F. J. Roethlisberger, *The Motivation, Productivity, and Satisfaction of Workers: A Prediction Study*, Boston: Division of Research, Harvard Business School, 1958, p. 114. Redrawn for this book.)

Case 17—Machine Shop

Data for this case were obtained from a study conducted by Zaleznik[3] in 1953 and 1954 in a small plant producing a variety of small precision instruments. Direct observations, informal interviews, and examination of records were the methods of obtaining data on the fourteen workers in the machine-shop room of the plant. In line with the research on human relations in industry conducted at the Harvard Business School, this study deals with the so-called informal social relations of workers. Specifically, it is an analysis of the congruency of status characteristics of individuals in relation to interaction patterns within the group of workers.

The technical characteristics of this work place and their demands on worker activity are very similar to those of the preceding case. Work is individually performed on lathes, drill presses, milling machines, and benches. References are made in other parts of the report to soldering, testing for water tightness, honing the bore of a cylindrical piece, and milling some small pieces.

---

[3] A. Zaleznik, *Worker Satisfaction and Development: A Case Study of Work and Social Behavior in a Factory Group* (Boston: Division of Research, School of Business Administration, Harvard University, 1956).

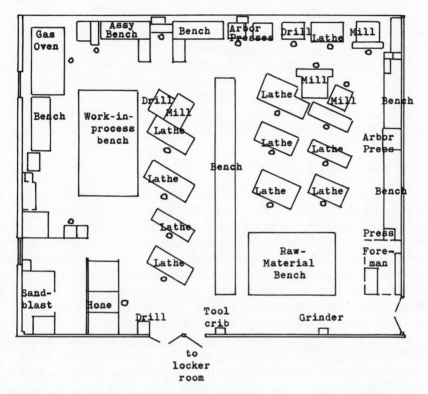

FIGURE 14. Case 17—Machine Shop (By permission of the publisher from A. Zaleznik, *Worker Satisfaction and Development: A Case Study of Work and Social Behavior in a Factory Group*, Boston: Division of Research, Harvard Business School, 1956, p. 15. Redrawn for this book.)

Spatial arrangements in the shop are shown in Figure 14. Machinists keep their toolboxes and do their layout work on the long bench extending from the foreman's desk. Sandblasting, soldering, and other finishing work take place near the opposite wall and are done by the less skilled "operators." Most of the center of the room is occupied by the machine tools. The foreman receives job orders and assigns them to individual workers. Machinists are supposed to be assigned the complex jobs; and operators, the finishing or simple machining work. When a worker has completed a job, he reports to the foreman for another assignment, and work does not move from one worker to another. Each job varies in its necessary processing steps, and batches are small. Workers are required to get tools from the tool crib and to move from one machine to another. (Zaleznik 1956, 13–16)

Precision instruments presumably consist of comparatively small pieces, so that we can assume that movement of materials is done by hand or hand trucks. Machine tools are used for the conversion of materials. (Code T3:R4-C1) As in Case 16, products are made in job lots and the operators are both skilled machinists and semiskilled machine operators. In this case, however, no clear indication is given that the machine operators have their jobs set up for them, and they do simpler machining jobs in addition to the finishing work. The technical constraints of this case are the same as those of the preceding case. (Code T4:1; T5:2; T6:3)

Case 18—Clicking Room

This case is based on a report by Roy,[4] who spent two months working with a small number of workers in the so-called clicking room of a manufacturing plant. The report describes how workers adapt to extremely monotonous work by individual revelries and the regular repetition of ritual occasions and conversational themes. Four clicking machines in a row side by side are located in a room separated from the main plant by a storage room. There is a cutting table at one end of the row of machines where operators cut small sheets of plastic material from rolls for use in the machine operation. All four machines are operated by men. A woman works at another table at the other end, using scissors to cut out intricate parts for raincoats. The machines are similar to punch presses on which a hammer, or punching head, descends to a wooden block on which a plastic sheet is laid. A die is moved by hand on the plastic sheet from one spot to the next for each cut. The hammer is moved down by pressure on a handle until an electrical connection is reached and a sharp, power-driven blow hits the die and cuts a piece of plastic. The hammer can be moved around a central column, and occasionally the sheets of material are shifted on the block. The material to be cut is either one sheet of leather or a stack of sheets of plastic.

The bulk of the work consists of hand and arm movements—placing the die, punching the clicker, placing the die, punching the clicker, and so on. Occasionally, fresh stacks of sheets have to be obtained, a box of finished work moved out of the way, and an empty box brought back. These occasional movements involve no more than a few steps. Other respites from regularity include variations in the color of materials, variations in the shape of the die, and the scraping of the block. (Roy, 158–161)

In Table 1 of Chapter II we suggested that we would classify a conversion operation as involving the use of machine tools when energy is supplied by the equipment and when the tool which actually performs the

[4] D. F. Roy, " 'Banana Time': Job Satisfaction and Informal Interaction," *Human Organization*, 18, No. 4 (Winter 1959–1960), 159–168.

conversion operation is held and manipulated by the machine. In this case the cutting tool, consisting of a die, is moved on the horizontal plane by hand and the actual cut occurs automatically by electrical contact when the operator moves down the hammer head with a handle attached to it. But the hammer head and the die are moved by the operator's hand in several directions confined by the central connection of the hammer head to the machine. In contrast, for instance, to the automatic lathe where tool movement along the work piece is started by the operator but continues automatically through the rotation of a spindle, this subpart of the operation is performed by the operator. The work piece is fed by the operator, and control over work cycles as well as over the planning of moves is in the hands of the operator. This case, then, can be categorized as involving the use of machine tools for conversion, even though the part played by the machine is somewhat smaller than in cases of more complex metal-working machine tools. All movement of materials is done by hand. (Code T3:R4-C1)

The simple two-phase moving of die and hammer and the feeding of sheets would be a highly habitual, repetitive set of acts, requiring continuous but only visual attention. Similar to the wiring and soldering operation of Case 14, cycles are so exceedingly short that they would be felt as mere duration. In addition to the clicking movements performed several thousand times a day, time is divided into slightly larger units by the feeding of new sheets of material from which several cuts are made, and into still larger but irregular segments by the required scraping of the block. Although one person in the room cuts sheets of material from large rolls for use by the four operators, each operator takes his work pieces from storage and returns them to storage. The operators work independently and are not connected by a work-flow sequence. Work stations are within talking distance and, for most of the time, workers are confined to a fixed position. We will not be concerned with the work of the woman at the cutting table, which is separated by shelves and stocks of materials from the remainder of the room. The tasks performed by the four operators are all the same. Their job requires surface attention, comprises very short, repetitive cycles of constant content and sequence, demands no thinking-through of the work, has highly habituated hand movements, and entails visual focus on hands and work piece. (Code T4:5; T5:1; T6:2)

Case 20—Weaving

The data for this case are from a study conducted by A. K. Rice as a part of the Tavistock Institute program for helping ailing work organizations. The study took place in the framework of a consultant-client relationship between Rice and the management of a textile company in India. A part of this work was first reported in three articles[5] concerned with the reorganization of work assignments in two experimental weaving sheds. One of these sheds contained automatic looms; the second, nonautomatic ones. The work with these two experimental reorganizations was reported subsequently in a book, together with reports about a third part of the consulting work concerned with management reorganization in the same company.[6]

Beginning in 1953, Rice made four visits to the mill in India for periods varying from 3 to 9 months. Information was obtained by discussions with groups and individuals from all levels of the organization, by direct observation, and through use of company records. The study aimed at increased productivity in the mill and at improved social qualities of work organization.

For the present case we focus attention on the work organization of the two experimental sheds. For both sheds we have information of the situation before and after a change was made. The detailed differences between these four situations are less relevant to our purposes than are their common technical and social characteristics. We will use the automatic weaving shed before the experimental change for the main description of our case.

The 224 looms are kept in operation by twenty-eight workers. These looms are fitted with a "warp-stop motion" which stops the loom whenever a warp thread breaks. The looms also have a bobbin battery from which the weft thread is fed. Bobbins on which the thread has broken, and empties, are automatically ejected and replaced. Each of the eight weavers is responsible for from 24 to 32 looms. Rice suggests the term "loom-end knotting" for this job which requires watching for broken warp thread and straightening out minor entanglements. When a warp thread breaks, the weaver knots a short piece of spare yarn to the broken end and draws it through the appropriate place in the heals and reed; he then restarts the loom. Repairing a single break takes between 30 and 60 seconds. Similar work is required on minor entanglements in the warp threads and on short or missing threads. Three smash-hands are weavers in training. Each smash-hand makes repairs on from 60 to 80 looms when the shuttle has

---

[5] A. K. Rice, "Productivity and Social Organization in an Indian Weaving Shed: An Examination of Some Aspects of the Socio-Technical System of an Experimental Automatic Loom Shed," *Human Relations*, 6 (1953), 297–329. A. K. Rice, "The Experimental Reorganization of Non-Automatic Weaving in an Indian Mill: A Further Study of Productivity and Social Organization." *Human Relations*, 8 (1955), 199–249. A. K. Rice, "Productivity and Social Organization in an Indian Weaving Mill II: A Follow-Up Study of an Experimental Reorganization of Automatic Weaving," *Human Relations*, 8 (1955), 399–428.

[6] A. K. Rice, *Productivity and Social Organization, the Ahmedabad Experiment: Technical Innovation, Work Organization and Management* (London: Tavistock Publications, 1958).

plowed through the warp threads due to untrue running of the sleigh or when a large number of warp threads breaks. Work on one smash takes anywhere from half an hour to several hours. On from 48 to 50 looms, each of five battery fillers keeps batteries filled with new bobbins. One bobbin carrier returns empty bobbins to the spinning department from all of the 224 looms. These seventeen workers keep the looms in the shed running during the actual weaving operation.

When the warp thread has run out on a loom and a roll of cloth has been completed, the loom is prepared for a new run. Each of the two cloth carriers is responsible for removing finished cloth from 112 looms. They might also cut off cloth during a run. Two gaters look after the setting up on from 80 to 112 looms. Warp thread is wound around a beam set into brackets at the back of the loom. The gater removes the exhausted beam and gates the new one. Each warp thread is fed through the heald which separates sets of warp threads during the operation to allow the weft thread to be passed through. The warp thread is then fed through the reed which bangs the weft thread into place. Finally, the warp thread is connected to the roller at the front of the loom which takes up the cloth. Two jobbers and two assistant jobbers divide the work of adjusting running looms and tuning looms after gating. One feeler-motion fitter keeps the bobbin-ejection device on all looms in the shed in working order. One oiler keeps all the parts of the looms oiled, and one sweeper removes fluff from under the

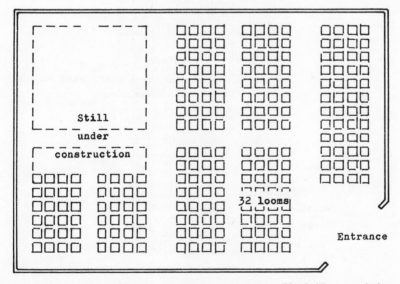

Figure 15. **Case 20—Experimental Automatic-Loom Shed** (By permission of the publisher, the author, and the Tavistock Institute of Human Relations, from A. K. Rice, *Productivity and Social Organization, the Ahmedabad Experiment,* London: Tavistock Publications, 1958, p. 67. Redrawn for this book.)

looms. These eleven workers do their work on any given loom primarily during setup time, which takes from 60 to 90 minutes. (Rice 1953, 306–310, 327; Rice 1958, 55, 57)

The nonautomatic looms in the other experimental shed do not have two of the important mechanisms of the automatic looms. When a bobbin is empty, the loom stops and the empty bobbin has to be removed and replaced by hand. This so-called shuttling takes about 20 seconds and occurs at intervals of from 3 to 12 minutes. Also, there are no warp-stop motions, and a break in a warp thread has to be observed and the loom stopped by hand. This observation is difficult to make, and cloth woven after a break must be unwoven and the break mended. Both of these characteristics require more time, so that one weaver can serve only two looms. The task of these weavers includes several components which are functionally differentiated in the automatic operation. (Rice 1958, 114–115)

In the reorganization of the automatic-loom shed, workers were divided into teams operating groups of 64 looms, each team with seven men. These seven men jointly performed all the operations initially described. The exact new distribution of task components as actually performed was not

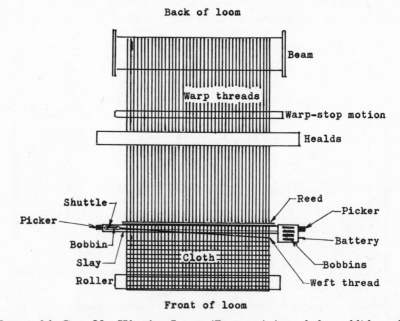

FIGURE 16. Case 20—Weaving Loom (By permission of the publisher, the author, and the Tavistock Institute of Human Relations, from A. K. Rice, *Productivity and Social Organization, the Ahmedabad Experiment,* London: Tavistock Publications, 1958, p. 53. Redrawn for this book.)

reported. The nonautomatic shed was reorganized by turning some rows of looms around to allow one worker to service only the back of 10 looms and another worker the front of 10 looms. Among any one such pair of workers, only 5 looms were shared in such a way that four workers together serviced 20 looms.

Movement of materials, consisting of beams, bobbins with yarn, and rolls of cloth, is done by hand along open lines of transportation. Conversion operations fit our category of "machine tools," with a variation between automatic and nonautomatic looms regarding the automatic feeding of bobbins from a battery and the automatic warp-stop motion. We must note, however, that only a part of the machine feeding is done by an operator, while the continuous feeding of thread during the operation takes place automatically. In this respect the case almost lies beyond category 4 of conversion operations. Similar characteristics both of machine feeding and task distribution can be found in mass-production metal-working operations. In automatic screw cutting, for instance, one man might keep a number of machines of the same type running, while other parts of the work (consisting of setting up and machine adjustments) are performed by specialized setup men. (Code T3:R4-C1)

The cycle from the putting in of a new beam to the taking off of a roll of cloth constitutes a loose temporal framework which we can compare to the situation at the coking battery of Case 9 to be described later. In contrast to the coking operation, the cycle here varies by type of cloth and by thickness of cloth roll desired. The beginning and the end of the cycle for each loom are not evenly spaced in time, as they are on the coking battery. Also, the required attention by any of the specialized operators to any given loom contains an element of chance in the breaking of threads. Rice suggests that most of the workers in the automatic-loom shed can be divided according to whether their work takes place on a loom in operation or on a stopped loom. Weavers work on running looms. Their work is irregularly cycled by thread breaks occurring in some chance sequence and requiring the weavers to move from loom to loom in irregular patterns tying broken threads together. The work on looms which are not in operation is also characterized by irregular cycles determined by the stopping and completing of cloth rolls.

In the automatic-loom shed, virtually none of the specialized tasks applies to the same set of looms. This means that the functional and temporal constraints are distributed in a complex pattern. Taking the weavers as central to the operation and as constituting the largest group, we find two types of attention requirements in combination. For some of the time, attention is focused on general indicators of the production process to determine whether one of two or three dozen looms has stopped. This is the attention requirement we have called watching, which involves little habituation and entails full awareness of what is going on.

When it comes to tying broken threads or undoing thread entanglements, the attention requirements of the weaver become very similar to those of most of the other workers. Then, vision is focused directly on the work of the hands, thinking-through of the procedure is necessary, hand movements are partly habituated, and time divisions are variable. These are conditions of detailed attention requirements.

While workers are likely to come close enough from time to time for verbal communication in spite of machine noise, the distances between the places at which workers are at any one time are usually greater. At the same time, workers are required to move through large parts of the shed. There is a very infrequent work flow in the sequence from the supplying of yarn to the loom to the carrying away of a completed cloth roll. Within the general organization of task distribution, task performances are technically interdependent. However, the work of any one worker is rarely immediately dependent on the work of another. The distribution of work creates substantial buffers between one task and another. While one loom is being set up or a smash repaired, a weaver continues to look after his other looms. Occasionally, when a battery filler has not kept pace, a weaver might not be able to restart a loom immediately. When we classify this case as independent and having no work flow, we need to recognize the limitations of this simple description in the face of the complexities of the actual situation. Some of the tasks are performed exclusively, and most of the other tasks are shared by several workers. (Code T4:2; T5:3; T6:3)

Case 19—Shoe Bottoming

The data for this case are from a study reported by Horsfall and Arensberg.[7] Horsfall made the observations for a period of one month between July and August 1938 in an American shoe factory. The factory produced from 7,500 to 10,000 pairs of inexpensive women's novelty shoes daily and employed about 1,000 persons. The study took place in the bottoming room, where twenty-eight workers performed machine operations on the underside of shoes before soling.

The research consisted both of direct observations for a general description of the organization of work in this department and of the systematic recording of the frequency and initiation of person-to-person interactions, defined as verbal communication without regard to communication content. The study is an attempt to quantify observations of interaction patterns and to describe differences in work-group structure by communication rates. It is also an example of a system of work allocation organized independently of management directives. It follows well-defined rules and

---

[7] A. B. Horsfall and C. M. Arensberg, "Teamwork and Productivity in a Shoe Factory," *Human Organization*, 8, No. 1 (Winter 1949), 13–25.

is regulated by the exchange of symbolic objects. These workers are on piece-rate payment, and their unofficial allocation system is designed to equalize work loads and pay among the four production lines in the room.

Figure 17 is an attempt to sketch the physical layout and work-station distribution in the department on the basis of information given in the report. In that figure the four production lines are shown side by side, but the report is not entirely clear on whether these lines were arranged as shown.

The same set of operations is performed on four production lines. On each line, seven workers perform five tasks. The piece-rate unit of work is a case or rack of 72 shoes. After the completion of a preceding operation, racks of shoes are pushed to the middle of the room. The rougher or pounder of a particular line moves the racks to the two trimmers. The trimmers take the shoes from the rack and put them on their bench. They remove tacks from the insole and trim excess leather at the shank and toe. The two girls face each other at the two machines which form one unit and put the completed shoes on the pounder's bench. The pounder is a man who smoothes the overlapping leather further by pounding and grinding at the toes and heels. His work is placed on the rougher's table at his side. In preparation for cementing, the next man holds the bottom of the shoe against a revolving wire brush to roughen the overlapping leather. The rhythm in the work of these two men can be perceived from the higher machine tone when the shoe is applied to grinder or brush in a sequence of front, side, other side, and heel of the shoe. Shanking is done by a girl who staples a metal strip in the center of the instep. At the end of the line, glue is spread around the edge of the shoe where in a subsequent operation the sole is cemented into place. These two girls then stick a small felt pad in place at the ball of the foot and place the shoes into boxes on racks. Girls considered moving to cementing as a promotion because the work required more skill, depended less on the machine, and occasionally required work on extra racks only to be cemented. From there, the racks were taken to be inspected and moved to the elevator. (Horsfall, 14–15)

All of the operators work on machines with which operations are performed on shoe parts. These machines fit our category of "machine tools" in the same way that the machines of the preceding case did. Work pieces move through the sequence of five work stations. As soon as an operation is completed on one shoe, the shoe is placed on an adjacent workbench holding the machine on which the next operation is carried out. Referring to our initial distinction in Chapter II, we find that energy for this transfer operation from station to station is supplied by operators rather than by equipment, but that the choice of routes of transfer is determined by the equipment setup rather than by the workers. Workers have control over

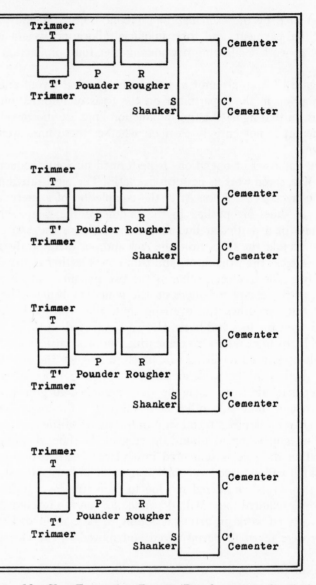

Figure 17. **Case 19—Shoe-Bottoming Room** (Based on text description in A. B. Horsfall and C. M. Arensberg, "Teamwork and Productivity in a Shoe Factory," *Human Organization*, 8, No. 1, Winter 1949, p. 23.)

the timing of work-piece movement. We have given this type of transportation of work pieces the label *dead line*. (Code T3:R4-C3)

The only indication of the time it takes to complete the work on one shoe is the 5 seconds apiece it takes the pounder during a playful speedup, when he tosses shoes directly to the rougher instead of putting them on the bench. (Horsfall, 19) Even during the normal run, there would be an exceedingly short and uniform cycle with constant content, requiring continuous attention, high visual discrimination, and an automaticity of individual movements—that is, the surface-attention requirement we have observed in some previous cases. Work stations in a given production line are in close proximity, functionally dependent, and connected by a work-flow sequence. We might note that, in addition to the very short cycle for work on one shoe, an additional loose framing of time is present in the succession of racks containing 72 shoes. Types of shoes may vary from rack to rack, but operators can interrupt their work and walk to the middle of the floor to sort out racks. The pounders and roughers often do this, within the limits of the number of shoes that their bench will accommodate when the operator preceding them on the line continues to work.

With the exception of picking up new racks, operators are confined to fixed locations. In any one of the four production lines in the bottoming room, two of the five tasks are shared by two operators, and the remaining three tasks are performed exclusively by one operator. On the other hand, the performance of all functions is shared within the department. But since the four production lines are technically independent of one another, we will say that some tasks are shared and some are exclusive. (Code T4:5; T5:15; T6:3)

Summary

In addition to the division into two types of technology, these cases exhibit further technical diversity. In Case 18 (Clicking Room), machine performance in conversion operations is mixed with hand work. Thus, the case has some characteristics of a Type II technology. Case 20 (Weaving), on the other hand, contains some self-regulating features in conversion equipment, which would be part of a higher level of technology. Finally, in Case 11a (Coal Mining II—Cutting), the work consists largely of the manual moving and maneuvering of heavy pieces of equipment, giving the case some characteristics similar to cases of technology Type I.

These differences seem related to some of the variation in technical demands. The attention requirements of Case 20 involve continuous watching (as in subsequent cases with an "automation technology"), as well as the detailed, intermittent attention characteristic of work on machine tools. In Case 18, we observed the surface-attention requirements similar to those of the assembly shops of the preceding chapter. Case 11a has the functional dependence and absence of work flow by which most cases of a Type I technology have been classified. Case 19 displays many characteristics of technical demands to be found in cases with an "assembly-line technology," discussed in the next chapter.

TABLE 15. CODING SUMMARY: TECHNOLOGY TYPES III AND IV

Technology: Type III (R4-C1) Machine Tools - Hand Transfer
Case 11a Coal Mining II (Cutting). Case 16
Machine Shop. Case 17 Machine Shop.
Case 18 Clicking Room. Case 20 Weaving.

Type IV (R4-C3) Machine Tools - Dead Line
Case 19 Shoe Bottoming.

T4: SPATIAL CONSTRAINTS

Relation of Workers to Work Stations	Talking Distance	Shouting Distance	Seeing Distance	Beyond Seeing
Open	16,17	11a,20		
Confined to fixed place	18,19			
Confined to mobile place				

T5: FUNCTIONAL CONSTRAINTS

Differentiation Pattern	No Work Flow		Work Flow	
	Independent	Dependent	Independent	Dependent
All tasks undifferentiated	18			
Each differentiated task shared	16,17	11a		
Some exclusive and some shared tasks	20			19
All tasks performed exclusively				

TABLE 15. CODING SUMMARY: TECHNOLOGY TYPES III AND IV (continued)

T6: TEMPORAL AND PERCEPTUAL CONSTRAINTS

Attention Requirements		Operation Cycles	
Low		Variable	11a,16,17,20
Surface	18,19	? seconds	18
Detailed	11a,16,17,20	5 and 10 seconds	19
External focus			
Watching			

   Central to the technology of Type III of this chapter are Cases 16 and 17 (Machine Shops). In these cases, detailed attention is required intermittently and tasks are not connected by functional dependence or work flow. In all but two cases in this chapter, workers are regularly required to move around in the larger work area; while in Cases 18 (Clicking Room) and 19 (Shoe Bottoming), this requirement applies only to a small part of working time. These latter two cases have persistently short operation cycles; in all other cases, cycle lengths are variable.

Chapter VII

ASSEMBLY LINE:
Hand Work on the Conveyor

Case 22—Auto Assembly II

The data sources for this case have been described in the discussion of Case 21 (Auto Assembly I). We are now concerned with operations on the main auto-assembly line and with the extended preparatory assembly lines feeding to the main line. Unlike most other cases, the picture here presented is a composite of the many and often quite varied conditions along the miles of assembly line. However, the dominant characteristics seem to be sufficiently similar to be put together into one case.

We begin with a brief description of a number of selected jobs found in various places of the original reports. At one point, jobs are classified by complexity of skills and, more specifically, by the number of distinguishable operations performed. In this classification a single operation is concerned with the use of the same tool and work on the same part. An example of a single-operation job is putting in screws and tightening them with an air-driven screwdriver. A man on a job which has several components might insert a set of screws in one metal plate, fix clips to another, and drill holes in a third. The job of a utility man is to relieve any of the men working in a particular section or department. His work requires the sum of all the knacks necessary for a whole series of routine jobs. Skill in the conventional, more encompassing sense is, for instance, required of the dingman. With a number of special-headed hammers, he dings out imperfections on the body of a car.

In the sample of workers interviewed, roughly one-third performed jobs containing one single operation; another third, jobs with from two to five operations; and the final third, jobs with more than five components. About 45 per cent do one or two operations, and the average time is from 1½ to 2 minutes. Following is a small number of descriptions of particular jobs.

An assembler of the baffle windbreaker in the trim department works on the moving body shell. First he puts in four screws. Then a chrome molding strip is attached at the bottom by nine clips. On another type of car, he puts in a piece of rubber that keeps the hood latch from rattling. Two screws are fitted into holes drilled through the rubber and metal. In the rear fender he attaches four clips on the rubber. On yet a different type of car, he puts two bolts in the trunk that hold the spare-tire clamp, in addition to the clips on the bottom molding. This man's job takes less than 2 minutes, for which he rides on the conveyor about 30 feet.

Working inside the car, another man puts in toe plates that cover the holes under the brake and clutch pedals. On a different kind of car, he attaches the shift lever instead.

A seat-spring builder works on a small circular conveyor off the main line. Walking a few steps on the periphery of this "merry-go-round," he shoots six or eight clips with a clip gun, putting together parts of the zigzag springs for front seats.

A wet-sander sprays water from a hose over a panel of the car body and then systematically sands certain parts, sometimes using both hands, sometimes one hand, to apply the piece of sandpaper. Giving ten strokes here, six strokes there, two or three strokes on a detail, and so forth, he applies a total of seventy closely counted strokes on one car. Every two cars, he replaces the sandpaper.

A spot-welder picks a jig from a bench, puts it in place, and welds the cowl to the underbody. He welds twenty-five spots in 1 minute and 52 seconds, walking along the moving line. He pulls off the jig, brings it back to the bench, picks up another one, and starts again. (Walker 1952, 41–42, 44–46; Walker 1956, 96; Guest, 499)

We now turn to the general technical characteristics of work on the line. Work at nearly every stage of assembly is done by hand, with hand tools and with power-driven tools manipulated by hand. All of the smaller parts are actually carried to the line as well. The main assembly, however, is of course carried past work stations on the continuously moving conveyor which is set, at any one time, at a certain speed. Among the hand tools used are files, hammers, sandpaper, welding guns, paint spray guns, hand polishing machines, clip guns, and air-driven wrenches. Working positions are either spread along each side of the line, or under the line, or inside the car. Men in some positions can speed up and work their way back up the line and gain a minute of rest. Working ahead or falling behind is in many cases restricted by power tools which are suspended and run along overhead wires only for a limited stretch. Even though adjacent work positions are generally quite close together, this distance is perceptually extended in many places by the noise from grinders, spot-welding guns, drills, clip guns, and overhead pulleys.

In hardly any of the jobs on the line is there functional dependence from one task to the next, or in fact anywhere within a section, in the sense that one man could not do his job without the preceding man's job having been done. There is interdependence between sections, and this is the problem for the foreman who regulates interdependent relationships with other sections, but who in turn looks after a collection of men working independently. In polishing, for instance, one man might polish the trunk-compartment lid; the next, the door on the right; another, the door on the left; and finally, two men might do each of the rear fenders. Each man can do his job without the other men having completed theirs. Similarly, a man might drill the holes for a molding, while only a half-mile farther down the line would the molding actually be put on.

Most of the work requires close but very limited attention. A worker must recognize the requirements of a particular assembly moving toward his station; he must find the right parts to match the car, the right jig, and the proper place to drill a hole. Each operation requires the coordination of eye and hand. In addition, the power tools and sharp metal edges are potentially dangerous. As indicated before, however, the number of components in a man's job is usually very small, and his work is therefore highly repetitive. The same few things to be done and watched out for recur again and again every 2 minutes or so. In the production process, there is a large number of variations because of the various makes, models, and styles assembled on the same line, the several dozen different colors and hundreds of color combinations, and the different accessories, instrument panels, and upholstery. The effects of this variation on any particular job are likely to be confined to changes in the odd work component and are also limited by the very extensive standardization of parts. Changes in the mix of makes and models and occasional changes in line speed necessitate redistribution of the elements performed by the men in a given section. (Walker 1952, 12–14, 38–39, 68–73, 80; Walker 1956, 7–8, 13, 53, 68–72, 78, 127; Guest, 499; Jasinski, 25)

Conversion operations in this case are performed by hand and with the use of hand tools; the transportation of work pieces takes place on continuously moving conveyors along fixed lines of traffic. (Code T3:R2-C5) With the exception of the short walk back up the line to the next assembly, workers are confined to a fixed place on the line. In the prevailing noise, they are primarily within shouting distance of the surrounding men. In most instances, there seem to be at least two men doing the same job. Furthermore, the dominant characteristic of these tasks is a time element into which different activity components are put as the line is constantly rebalanced. The changeable performance element is shared by many workers. Work stations are clearly linked by work flow, but workers in the same vicinity perform independent tasks. The requirements of surface attention describe the dominant temporal and perceptual constraints. (Code T4:6; T5:10; T6:2)

Case 23—Candy Wrapping

This case results from a short part of a report by Wyatt and Langdon[1] on machine-feeding processes. The study is part of a research program conducted over many years by the British Industrial Health Research Board into questions of fatigue and monotony in industrial operations. One part of the report is concerned with the reactions of women who independently feed toffee-wrapping machines. We are focusing here on another part, concerned with conveyor work. Four operations on moving belts are briefly described in the report.

The data are the result of interviews with all workers in the four operations to be described. In the first process each of sixty-two chocolate coverers takes a piece at a time from a supply of centers and dips it in a bowl of chocolate. The coated center is then marked with a simple decorative design and placed on the moving belt. The girls sit close enough together for conversation among immediate neighbors, and experienced operators are able to talk or to "indulge in detached thoughts." In each of the next two sections, forty-four chocolate packers fill boxes with assorted chocolates from a conveyor. A memorized pattern governs the packing of chocolates. Working speed is regulated by the moving belt. Attention requirements are greater than in the chocolate-covering operation. In the fourth sequence, thirty-four chocolate packers are seated on both sides of the conveyor which carries the continuous supply of chocolate blocks. Each worker takes off a block, wraps it in gummed paper, and puts it back on the conveyor. (Wyatt, 37–38)

This is work performed by hand on a continuously moving conveyor. (Code T3:R2-C5) Close visual discrimination is necessary in the handling of small items, hand movements are automatic, and attention is continuously required. The exact time it takes each operator to complete the work on one piece is not given, but we might assume that it would take only a few seconds for the first and the last operations and perhaps not more than a minute or so for the workers filling boxes with chocolates. Operation cycles are uniform and short and have a constant work content. All workers on any one of these lines perform the same work, and only the section as a whole is functionally connected with other sections. The operations performed by the workers within a section are functionally independent, but work stations are connected by a work-flow sequence. Operators are within talking distance of one another. All workers in one section share the performance of the same task. They are confined to fixed work locations. (Code T4:5; T5:9; T6:2)

---

[1] S. Wyatt and J. N. Langdon, *The Machine and the Worker: A Study of Machine Feeding Processes*, Great Britain Medical Research Council, Industrial Health Research Board, Report No. 82 (London: HMSO, 1938).

Case 24—Equipment-Assembly Line

This case is based on a small part of a study describing the organizational problems faced by one particular foreman, Tony. The study was conducted by Abraham Zaleznik at the central assembly section of an American plant manufacturing electrical products. As a result of direct observations, the report describes foreman-training conferences and a series of events relevant for the behavior of a foreman on the assembly line.[2] Some aspects of this study are summarized at the end of a later study by Zaleznik.[3] The purpose of the study was to provide an answer to the question "Did this particular training help the supervisors to act more effectively on their jobs, and what else should have been done?"

The product made on this assembly line is the central and most important component of an electrical consumer item. The mechanized conveyor is about 460 feet long. Work stations are set up on only half of the line, and completed units run all the way through the unoccupied half to the end for transfer to an overhead conveyor. About fourteen workers are repairmen and stock clerks off the line. We will be concerned with the thirty-six operators on the line—of whom six are men who assemble heavier parts, and the remainder are women. Each operator on the belt is expected to complete her work in a space of about 3 feet and within about 4½ minutes. An inspector is placed between every twelve or thirteen positions to check the work done on the preceding stations. In addition to these three on-line inspectors, there are quality-control inspectors at the end of the line.

Taking small parts from bins within arm's reach, each operator performs a series of simple operations on each unit. The work is done with the use of hand pliers, soldering irons, air-driven nut runners, and screwdrivers. Preparatory work on all the parts used in the assembly is done by the time the parts reach the line. The parts are assembled to a base which is moved to the first station on an overhead conveyor. The heavier work is performed at the first two stations, which are not on the main line. Instead, the first operator passes the assembly base to the next by hand, and from there it goes to the first station on the conveyor. Design changes are fairly frequent and sometimes require reshuffling of operations and stopping the line temporarily. The process requires no interaction between workers, and each operation—though necessary to the whole product—is self-contained. (Zaleznik 1951, 93–96; Zaleznik 1956, 120)

The equipment used for conversion operations consists of hand tools:

---

[2] A. Zaleznik, *Foreman Training in a Growing Enterprise* (Boston: Division of Research, Graduate School of Business Administration, Harvard University, 1951).

[3] A. Zaleznik, *Worker Satisfaction and Development: A Case Study of Work and Social Behavior in a Factory Group* (Boston: Division of Research, Graduate School of Business Administration, Harvard University, 1956), pp. 120–122.

pliers, soldering irons, nut runners driven by compressed air, and screwdrivers. Work-piece transfer takes place on a continuously moving conveyor, on which thirty-six operators perform segmented assembly tasks. (Code T3:R2-C5)

Continuous attention is technically required, and there are high visual discrimination and habituation in hand movements. Operation cycles of about 4½ minutes are uniform and short, with constant work content. Operators are confined to fixed work stations which are within talking distance of one another and are connected by a work-flow sequence. No sufficiently precise information is given on whether each operation is functionally dependent on the preceding operation, in the sense that one operation could not be performed unless the preceding operations had taken place. As in automobile assembly, there is temporal and spatial interdependence, since each operator has only so much time to perform his operation in the space of a given section of the belt. But we might assume, in addition, that when thirty-six operators complete the major component of the finished product, at least a large proportion of the operations are functionally interdependent, so that many operations could not be performed without the completion of preceding ones. Each operator presumably performs a different task in the assembly of the total product. (Code T4:5; T5:16; T6:2)

Two particular characteristics of this case should be mentioned:

1. We have called the work content of operation cycles constant, even though the report suggests that frequent changes are made in product design. We noted the variability of the content of uniform operation cycles on the automobile-assembly line which was due to changes in line speed and to the variety of models and styles of assemblies coming down the line. But in this case, for any given period of time, the product remains the same, and many design changes apparently did not greatly affect the work operations to be performed.

2. Unlike the auto-assembly operation, belt speed remained unchanged in this case. In fact, a large part of the story of the problems faced by the foreman, Tony, is concerned with breakdowns in line production as operators do not complete their work within the allotted time and space and thus get in each other's way.

Case 25—Garment Line

The report for this case by Treinen[4] is part of a series of papers, on the use of the so-called interactiogram developed by Peter Atteslander. The

---

[4] H. Treinen, "Eine Arbeitsgruppe am Fliessband: Sozialstruktur und Formen der Beaufsichtigung," *Kölner Zeitschrift für Soziologie und Sozialpsychologie*, 8 (1956), 73–83.

report records observations of workers' behaviors on four belts in a sewing department of a German garment factory. Specifically, the report focuses on the so-called informal organization of workers and on an analysis of interaction counts for the four belt leaders. The description of technical characteristics is short and does not contain information on several points we would require for complete classification.

Materials are supplied to the four lines from the cutting room on the same floor. Each conveyor consists of a frame about 25 yards long on which the belt runs. Belts are divided into boxes into which materials are thrown. About forty girls sit at each conveyor, one behind the other; half are on one side, facing the beginning of the belt, and half are on the other, facing the end. Changes in production orders require reshuffling of seating order and result in the redistribution of girls over the four lines, with a difference of up to twelve persons per belt. Two inspectors and some workers on special machines are located at the end of the belt, facing each other. The end man on each belt performs a special task and has work piling up if work pieces do not arrive at his station at a regular pace. From this information we might tentatively conclude that work pieces move from operator to operator through functionally dependent operations, since completed pieces would always arrive at the end of the belt with some chance irregularity if work pieces traveled directly from each worker to the end.

The report gives no indication of whether the sewing operations are performed by hand or with machines. For purposes of our analysis, the difference between sewing by hand and by machine would appear minor, and we will classify the case as involving the presence of conversion operations by hand or with hand tools on work pieces moved along fixed lines by a continuously moving conveyor. (Code T3:R2-C5)

The information provided is too insufficient for any more than a very tentative coding of the case. We will assume that sewing work in garment manufacture carried out in segmented tasks along a conveyor belt requires surface attention. Operation cycles in this case are somewhat similar to the candy-wrapping operation described in Case 23, by the fact that work pieces are taken off the line to be worked on and put back after completion of a task. In such a case, a worker's pace is not as strictly governed by the speed of the belt as it would be if the work piece remained on the belt. The text does suggest the possibility of an uneven distribution of work pieces on the belt due to variations in the speed with which operators do their work. But on a line of this kind it is likely that attempts are made to balance the distribution of work components over the line. This would result in uniform work cycles, at least by technical design. In the presence of design changes, there would be some variation in work content within operation cycles. We also assume that cycles are comparatively short. Work stations are within talking distance although, as indicated, this

TABLE 16.   CODING SUMMARY: TECHNOLOGY TYPE V

Technology: Type V (R2-C5) Hand Tools - Live Line

Case 11b Coal Mining II (Filling).   Case 22 Auto Assembly II.
Case 23 Candy Wrapping.   Case 24 Equipment-Assembly Line.
Case 25 Garment Line.

T4: SPATIAL CONSTRAINTS

Relation of Workers to Work Stations	Talking Distance	Shouting Distance	Seeing Distance	Beyond Seeing
Open				
Confined to fixed place	23,24,25	11b,22		
Confined to mobile place				

T5: FUNCTIONAL CONSTRAINTS

Differentiation Pattern	No Work Flow		Work Flow	
	Independent	Dependent	Independent	Dependent
All tasks undifferentiated			11b,23	
Each differentiated task shared			22	
Some exclusive and some shared tasks				
All tasks performed exclusively				24,25

TABLE 16. CODING SUMMARY: TECHNOLOGY TYPE V (continued)

T6: TEMPORAL AND PERCEPTUAL CONSTRAINTS

Attention Requirements		Operation Cycles	
Low		? seconds	11b
Surface	11b,22,23,24,25	1½ minutes	22
Detailed		? seconds	23
External focus		4½ minutes	24
Watching		? minutes	25

distance is extended by noise. In this respect the report gives conflicting observations; operators are reported as talking among themselves, and talking is used as a measure for interaction. Work stations are connected by a work-flow sequence and are assumed to be functionally interdependent. Although many of the tasks performed on any one line might be performed exclusively by one person, workers are frequently moved around among the four belts, with the exception of the workers at the end of each line. (Code T4:5; T5:16; T6:2)

Summary

Table 16 contains a summary of technical demands for the four cases discussed in this chapter. It also includes Case 11b (Coal Mining II—Filling), which was coded in the preceding chapter together with Case 11a.

Our summaries indicate that the characteristics of this cluster of cases are quite uniform. In all these cases, conversion operations are performed by hand and with hand tools, and work pieces are transferred by continuously moving belts or conveyors. However, both in Case 11b (Coal Mining II—Filling) and in Case 23 (Candy Wrapping), work pieces do not move through adjacent work stations to have operations performed on them at each station, as in the other three cases. Instead, work pieces are placed on the belt by operators and then move away from the operators without being worked on by other workers on the particular section of the line. Furthermore, in Case 25 (Garment Line), work pieces are taken off the belts and put back on the belts after an operation has been performed. This means that, in these three cases, working pace is not strictly governed by the speed of the belt. Workers have a degree of choice over the disposition of activities in time, limited by supervision and, in Case 25, by functional interdependence.

Surface attention is required in all of these cases (with less visual discrimination necessary in Case 11b), and operation cycles are short. Work stations are connected by work flow but, as indicated, only in two cases are they functionally dependent. Distances between stations are short. In the two cases of functional interdependence, the exclusiveness of task performance is also higher than in the other cases. Workers are confined to fixed work locations.

Chapter VIII

MACHINE LINE:
Remote Control of Connected Machines

Case 26—Wire Rolling

Of the cases in this chapter, this first case and six of the remaining eight have their source in the two publications by Popitz and his associates,[1] referred to in Cases 3 and 5. Also, as suggested in Chapter IV, four of the nine cases in this chapter will be divided into two parts. One part will be classified as technology Type I. This classification will include work on mill changes in Cases 26, 28, and 29, and the work of subcrews in Case 6.

The work descriptions available for Case 26 include all of the operations of a hot-wire rolling mill. They concentrate primarily, however, on the central part of the operation in the so-called finishing mill illustrated in Figure 18.

The operations preceding the finishing mill take place in the billet storage area, the oven used for heating billets, and the pre-rolling mill in which billets are reduced in diameter and extended in length in the continuous operation of 9 roll stands. The length of wire or rod coming out of the pre-rolling mill proceeds through the finishing mill to a spooling station and hotbed, going from there through a binding and sorting operation to a loading station. Billets come out of the oven and are cut to required lengths on shears and are then fed into the pre-rolling mill. Once the steel has entered the pre-rolling mill, the operations performed on it are continuous until the completed wire reaches the spooling station. Speed throughout this continuous part of the operation is preset, each successive roll stand running at a higher speed than the preceding one. Our analysis will be concerned only with the finishing mill.

The finishing mill consists of 8 roll stands arranged side by side. As the wire enters a roll stand from one side, it passes through the rolls, its diameter is reduced, its cross-sectional shape changed, and its length extended. Coming out of the other side of the roll stand, the wire is

---

[1] H. Popitz *et al.*, *Technik und Industriearbeit* (Tübingen: Mohr, 1957); H. Popitz *et al.*, *Das Gesellschaftsbild des Arbeiters* (Tübingen: Mohr, 1957).

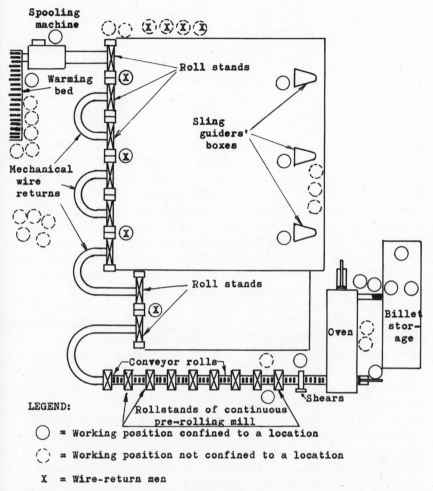

FIGURE 18. **Case 26—Hot-Wire Rolling Mill** (By permission of the publisher and authors from H. Popitz, H. P. Bahrdt, E. A. Jüres, and H. Kesting, *Technik und Industriearbeit*, Tübingen: Mohr, 1957, p. 95. Redrawn for this book.)

redirected in a semicircle and enters the next roll stand. On every second turn, that is, all along one side of the finishing mill, the wire is redirected mechanically; on the other side, the wire is returned to the next stand manually. The finishing-mill crew consists of twenty-one men: a foreman, eight rollers, six sling men, five men who look after the mechanical wire return on the other side, and a grease man. Half of the rollers and sling men work in rotation on half-hour turns. Four rollers redirect wire between roll stands on the manual side, and the other four stand by, recuperate, and watch carefully in order to prevent accidents from happening to the four working rollers. The three sling men on the relief turn help on the scrap spooler and remove scrap from the finishing mill.

During his half-hour working turn, a roller stands in front of two roll stands, facing the point at which the two stands are joined. With a long-handled pair of tongs, he grasps the white-hot wire shooting out of the rolls on his left, turns counterclockwise swinging the tongs with the wire with him, and then sticks the wire into the rolls on his right. The wire then proceeds through the mechanical return on the other side and comes out of the next roll stand, where it is grasped by the next roller who in turn performs the same operation. Thus, the wire runs mechanically from the pre-rolling mill into the first roll stand and snakes through the succeeding positions until the last man, the so-called finishing roller, passes the wire through the last rolls from where it moves onto the spooling machine and the warming bed. The sling men sit in a kind of tub about 10 yards behind the rollers. With long tongs they slow down the speed of the wire, prevent it from jumping, and keep the several passing wires from being entangled.

Wire shoots out of the roll stands at the speed of a fast train, at the rate of about 250 times each half-hour turn. This would be a cycle of slightly over 7 seconds. When the wire has been stuck into the roll stand to the right of a given roller, the end of the same wire has not yet left the stand on the left, and thus forms a loop around the roller. With the moving loop of the first wire still around his back, the roller grasps the next wire and resticks it, thus forming a second loop, and so forth. About three wires run simultaneously at the beginning of the finishing mill, and about seven at the end. The flow of these several wires through the rolls is regulated by guide boxes with a row of holes into which the wire is successively stuck.

The characteristics of the work of the men placed along this production sequence change, then, from position to position. From the beginning to the end of the finishing mill, the number of wires running at the same time increases, as well as the speed of the wires. Successively less energy and more skill is required. In the first two positions the wire can be seen coming out of the preceding stands and provides a visual cue for the time of grasping the wire. The succeeding two men can orient themselves only by a cracking sound when the wire enters the preceding rolls. The first man is most often required to cut the deformed head of the wire with foot-operated shears.

The rollers must maintain the specified wire profile, and they do this by a few manipulations on the roll stands. When a roller is endangered by a wire loop closing in on him, it becomes necessary for a man on his off-turn to jump in with a wire cutter and cut the loop before it hits a man who might not even be aware of the danger. Similarly, men must be aware of the possibility that a wire might be missed in grasping and shoot out uncontrolled. On each shift between 20 and 30 minutes are required for resetting the guide boxes on the roll stands. From 45 minutes to an hour or more is needed for a change of rolls for a new production order. These two elements will be analyzed in a later section on setup operations in rolling mills. (Popitz 1957a, 94–112, 164, 199; Popitz 1957b, 251–255)

Rollers and sling men during their working turn are narrowly confined to a specific position defined by roll stands and wire flow. The noise from a number of continuously running rolls is likely to be high and the distance between work stations can at best be overcome by shouting. Tasks in successive positions along this production line are sufficiently differentiated that new learning is required when a worker moves from one place to the next and that changes in jobs from the beginning toward the end of the line are considered advancements in terms of skill. Positions are part of a continuing work flow, and dependence of one task on another is very high. The attention requirements of this case do not fully fit one of our five categories. Cycles are short and repetitive, but at the same time a high and continuous involvement in the process is necessary—demanded by danger and the split-second grasp for a white-hot wire which has not yet appeared in sight. The visual and auditory focus of attention is directed not only to a tool and a work piece immediately in front of a man, but also to the nearest two work stations. Recognizing these complexities, we will classify the case as requiring detailed attention.

We have considered the feeding of machines as part of a conversion operation. In this case the dominant characteristic of the work of the wire roller does not lie in the moving of work pieces from one work station to another, since the quality of the product—the attainment of specific profiles and diameters—depends on his performance. Conversion operations are, then, performed jointly with the use of machine tools (the roll stands) and of hand tools (the tongs used by rollers and sling men). Although quite different from a continuously moving assembly-line conveyor, this operation has the same characteristics: the speed and movement of work pieces are determined by the machine and cannot be controlled by the worker. Instead, the worker's movements are controlled by the machine in even greater detail than they are on the continuously moving assembly line. (Case 26a: Code T3:R3-C5; T4:6; T5:16; T6:3)

The classifications so far provided for this case apply to work when the mill is in operation. This major part of the case we will call Case 26a. The case reports indicate that a further part of the work on the finishing mill consists of mill changes, that is, the shifting of guide boxes and the exchanging of rolls. The equivalent type of operation is also found in Cases 28 and 29 (Tube Rolling I and II). We will code these three partial cases (26b, 28b, and 29b) at the end of the discussion of Case 29.

Case 27—Bloom Rolling

This case is again based on the report by Popitz and his associates and is concerned with the operation of a heavy rolling mill on which large heated steel blocks (ingots) are rolled into blooms. Figure 19 is an illustration of the installation, showing the layout of the mill and the positions of the operators. This rolling mill has only one roll stand, a cross section of which is shown below the layout sketch in Figure 19. This is a two-high reversing mill. Glancing at the layout, we can see that the block moves from the right to the left through the roll stand, is then run back and forth through several passes, and finally is moved away to the left. A look at the cross section of the roll stand shows that there is a succession of passes from left to right through the calibers, with decreasing distance between rolls.[2]

Three men, and sometimes four, operate one mill. The mill is driven by steam, has a two-high reversible roll stand with six calibers, and a remote-controlled canting device. The steering operator and the canter operator have their positions side by side on a raised, glassed-in platform. From this position they can see the operation on one side of the roll stand, but not the area behind it. When a new ingot is to enter the mill, it is placed at the beginning of the mill. With one of four levers, the steering operator controls a skip from which the ingot is slid onto the supplying roller conveyor. With a second lever, this conveyor is set in motion and the ingot is moved toward the center of the mill. It runs onto the working roller conveyor regulated by the steering operator with his third lever. With this working conveyor the steel block is moved to the roll stand and, on a return pass, away from it. A fourth lever allows the steering operator to change the distance between rolls in the roll stand, using a numerical indicator as a guide. Thus, the first two levers are used only at the time of putting a new block into the process, while the other two are used continuously during the actual rolling operation.

The canter operator controls the working roller conveyor behind the roll stand with his first lever. This conveyor receives the block after a forward pass through the roll stands and returns it to the roll stands for a reverse pass through the same caliber. It is also used to move the finished bloom away to the shears. The other two levers used by the canter operator regulate horizontal and vertical movement of the canting machine. This canter is positioned above the working conveyor in front of the roll stands. It is used to shift the rectangular steel block sideways for entry into the next caliber and to tip it for the next pass. The block is then reduced in size by pressure of the rolls on the two horizontal sides of the block which were vertical on a previous pass. The position of the roll-stand operator is beside the roll stand where he, like the other two operators, can see the

---

[2] "For good rolling economy, the reduction should be rapid, a common rate being that of rolling an ingot of 23 inches square down to a bloom 6 inches square in about 2 minutes. For this purpose, approximately 17 roll passes are needed. During the blooming step the work piece is processed in a reversing mill or several continuous mills; in either case the bloom is turned 90 degrees between reduction passes to work uniformly on all sides." J. L. Morris, *Modern Manufacturing Processes* (Englewood Cliffs, N.J.: Prentice-Hall, 1955), pp. 139–140.

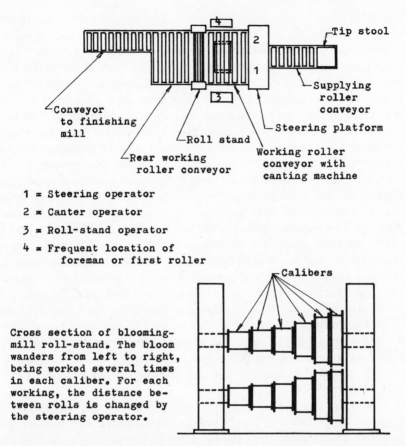

1 = Steering operator

2 = Canter operator

3 = Roll-stand operator

4 = Frequent location of
foreman or first roller

Cross section of blooming-
mill roll-stand. The bloom
wanders from left to right,
being worked several times
in each caliber. For each
working, the distance be-
tween rolls is changed by
the steering operator.

FIGURE 19. **Case 27—Blooming Mill** (By permission of the publisher and authors from H. Popitz, H. P. Bahrdt, E. A. Jüres, and H. Kesting, *Technik und Industriearbeit*, Tübingen: Mohr, 1957, pp. 55, 56. Redrawn for this book.)

process in front of the roll stand but not behind it. Indications of events behind the roll stand come to him by reflections from the white-hot bloom, by occasional signals from the foreman, and by changes in vibration transmitted to his hands through the levers. His first lever regulates the flow of steam for forward motion of the rolls at varying speeds, and the second lever is for reverse passes. A third lever cuts off the steam supply entirely.

The movements of the steel block are controlled by the working conveyors in front of and behind the roll stand, by the canter, and by the roll stand. These are in turn regulated through remote control by the three operators. Occasionally a foreman helps in coordinating their movements. When the steering operator moves the block toward the roll stand, the roll-stand operator gets ready for the rolls to grasp the work piece. In order to make possible the entry of the block into the rolls, the steering operator slows down the movement of the block by reversing the conveyor. At the same time, the canter operator places the lifting arms of the canter under the block and raises it slightly for entry into the rolls. Except for aid by the canter, the same coordinated action takes place on the return pass. When the steam put in by the roll-stand operator is insufficient to complete a pass, he reverses the rolls and tries again. Sometimes it becomes necessary for the steering operator to open up the rolls in order to inspect the work piece and, if necessary, to return it to the conveyor for another try. The steel block becomes increasingly longer with every pass, and canting and shifting cannot be done in rectangular movements. Smooth movement requires close coordination between the steering operator and the canter operator. The extended bloom often becomes bent in the process, and the canter operator moves the canting arms against the bloom in order to straighten it while it moves through a pass. The precise speed, acceleration, and position of the pieces of equipment are to a great extent a matter of trial and error by moving levers quickly back and forth until the right point is reached. This is particularly important during the final finishing passes, when the specified dimensions for the finished bloom are obtained. When a block approaches the roll stand at the wrong time—that is, when the rolls have accelerated too far or not far enough, the roll-stand operator must be prepared to stop the rolls and prevent the block from entering a pass. (Popitz 1957a, 56–59)

The report also describes the part played both by the first rolling-mill operator (a kind of lead hand) and by the foreman. The foreman gives instructions and production specifications to the canter operator and the steering operator and watches that the rolling material is worked according to specifications. The first man aids the foreman and coordinates the work of the three operators on one of the blooming mills, with the use of whistle signals. He does this especially during the time that the bloom is behind the roll stand and cannot be seen by any of the three operators. He is also responsible for adjustments on the roll stands and for lubrication and cooling of the blooms. Occasionally he might cant a bloom by hand with the use of a "canting key." He also checks the dimensions of the blooms.

In this case, conversion and transfer operations are intricately intermeshed both in what machines and in what operators do. Conversion takes place by the use of "steered automatics." Energy supply, tool and work-piece manipulation, and feeding are performed by equipment; control over operation cycles and over "planning" is performed by operators. Similarly, movement of work pieces takes place on a "steered line," with an external power supply and the choice of lines of work-piece movement determined by machine design. (Code T3:R5-C4)

The original report stresses repeatedly the particular intensity of attention required of the operators running the mill. The requirements change somewhat with every bloom rolled, due to ingot temperatures and the variability of joint control of work-piece movement by the three operators. This variability, the requirement for any one operator to coordinate his moves precisely with those of the others, and the very rapid passing back and forth of a very large and white-hot block of steel require continuous sharp attention and high visual discrimination. Similar to other cases in which we speak of "steering," attention is here not focused on one's hand movements but on events external to one's immediate location. Hand movements for the manipulation of several levers must be highly habituated for a successful operation. A major difference in attention requirements between cases of machine feeding and assembly operations and cases of remote control of large pieces of machinery lies in the direction of the focus of attention. In the first type of case, attention is focused on what is immediately before the operator. In the second type, attention is focused on events external to the operator's immediate work location. At the same time, this kind of operation requires conscious participation in the process. What we have called the requirements of "externally focused" attention combines the habituation and speed of surface attention and the cognitive involvement of detailed attention. Added to these is the focus on the larger production process necessary for coordination of the intermeshed movements of several men.

Operation cycles in this case are of two kinds: one consisting of the time from the intake of the raw block to its departure to the shears; the other, the time for a forward and return pass of the bloom. If this operation only approaches closely the time requirements given in the quoted statement from the engineering text (note 2 above), both of the inner and outer operation cycles are still very short, extending about 2 minutes on the one hand and about 7 seconds on the other. Built-in machine speeds allow comparatively little variation from a uniform and short cycle. Although many minor variations for every run are crucial for the concentrated attention required, the kind of work done during every cycle remains the same. (Popitz, 1957a, 60–65, 144, 186–187, 194–196)

Work stations are connected by a work-flow sequence which has the following characteristics: during any one larger cycle, the work piece moves back and forth several times, renewing in each case a chain of interdependent manipulations performed by each operator. There is also a "flow" of passes from the left to the right of the roll stand. Each pass, once performed, is irreversible, and the shape of the bloom has been changed. The three or four men on the mill are within seeing distance of one another, but the steering operator and the canter operator stand side by side in an enclosed cubicle. The working positions of operators are certain fixed locations. Each task is performed exclusively by one operator. (Code T4:7; T5:16; T6:4)

Case 28—Tube Rolling I

The basis for this case is a report by Charles Walker of research conducted in a steel-mill town in the United States.[3] The study describes reactions to a plan for moving the local tubing mill to another city. As part of the report, the central operation in the tubing mill is described and that part is the basis of our case. The study was carried out from the fall of 1946 to the fall of 1948. Interviews with a sample of workers were conducted in their homes. The next case will be based on a later report by Walker, concerned with a technically more advanced tubing mill. In that report, frequent comparisons are made to the operations in the older mill. The description of the operation is based on direct observations and formal job descriptions underlying wage classifications. The mill is illustrated in Figure 20.

The five mills of the hot-mill department in this plant produce seamless steel tubes, usually operated on three shifts. A shift crew on one hot mill has between fourteen and twenty-two men. Steel blooms are delivered to the plant and converted into round billets weighing from 30 to 3,000 pounds, and these constitute the raw material for the hot mills. As a first step in the operation, billets are heated to a temperature often exceeding 2,000°F in the continuous roll-down furnace. The heater and his several helpers charge and discharge the furnace and roll the billets through it with steel hooks. When the billet is at forging temperature, it slides down a skip to a conveyor leading to the piercer. At the outlet side of the piercer, the plugger lifts a pointed plug from a water trough and puts it in front of a long bar. The piercer operator controls all of the following operations by a series of levers. He operates kick arms to raise the billet from the conveyor, to roll the billet into the inlet trough, and to close a lid over it. Almost simultaneously, a ram pushes the billets between the two rolls of the piercing mill from one side, and the long bar moves the plug in from the other. The two rolls then squeeze the billet in a forward rolling motion and create a weak point in the center of the billet. This process permits the steel to "flow" over the plug and bar to form a shell from three to six times the length of the billet. With his remote controls the operator then pulls the bar from the tube, clears the tube from the piercing mill, and kicks it onto skids from where it moves to the next operation. The piercer plugger puts the used plug into the water trough and puts another in its place. The piercer operator can see the conveyor from the furnace; he can also see the piercing mill, its intake and outlet sides. When the work is held up at the piercer or beyond, he blows a whistle for the furnace to stop discharging. A piercer dragout and sometimes another helper as well work on the piercer.

---

[3] C. R. Walker, *Steeltown: An Industrial Case History of the Conflict Between Progress and Security* (New York: Harper, 1950).

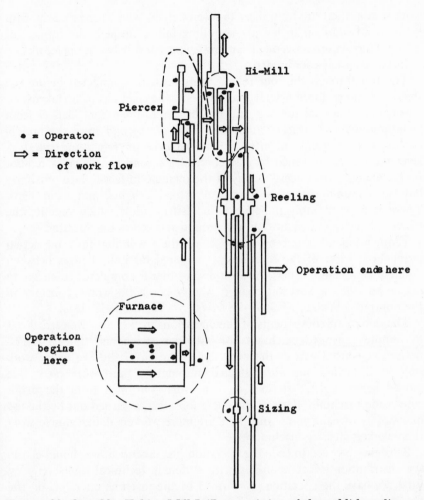

Hi-Mill

Piercer

• = Operator

⇨ = Direction
  of work flow

Reeling

⇨ Operation ends here

Furnace

Operation
begins
here

Sizing

FIGURE 20. **Case 28—Tubing Mill I** (By permission of the publisher, diagram entitled "Technology Determines Teams and Subteams" from *Steeltown* by Charles R. Walker, Harper, 1950, p. 54. Redrawn for this book.)

The succeeding three operations are similar in their organization to the piercing mill. The roller controls the hi-mill and has three helpers. He regulates the equipment with two electric controls and eight air levers. Two reeler men and two helpers operate the two reeling machines. Two sizing mills are controlled by one operator, and from there the finished tube moves to the cooling table to be inspected and tagged and sent for further processing. The complete operation contains five major work stations for heating, piercing, hi-mill rolling, reeling, and sizing. Each machine is controlled by an operator who regulates the conversion process in his machine and the conveyor movement between machines. On each work station there are from three to seven helpers who work primarily with heavy hand tools on such work as rolling billets through the furnace or lifting plugs. Work movements among helpers and between operators and helpers are closely coordinated.

The run through the four rolling units must be completed before the steel cools down too much. If that happens, the steel has to be taken out, reheated in a special furnace, and put back into operation. Danger from "whipping cobbles" (accidentally dislodged tubes) and from the rapidly cooling steel demands an intricate balance between safety and speed. A lever movement mistimed by a fraction of a second can "wrap a red-hot tube around a man's neck." Many of the men are in face-to-face proximity but can communicate only by way of whistles, lights, and hand signs. There is a small interval between successive billets which permits the piercer plugger, for instance, to turn around and yell to the operator.

Workers spend about 60 per cent of their working time on actual production. Most of the remainder is required for mill changes between different production orders. As soon as an order is completed, each group begins work on the next mill change. A wage bonus ties workers' income to their output. (Walker 1950, 53–59, 64–66, 82; Walker 1957, 44)

The dominant components of the operations in this case are carried out by remote-controlled machines, for both conversion and transfer operations. The central part of the work done on each of the five major work stations is carried out with "steered automatics," and work pieces are moved between these stations on conveyors controlled from the major conversion machines. Parts of the operation are also carried out by the use of a variety of hand tools, and there are more workers doing muscle work than workers steering machinery.

Before we proceed to code the operation just described, we should clarify the distribution of components with different technical characteristics. First, we have the operations performed by the machine operators on the five major pieces of equipment. This is the component we will classify now as Case 28a. Second, there is the work done by the other men of each subcrew under the direction of a machine operator. This component is similar to the work in Case 26 (Wire Rolling), as it involves the use of both hand and machine tools at the same time. But in Case 26 machines were running continuously without being regularly controlled by operators. Here the machines are controlled by the machine operators. The descriptions in the case material are too insufficient for use as a separate case. This component will be omitted, then, from subsequent analysis, but its presence might be recognized from time to time. Finally, the case contains descriptions of work during mill changes, and these will be coded later as Case 28b.

Focusing on the machine operators and the relations between their tasks and work stations, we can classify Case 28a as one in which both conversion and transfer operations are remote-controlled through steered automatics. (Code T3:R5-C4)

The report indicates that there is a short interval between work pieces moving down the line. To a limited extent, this would indicate that attention requirements for the operators are intermittent. This is perhaps related to the work performed by the hand workers in a given crew, and this work seems to fall in part between the operations performed by machine operators. The regulation of fast-moving work pieces requires high visual discrimination and automaticity of hand movements. Attention must be focused, however, on events external to the immediate location. Cycles are uniform and short and have a constant work content. The five major work stations are connected by a clear one-way work-flow sequence, and the tasks performed at one work station are dependent on those performed at another. With the exception of the work of the two reeler men, all machine-operating tasks are performed exclusively and helpers' tasks are shared. Although comparatively close together, work stations are separated by machine noise and smoke to what we have called seeing distance, overcome only by signals and hand signs. Operators are confined to a fixed work place while the mill is running. (Code T4:7; T5:15; T6:4)

Case 29—Tube Rolling II

The case material is from a study conducted by Charles Walker between 1949 and 1952 in an American semiautomatic seamless-tube mill during its first three years of operation. The report describes the operations in the plant and the reactions of workers to the three-year debugging period beginning with the starting of operations in the new mill. Data were obtained by direct observations and informal interviews on the mill floor, by three separate interviews with selected workers in their homes, by discussions with management personnel, and by the use of company records.[4]

The operations performed in this mill are similar to those of the last case. However, the crew consists of only nine men, and the bulk of the work can be performed automatically. Much of it is controlled by electric eyes, timing devices, limit switches, and rotary controls, which in turn regulate various hydraulic, mechanical, and electrical mechanisms. There are also five major operating positions: the furnace, the piercing mill, the nine-stand mandrel mill, the stripper, and at the end the alternately used twelve-stand reducer and the sizing mill. With the exception of parts of the work on the furnace and on the piercing mill, the production process runs automatically. However, all of the operations except the transfer of

---

[4] C. R. Walker, *Toward the Automatic Factory: A Case Study of Men and Machines* (New Haven: Yale University Press, 1957).

work pieces from machine to machine can be switched to "manual" control, by which step-by-step operations are remote-controlled. The discharging of billets from the furnace and the entry of billets into the piercing mill are always controlled "manually." There are two jobs involving physical labor: part of the work of the furnace-inlet man, and all of the work of the piercer plugger. The piercer plugger's job is a holdover from the older operations described in the preceding case and has changed little. An illustration of the plant layout is given in Figure 21.

Billets are round pieces of steel from 8 to 14 feet long, 5½ inches in diameter, and weighing from 380 to 1,200 pounds. The finished product may be a pipe 2⅜ inches in diameter and 140 feet long.

One of the nine operators is a relief man, who spells the other eight and burns away pipe caught between rolls. The furnace-inlet man controls the movement of billets from storage racks to the automatic charger and coordinates the charging with the discharger operator, who sets the pace for the operation. The discharger operator watches the automatic heating of billets in the furnace (which can also be run "manually") and controls the jaws which withdraw the heated billet from the furnace and drop it onto skids from where it moves to the piercing mill on a conveyor. The discharger is expected to push for speed and to coordinate the output of the rotary furnace with the piercing mill. The piercer operator sits in an enclosed pulpit and produces a hollow shell from the solid billet by remote control, in a fashion similar to that described in the preceding case. He can see the operating units of the whole mill and is required to level out the production process. The piercer plugger exchanges the heavy plug manually with a pair of tongs, coordinating his movements with the rapid production of the piercing mill. The inserter operator observes, and corrects irregularities of, the automatic inserting of the long mandrel into the shell on two sets of conveyor chains. The tube and mandrel bar then move into the mandrel mill, whose operator is the technical leader of the crew under the foreman. The position of the stripper is on an elevated bridge facing a panel of levers and buttons. He observes the automatic removal of the bar from the shell. The sizer-reducer operator performs a job second in skill and pay to that of the mandrel-mill operator. At the beginning of a new order, his equipment must be quickly adjusted in order to reach regular production quickly in which output meets inspection standards. (Walker 1957, 5–6, 11–17, 90, 194, 195)

Among the nine men comprising the crew in this case, six are operators of machines. Among these six, one operator, the furnace discharger, is in control of equipment half of which is self-regulating and half remotely steered. The work of the piercer operator is always performed by what the report calls "manual" operation, that is, by the steering of machinery through remote controls. The remaining four operators are in charge of equipment which is designed to be controlled by self-regulating features

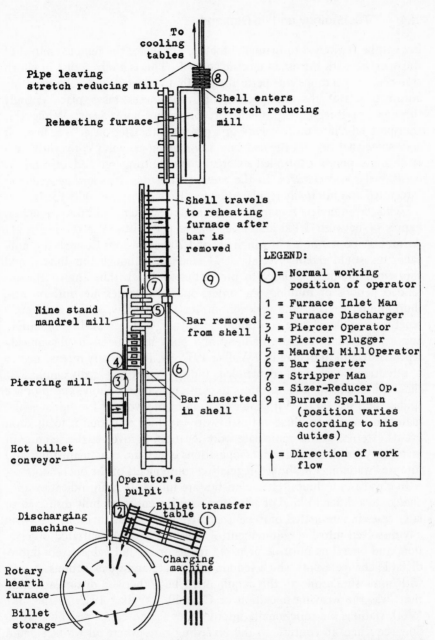

To
cooling
tables

Pipe leaving
stretch reducing mill

⑧

Shell enters
stretch reducing
mill

Reheating furnace

Shell travels
to reheating
furnace after
bar is
removed

⑨

LEGEND:

◯ = Normal working
position of operator

1 = Furnace Inlet Man
2 = Furnace Discharger
3 = Piercer Operator
4 = Piercer Plugger
5 = Mandrel Mill Operator
6 = Bar inserter
7 = Stripper Man
8 = Sizer-Reducer Op.
9 = Burner Spellman
(position varies
according to his
duties)

↑ = Direction of work
flow

⑦

⑤

Nine stand
mandrel mill

Bar removed
from shell

④

③

⑥

Piercing mill

Bar inserted
in shell

Hot billet
conveyor

Operator's
pulpit

Billet transfer
table

①

Discharging
machine

②

Charging
machine

Rotary
hearth
furnace

Billet
storage

FIGURE 21. **Case 29—Tubing Mill II** (By permission of the publishers from
C. R. Walker, *Toward the Automatic Factory: A Case Study of Men and
Machines*, New Haven: Yale University Press, 1957, p. 18, and of the United
States Steel Corporation from "The World's First Continuous Seamless Pipe
Mill," *U. S. Steel News*, vol. 14, No. 4, October 1949, p. 22. Redrawn for this
book.)

but can be "switched to manual," that is, run under the remote control of the operator with the use of electric controls. This is a mixed case in which conversion operations are performed both by steered and self-regulating automatics. But the transporting of work pieces takes place entirely through a self-regulating system of continuous movement. While this transport falls into our category of work-piece transfer on a "live line," it goes somewhat beyond the continuously moving assembly conveyor which is at some points controlled externally by shutting on and off and by occasional speed changes. In the present case, the transporting system is integrated and internally regulated by feedback devices. (Code T3:R6-C5)

Reported interview responses with hot-mill workers indicate production figures of between 1,100 and 1,300 pieces per shift. (Walker 1957, 34) Assuming about 7 hours in which about 1,200 pieces run through the mill, each run would extend over about 21 seconds. Although this time would vary from production order to production order, within any of the extended periods of running one order, operation cycles are uniform and short and have a constant work content for all operators. Such a rapid cycle repetition would require continuous attention, high visual discrimination, and a habituated response of hand and body movements to the quickly repeated technical demands. (Walker 1957, 44, 104) A very intense degree of attention is technically demanded, and the report repeatedly emphasizes the requirement for the operators to constantly watch, think, and produce split-second reactions. With the exception of the work of the furnace-inlet man and the piercer plugger, this is work in which attention is focused on events external to the immediate work location. It involves the steering of machinery for those parts of the operations which are run "manually," and intense "watching" in the self-regulating components of the operation.

In this case, technical characteristics are mixed. It is an indication of a change to a different kind of attention requirement more fully displayed in later cases in automated processing plants. There, time divisions are virtually dissolved into the requirement of constant and concentrated observation, and operators must be prepared for recurring but subjectively unpredictable chance events which require immediate and quick actions. A case with some similarities to this requirement but otherwise dissimilar conditions was the weaving operation of Case 20. (Walker 1957, 31, 33, 88) Work stations are functionally interdependent and connected by a work-flow sequence. In contrast to the preceding case, where all workers could see all of the operation because they were crammed together in a comparatively small space, other stations in this case can be seen only from very few positions. (Walker 1957, 40) In fact, the distance had to be overcome by the installation of a public-address system. Six of the nine workers are confined to fixed locations while the mill is running. Their tasks include the setup work of mill changes, and of the emergency work required when pipe gets stuck in a machine or becomes entangled in the reheating furnace. (Walker 1957, 85) There are clearly no shared functions in this work place, but we should notice that here, as for instance on the main auto-assembly line, we find a man whose job consists in spelling other workers when they have to leave their work station. (Case 29a: Code T4:8; T5:16; T6:4 and 5)

Cases 26b, 28b, and 29b—Mill Changes

We can now classify the parts of Cases 26, 28, and 29 concerned with mill changes which had been separated and left out in the preceding analysis. Although we retain the original case numbers, the information we have is only sufficient to code these three subcases together.

No conversion operations take place during the periods of change-overs. Although overhead cranes are occasionally used to bring heavy equipment parts to the work area, most of the work consists of moving and adjusting equipment parts by hand and with hand tools. Mill-change operations in these three cases are classified, then, as technology Type I together with the cases discussed in Chapter IV. (Code T3:R1-C1)

The distribution of work in these mill changes has no recognizable operation cycles. The work content is variable, depending on the specifications of the next production run. In the taking apart and putting together of heavy equipment components to requirements of precision and speed, tasks are likely to be shared by several men who are functionally interdependent but not connected by work flow. The major part of shifting heavy equipment parts would seem to require partly habituated movements, a focus on hands and tools, and thinking-through of the process only at certain crucial moments and by the man in charge of the particular equipment. The work makes it necessary for workers to move around more freely, and workers are within talking distance. (Code T4:1; T5:6; T6:1)

Case 6—Blast-Furnace Feeding I

In the discussion of Case 5 (Blast-Furnace Batching I) in Chapter IV, we indicated that we would deal with Popitz's descriptions of the operations of supplying blast furnaces with raw materials in three cases. Popitz described two kinds of installations: an old one, and one of comparatively recent construction. We divided the information on the older installation into two cases. The first (Case 5) contains the work of drawing ore, coke, and lime from bunkers and of hand-pushing wagons filled with these materials to a scale and then to an elevator. The second (Case 6) is concerned with the work of moving ore wagons from the bottom to the top of the elevator and of feeding the materials into the blast furnace. Case 6 will be further divided. In Case 6b, we will focus separately on the crew at the bottom of the elevator, on the crew at the top, and on the technical relations among tasks within each crew. In Case 6a, we will be concerned with the elevator operator and the technical relations of his task with the work performed by the two crews. Finally, in Case 7, we will classify all of the batching and feeding operations of the newer installation.

Two wagons loaded with ore or coke are moved by a steam-driven vertical elevator from the batching floor to the feeding platform at the top of the blast furnace, while two empty wagons move down. Two men are positioned near the elevator on the feeding platform and pull out the two loaded wagons. These wagons are then taken over by the other two men, who move them to the hopper and dump the load. At the same time, the first two men push two empty wagons into the elevator. The important knack in this operation is to keep the full wagons in motion after they have been pulled out of the elevator while they are taken over by the second pair of men. Two setters at the bottom receive the loaded wagons from the scales and move them into the elevator after the empty wagons have been pulled out. The position of the elevator operator is in an enclosed operating room halfway up the side of the blast furnace. When the setters have put the loaded wagons in position inside the elevator below, and the feeders at the top have their empty wagons in place, the elevator is ready for operation. However, only when the setters have given an electrical signal that they are clear below can the feeders give their signal from above. Both signals must be given before the elevator is put in motion. However, it is the feeders who can push for speed by filling the hopper to the limit and thus gaining time for a break or raising the bonus for additional loads. In the process, the weakest of the group begins to fall behind and the others make up for this by a subtle redistribution of effort. (Popitz 1957a, 74–77, 181–182)

Disregarding for the moment the elevator operator and focusing on the internal characteristics of the crew of setters and feeders, we can classify Case 6b. This operation does not directly contain conversion of material, and transfer operations consist of manual pushing and pulling of ore wagons into and out of the elevator and to the blast-furnace hopper. (Code T3:R1-C1) Assuming twenty-eight wagons required per "load," about thirty loads per shift, and two wagons for each elevator run, we detect a quite uniform and short cycle of approximately 1 minute for one up-and-down movement of the elevator. The content and sequence of work components are constant. In the rapid movement of wagons to, and away from, the elevator, particularly in the smoothly flowing "relay" among the four men at the top, these men's visual focus is directed toward their hands and the immediate movement of the wagon being pushed or pulled. Moving this heavy equipment would seem to require partly habituated movements and little cognitive involvement. These are the conditions for what we have called low attention requirements.

Each of the three differentiated tasks is shared by two men; and within each of these crews, either at the bottom or at the top, there is interdependence of tasks, not because workers perform successive operations on the same work piece but because they are bound by a shared-time requirement and by part of the equipment. Except for the movement of wagons between the two pairs at the top, tasks within each crew are not linked by work flow. Workers within a team are within talking distance of one another and are required to move about in their work area (even though along a very fixed pattern). (Code T4:1; T5:6; T6:1)

For Case 6a we will now consider the work position of the elevator operator in relation to the work positions at the top and bottom. The operator does not share the load bonus paid to the setters and feeders when more than twenty loads per shift are run. However, the 2 seconds or so by which he can vary his performance on each run affect the whole work sequence, and it is the elevator operator who translates speed variation at one end of the operation to the other. As soon as the signals from below and above are given, the operator releases the brake and turns on the steam, and the loaded elevator basket is pulled up. As the basket moves up, the operator has to exercise judgment over when to reduce steam and put on the brakes. If he performs these operations too soon, the steam may be insufficient and the load may drop. From his enclosed cubicle he can see only a small portion of the elevator and, especially, he cannot see upwards. An indicator in front of him shows the relative position of the basket but is too imprecise for him to judge how close the basket is to the top. In addition, he may rely on markings on the cable or the cable drum, or he may go simply by generalized experience. He has to be concerned with specified maximum loads and with the safety of the operators above and below, who must be clear of the elevator when it is put in motion. (Popitz 1957a, 210; Popitz 1957b, 36–38)

There is no conversion of materials in this operation, and the movement of materials of which the operation consists is regulated by remote control. With a transfer technology of a "steered line," energy supply and choice of direction are built into the equipment, but the operator has control over operation cycles. (Code T3:R1-C4) Operating positions in this work sequence are beyond seeing distance, and the operator confined to a fixed work station. The operator's task is performed exclusively, while the other workers' tasks are shared. Working positions are related by work flow and functional dependence. The operator performs habituated movements with a visual focus external to his immediate environment, represented by signal lights, indicators, the cable, the cable drum, and part of the elevator. The work requires high concentration and relatively full involvement in the process. Operation cycles have a constant content and sequence and are short and repetitive. (Code T4:8; T5:15; T6:4)

Case 7—Blast-Furnace Batching and Feeding II

We now turn to the newer installation for the supply of raw materials to a blast furnace, as described by Popitz. This process is fully mechanized, and the two parts (batching and feeding) are mechanically so closely interconnected that they will be treated as one case. Here we no longer find men working at the top of the blast furnace. There still is the elevator operator, now in the company of a helper. Together, they run a large piece of conveying machinery which, unlike a simple vertical elevator, runs at a steep angle from the top of the blast furnace directly to the side of the bunkers. The ore and coke handlers now drive powered cars on rails. Sketches of the plant are shown in Figures 22 and 23.

The crew of the feeding plant of this blast furnace consists of seven

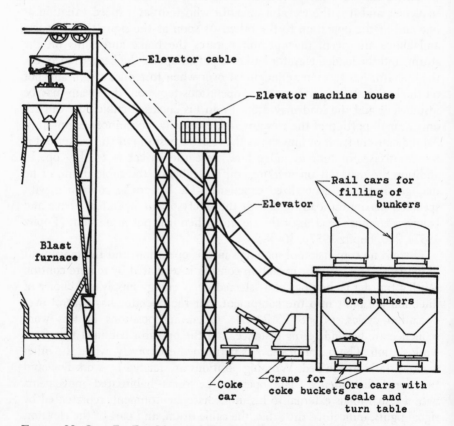

FIGURE 22. Case 7—Batching and Feeding Plant of Blast Furnace II (By permission of the publisher and authors from H. Popitz, H. P. Bahrdt, E. A. Jüres, and H. Kesting, *Technik und Industriearbeit*, Tübingen: Mohr, 1957, p. 85. Redrawn for this book.)

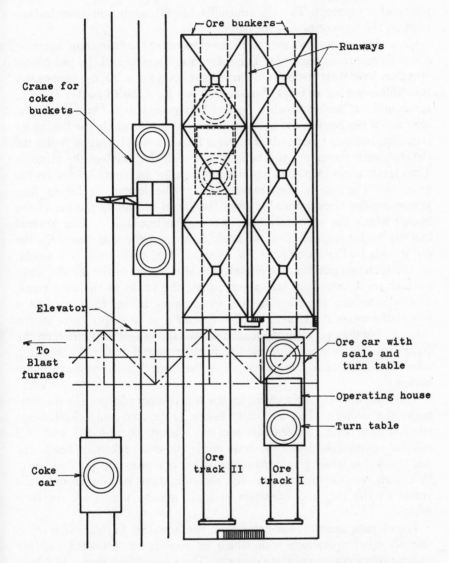

FIGURE 23. Case 7—Batching and Feeding Plant of Blast Furnace II (By permission of the publisher and authors from H. Popitz, H. P. Bahrdt, E. A. Jüres, and H. Kesting, *Technik und Industriearbeit*, Tübingen: Mohr, 1957, p. 87. Redrawn for this book.)

workers. Three of these will be of little concern to us, as they perform various maintenance and ancillary functions. The first of these is the elevator operator's helper, who is in training, watches the cable and cable drum, keeps the operating room clean, gets coffee, and occasionally relieves the operator. The grease man is responsible for lubrication on the various pieces of equipment. The ore controller keeps records and gives instructions on the composition of the batch.

Central to our interest are the elevator operator, the coke-crane operator, and the two ore-car operators. The coke-crane operator and the two ore-car operators have their positions on large track-bound cars. An ore car has two turntables: one for an empty bucket, and one for a loaded bucket. The car is run under a bunker which is opened by a push button. As the material runs out of the bunker, the operator turns a switch to rotate the bucket for even distribution of materials. The car is then moved in position under the elevator, with the empty turntable in line with the "cat" of the elevator. The elevator runs on a steep incline and deposits an empty bucket on the turntable. The car is then moved to put the loaded bucket in line, permitting the hook suspended from the cat to slip under the bar of the bucket which has previously been raised. The turntable is then lowered and the bucket suspended on the hook. As soon as the load moves up, the car returns to the area under the bunkers. The coke crane is a similar vehicle with two positions for buckets, but also a crane in the middle. Coke buckets are delivered on rail cars alongside the tracks of the coke crane. The operator uses the crane to pick up an empty bucket from one of the two platforms on the train car and to deposit it in an empty space on the coke car. He then picks up the loaded bucket and puts it in position on the crane car. The whole crane vehicle is then moved under the elevator, where the filled bucket is picked up in the same fashion as was the ore bucket.

The work of these three operators has two distinct phases: (1) the time under the elevator when an empty bucket is received and a loaded one released, and when movements are very closely coordinated with the elevator operator; and (2) the time under the ore bunkers or beside the coke track for hauling raw materials, when operators are on their own. When an operator arrives near the elevator, there is a break until the arrival of the cat, and operators perform maintenance work on their vehicles.

The elevator operator has before him two armature boards which represent all other operations with which he coordinates his work and the corresponding communication contacts. These boards are shown in Figure 24. In addition, there is a vertical indicator which shows the position of the bucket-lifting mechanism at any one time. Two lamps show what the current load contains (ore or coke) and indicate to the operator where to pick up the next load, ore and coke being run alternately. Several lamps light up when neighboring furnaces are being fed. When the hopper of the nearest furnace is open, this furnace cannot be fed. Four lamps are connected with corresponding bells for communication with the operators below and with the top. Red and green lamps on the other board indicate when the hopper on top of the blast furnace is open or closed and whether the materials cars

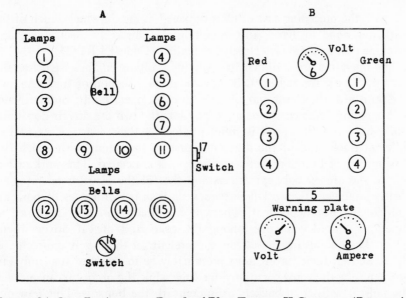

FIGURE 24. Case 7—Armature Boards of Blast Furnace II Conveyor (By permission of the publisher and authors from H. Popitz, H. P. Bahrdt, E. A. Jüres, and H. Kesting, *Technik und Industriearbeit*, Tübingen: Mohr, 1957, p. 88. Redrawn for this book.)

below are in their correct position for pickup. A warning light permits men on the smelter crew to interrupt feeding. An ampere meter shows to what extent a bucket at the top has emptied. There are also speaking tubes for direct verbal communication. Finally, certain positions of the cat automatically lock the ore and coke cars in their position and vice versa.

Once a coke bucket arrives at the top, it empties automatically into the hopper. The operator controls the movements of the elevator with a number of switches and controls, especially a speed regulator, with several gradations for speed both up and down, and two brake levers. When the empty bucket descends, the elevator operator communicates with the car operator by bells and signal lights for the operation of exchanging buckets. In the process he watches his armature boards, the vertical indicator, and markings on the cable drum. Loading and unloading of buckets on the batching floor require temporal and spatial precision: cars have to be moved to within inches of a certain position; and the raising and lowering of turntables, as well as the movements of car and cat, have to be closely coordinated. The elevator operator cannot see the conveyor during the operation. (Popitz 1957a, 84–91, 120–121, 170, 200)

This operation contains no conversion of materials. All the machines used are "steered" by their operators, and they are steered along entirely fixed lines—the ore and coke tracks and the sloped conveyor. In compari-

son with the preceding case of blast-furnace feeding, in which much of the
work was done by hand, this operation is completely mechanized and
machine processes are very closely integrated. (Code T3:R1-C4)

The operators are confined to a specific position on their vehicles, and
the vehicles are limited in their movements to a section of track. As only
one car is near the elevator at any one time, the operators are ordinarily not
within seeing distance of one another. Only the two ore drivers do similar
work, but even this work is differentiated by their assignments to two
different tracks and by the different demands for timing with which this
distribution of functions between the two is associated. The work of any
one of the ore- or coke-car drivers and that of the elevator operator are
clearly arranged in a work-flow sequence. Task performances of both are
functionally interdependent. There is no direct work-flow sequence or
functional interdependence among the coke- and ore-car drivers themselves. These kinds of connections are present for them only indirectly, in
the sense that their travels must presumably be so arranged that only one
of them is by the conveyor at any one time while the other two are away at
the rail car with coke buckets or underneath the bunkers. This temporal
requirement for the presence of only one car at the conveyor every third
time around makes indirectly for something similar to a work-flow sequence and for at least temporal interdependence. With from eight to ten
runs per hour, the cycle of the conveyor is repeated about every 6 or 7
minutes. The reported time for one up-and-down run is 3 minutes, on the
average. With each of the three supply-car operators having to have a load
ready for every third run, the cycle would be about 20 minutes long. The
report emphasizes the necessary habituation in manipulating levers and
controls. At the same time, the operators' perception would be focused
almost entirely on the complex technical processes external to their immediate position on their equipment. The process requires concentration and
conscious involvement, especially for the elevator operator. (Code T4:12;
T5:16; T6:7)

Case 8—Bridge Crane

This short case describes the work of a single man who runs a rapid-
transit bridge crane in a heavy rolling mill. A few observations of this
operation are reported in several parts of the first volume by Popitz and his
associates; the remainder comes from an interview with a crane operator, in
the second volume. Although these cranes apparently perform a variety of
different jobs, the interview refers more specifically to the work of supplying large, heated steel ingots to a rolling mill. In addition, the cranes are
used to move scrap to railroad cars. Ingots must be moved very rapidly and
at the right time. They must reach the rolling mill at a temperature which
allows the completion of the rolling process before the block cools down to
a point where it no longer can be rolled.

The rapid-transit crane runs high above the large hall containing a multitude of rolling-mill operations. The operator sits in a glassed-in cabin attached to the crane and travels with it as it traverses the large hall. He is subjected to the heat and gases from the reheating furnaces. The operator receives his order from the foreman. He must be familiar with the rolling program in order to pick up the right ingots at the right time. The ingots are marked with order numbers which disappear in the reheating process. Ingots are picked up from storage with the aid of signals given by men on the floor. Before the operator raises the load, he must know that the load is clear both near the pickup point and on the way where the second crane may, for instance, service a repair crew. The operator controls simultaneously the three movements of the crane: back and forth, up and down, and the tipping of the crossboom to which the hook or grasping device is attached. Distances downward are difficult to judge, and the operator may think that the hook has reached the ground while it is still several yards above it. Instead of first raising the load and then starting the forward movement of the crane, a skilled operator will combine these movements into one smooth flow, which requires confidence and familiarity with the route traveled. When heat and gases prevent the operator from seeing through his window, he has to orient his movements solely by certain indicators in the hall constructions. In fact, he must be familiar with a great variety of events in his very large working space in order to move both rapidly and safely. The rolling mill which he supplies relies for its continuous operation on his movements. (Popitz 1957b, 30–33; Popitz 1957a, 122, 166–167)

As in the preceding two cases, there is no conversion operation involved here, and the movement of materials takes place by steering a piece of equipment along a comparatively fixed line. (Code T3:R1-C4) The operation requires clearly habituated movements in regulating the controls of the crane; at the same time, it requires paying close attention over extended distances to the movements of the crossboom and the position of the crane when picking up, transporting, and setting down materials. This is the requirement for externally focused attention similar to that of driving a car. The crane is a central component in a sequence of closely timed work flow and dependence with the tasks of the men at the pickup point and the rolling mill. At any given time, the crane operator's task is performed exclusively, even though he has a second man with whom to alternate for reasons of safety. He is confined to a mobile work location, and he is within seeing distance of other workers in the process. (Code T4:11; T5:16; T6:4)

Case 9—Coking Battery

In three preceding cases based on the reports by Popitz and his associates, it was recorded that coke was used as a raw material in blast-furnace operations. In this case, we go to the place where coke itself is produced in three coking batteries of 48 chambers each. In addition to coke for the blast furnaces, this plant produces coking gas for the whole steelworks and various by-products of coking gas. Our focus here is on only one coking battery, put into production in 1953. It is illustrated in Figure 25.

A filling car runs on top of the battery and hauls coal dust from the coal tower at the end of the battery to the individual chambers. A machine runs on tracks along one side of the battery. It mechanically lifts out the chamber doors, pushes the hot coke out of the other end of the chamber with a power ram, spreads the coal dust dropped from the top, and puts the doors back in. Along the other side of the battery runs another carriage which also lifts out chamber doors mechanically and guides the hot coke into the hot car when it is pushed out of the chamber from the other side. We have, then, the filling car on top with two men, the ram car on one side with its operator and helper, the guide car on the other side with one operator, and the hot car on railroad tracks beside the battery. The chambers are heated by combustion of gas within the walls between the chambers. The heating equipment is underneath the chambers and is operated by one man who has no direct connection with the operations on the two sides and top of the battery.

Of the two men operating the filling car on the roof of the coking battery, the first filler is in charge of the whole battery. He connects and disconnects the chambers for the coking process proper; is responsible for the positioning of the ram car, guide car, and hot car before finished coke is pushed out; and gives the order for pushing out. He opens, closes, and greases the lids through which coal dust is filled into the chambers. He does part of the steering and maintenance of the filling car. The second filler is a helper, who performs the ancillary work of weighing coal and does part of the actual running of the filling car. Both of them are jointly involved in drawing the coal, opening the hoppers on the filling car, and starting the various motors.

The ram operator and the door man on one side of the battery are in a similar relationship of operator and helper. The ram operator controls the three components of his equipment. He lifts out chamber doors with a special device fitted to the ram car. By controlling the forward movement of the ram proper, he pushes the hot finished coke out of the chamber. He also controls the leveling bar which levels coal dust being filled into the chamber from the top. His helper, the door man, opens, closes, and locks chamber doors by turning air pressure on and off. He sweeps together the coke that drops out of the chambers and scrapes tar out of the door frames with a long bar after the door has been lifted out.

Doing similar work, the guide-car operator on the other side combines the work of an operator and helper. With his equipment, he lifts out the doors on his side and extends the guiding pan over which the hot coke

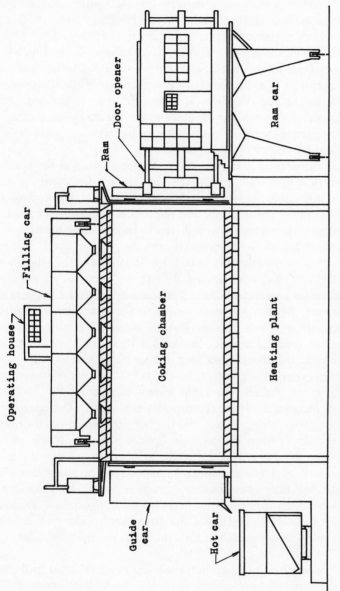

FIGURE 25. Case 9—Coking Battery (By permission of the publisher and authors from H. Popitz, H. P. Bahrdt, E. A. Jüres, and H. Kesting, *Technik und Industriearbeit*, Tübingen: Mohr, 1957, p. 79. Redrawn for this book.)

drops from the chamber into the hot car. He also sweeps up coke and removes tar from the door frames. The hot-car operator runs the hot car on railroad tracks between the coking battery, the quenching tower, and the point to which the finished, cooled-off coke is delivered.

The major work sequence in this operation is as follows. Coal dust is moved from the coal tower to a chamber. The chamber is filled with coal and leveled off. Then follows the 20-hour coking process, which requires no work by the operators. The finished coke is pushed out of the chamber and dropped into the hot car. The hot car moves the coke to the quenching tower. The operators of the filling car and the ram car cooperate during the filling process of the sequence. The operators of the ram car, guide car, and hot car cooperate during the pushing-out process.

Each of the three main elements—filling, pushing out, and the intermediate maintenance and waiting period—will now be described in more detail. The filling car is moved under the coal tower at the end of the battery. The operators pull the lids, and the coal runs into the hoppers on the car. The car is then weighed and driven to the chamber opening. The chamber lids have already been opened during the previous cycle. The ram car moves in front of the chamber to be filled, the upper part of the door is removed, and the leveling bar is extended. Both the filling-car crew and the ram-car crew are now ready for filling. The fillers open up the hoppers and turn on vibrators. As the coal dust runs into the chamber, the ram-car operator distributes it evenly with the leveling bar which is going back and forth. When the required amount of coal has been filled in and leveled, the lids on top and the doors on the ram side are closed and locked.

Both the ram car and the guide car now move to the next chamber, with finished coke to be pushed out. Light signals connecting the two sides indicate when the two machines are correctly positioned. The operator of the approaching hot car rings a bell, and the hot car soon comes into sight. By use of the door-lifting devices, the operators on each side of the chamber remove the doors, and the guide-car operator extends the guide pan. Light signals go back and forth to indicate when all positions are ready, and the first filler gives the order for pushing out. By extension of the ram, the hot coke is pushed out over the guide pan into the hot car which is moved slowly to distribute the coke evenly. The hot car then moves to the quenching tower, and the ram car to the next chamber to be filled.

While hot coke is being pushed out, the fillers move their car to the coal tower, fill the hoppers, and weigh the coal. They then move to the chamber which had been emptied in the preceding cycle and wait until the ram car arrives to commence the next filling. When the filling is completed, the operator and helper on the ram car clean up and take a break until the hot car turns up again. When the pushing out is completed, the guide-car operator cleans up and takes a break until the next cycle. (Popitz 1957a, 77–82)

While this case involves conversion from coal dust to coke, the work of the operators on whom we focus is not concerned with the conversion process itself. Even the coking cycle of 20 hours is not the work cycle of the operation performed by these men. It exceeds the time period of a shift and does not coincide with shift periods. The operation in which these men are involved consists, then, entirely of the moving of materials, and this moving is performed by means of steered vehicles along fixed lines. (Code T3:R1-C4) The operation is divided into distinct, interconnected phases, and the attention required of the operators is intermittent. No minute distinctions must be made by visual means. Although the work of the operators here consists primarily of the steering of track-bound vehicles similar to the work in the blast-furnace feeding of the newer plant in Case 7, the operators here do not perform the steering component of their performance with an automaticity comparable to that case. There, the distances covered are the same, with only minor variations. The back and forth movements along the same route, and the loading operation at each end, are repeated without variation. In the present case, there is a clear separation between the times at which quite different functions are performed. The actual place of performance constantly changes, as the beginning of a new cycle also requires moving to a different heating chamber. (Popitz 1957a, 122) During the main phases, the operators on each of the four machines observe the process while controlling large pieces of machinery by habituated hand movements.

For any one heating chamber, it takes about 20 hours from the time of filling in of coal dust to the time of pushing out of completed coke. Assuming that a continuous shift is operated and that workers must have completed the work on each of the 48 chambers when beginning to work on a chamber which has been filled 20 hours earlier, we can calculate that each work cycle would be approximately 25 minutes long. (Popitz 1957a, 151)

While we would suggest that operation cycles here are uniform and long and that the work content is constant, this classification does not indicate the relative complexity of interconnections between cycle components in comparison to the simpler cycle content of other cases. This complexity is also indicated in the work-flow characteristics of this case. In some other operations, work pieces or materials persistently flow past successive work stations. In this case, materials move from the coal tower to the chamber to the hot car, and this flow connects the mobile work stations of the operators to some extent. However, for each operation cycle (not the coking cycle), they move to another chamber and, in a sense, to another segment of the work flow. Work stations are functionally interdependent and at the same time beyond seeing distance of one another. A different function is performed by each operator. Workers are bound to work places which move along fixed lines. (Code T4:12; T5:16; T6:4)

It might be noted that this operation contains a certain hand-work component in work on lids on top of the battery and in the scraping of door frames on the sides. Part of their work connects two operators in the pairs on the filling car and the ram car in a technically different fashion than is found in the relations between the different work stations. We could have attempted to distinguish analytically a separate subcase, involving primarily hand work. The same could have been done with the conveyor operator and his helper in Case 7. In both cases, however, recorded observations are insufficient. In addition, the technical relationship between the tasks of a helper, who might also be in training and perform various menial jobs, and those of an operator is a peculiar one requiring more detailed data than are available. Subsequently we will focus, then, on the whole work crew and the relations among the four major work stations.

Case 32—Soaking Pit

The material for this case is found in the interview responses of one soaking-pit operator, reported by Popitz and his associates.[5] A soaking pit is a furnacelike arrangement below floor level in which heat is applied to large pieces of steel from an external source. It equalizes sectional temperatures for subsequent rolling to avoid cracks and fissures in the ingot, and brings the ingot up to rolling temperature.[6]

The soaking pit is operated from a control platform. The pit is covered by heavy doors. When a block is to be put in or taken out, the appropriate door is opened and closed by remote control. This is apparently a recent installation designed for automatic operation by remote control. It still has many "bugs," making it necessary, for instance, for the operator to actually go and look into the pit to observe at what stage of heating certain ingots are, and requiring a longer time for the heating process than anticipated. In the interview, the operator indicated a period of 4½ hours for the heating of certain blocks, whereas 2 hours had been expected. A certain maximum temperature must not be exceeded. Temperatures and gas and air supply are continuously measured and automatically recorded on paper tape. The operator is dependent on the dispatcher, who apparently keeps a continuous record of heated ingots together with heating times and regulates the flow of ingots, presumably for several soaking pits. Ingots arrive on railroad cars, are lifted into the pit, and are taken out and moved to the rolling mill by crane. The dispatcher communicates with the pit operator by signal lights, read by the operator on his control platform. The operator,

---

[5] Popitz et al., Das Gesellschaftsbild des Arbeiters, pp. 40–43.
[6] Morris, Modern Manufacturing Processes, p. 125.

in turn, can telephone the dispatcher when the latter has made a mistake, for instance, in ordering the removal of ingots which have been in the pit for only half an hour. The superintendent can also call the operator by telephone when ingots do not arrive at the mill as required. Communication with train and crane operators is by hand signals.

The dispatcher gives instructions to the operator of the train engine to move ingots loaded on the railroad car close to a particular furnace. The soaking-pit operator receives instructions by signal lights "from the board" (that is, the dispatcher) on where to place the ingots in the furnace. He receives another light signal when the ingots are to be removed. He opens the furnace by remote control and directs the train operator to the ingot, which is then picked up by the train and moved to the rolling mill. Once the operator knows which batch of ingots is to be pulled, he has to make sure that the next one is pulled on time. Indicators of conditions in the furnace are not sufficient to show if ingots are properly heated. The operator can better judge this by observing how "soft" the ingot is when it goes through the rolling mill. From his position he cannot see the mill clearly and actually goes over to the mill to see for himself. When work proceeds rapidly, 130 ingots might be pulled in one shift. In that event, he cannot go and look for himself, and the regulation of the heat is left to the foreman. Important requirements for the soaking-pit operator are that he must not burn ingots or abuse the furnace, and he must have material ready for rolling when it is required. (Popitz 1957b, 40–43)

The conversion operation which takes place in this case, that is, bringing ingots from one temperature state to another, takes place by self-regulating automatics watched over by the pit operator. But the operator regulates parts of the operation, including the opening and closing of doors, by remote control. There is, then, a mixture of steered and self-regulating automatics. Work pieces are moved by operator-driven vehicles running along fixed lines. (Code T3:R6-C4)

Operation times relevant to the soaking-pit operator are regulated by the arrival of batches of ingots, the removal of reheated ingots to the rolling mill, and the heating cycle itself. An example is given in the interview where twelve ingots are put into the soaking pit at one time, eight of which are successively removed later, and half an hour later the remaining four, while the eight ingots removed first might have been replaced with ingots from a new batch. The size of the batch is determined by the quantity of steel drawn from a converter or open-hearth furnace during one tap.

During a shift with a fast-running operation, 130 blocks move through the soaking pit, a subcycle of from 3 to 4 minutes. Thus, several cycles overlap or are built into one another. The output of the pit going to the rolling mill presumably follows a somewhat more regular pattern than does the input. Since ingots enter the pit at varying stages of heat still contained by them, and since they enter at different locations with perhaps varying temperature, time cycles relevant to the operator are likely to be variable but encompass a fairly constant content. Watching of signal lights requires continuous attention but attention which varies in intensity over different time periods separated by the repeated opening and closing of furnace doors. A part of the operator's performance is likely to consist of habituated hand movements in the regulation of the furnace and its doors. In short, some components of this job require externally focused attention; and some components, "watching." There are a work-flow sequence and a functional interdependence between the operators of the delivering train, the soaking pit, and the crane. In addition to the flow of work pieces, there is a flow of information with functional interdependence between the dispatcher and the soaking-pit operator. All functions within one work-flow sequence seem to be performed exclusively by one man at any one time. Operators in the work-piece flow are within seeing distance of one another, and operators connected by information flow are beyond seeing distance. Except for his occasional walk to the rolling mill, the soaking-pit operator is confined to his position by the furnace. (Code T4:7–8; T5:16; T6:4–5)

Summary

Six classifications of technology were represented among the cases in this chapter. Cases 26b, 28b, 29b, and 6b are of the same kind of technology as the cases described at the very beginning, with no conversion operations and with transfer operations performed by hand. The technical demands for these cases are separately classified in Table 17. It can be seen there that these cases display much uniformity among themselves and in comparison to the cases of Chapter IV. Somewhat of an exception is Case 6b (Blast-Furnace Feeding I). The work described in this case is built into a rapid and demanding work flow, unlike most other cases of Type I.

The classifications of technical demands for the remaining nine cases are summarized in Table 18. In the listing of cases by type of technology, we have distinguished two types. Case 26a (Wire Rolling) was called Type VI. It is a case where the conversion operations clearly combine components of hand and machine work in the activities of the same operators. The remaining cases have all been assigned to Type VII, even though they display the characteristics of four different classifications in our original typology. Cases 6a, 7, 8, and 9 are cases with no conversion operation and a steered-line transfer technology. The data suggest that the characteristics of these operations do not warrant a separation from Cases 27 and 28a where both conversion and transfer are regulated by remote control.

In actual technical development, Case 29a (Tube Rolling II) is the successor of Case 28a. In contrast to Case 28a, all transfer operations are self-regulating, and parts of the conversion operations also have self-regulating mechanisms. The report indicates, however, that two of the work

TABLE 17.   CODING SUMMARY: TECHNOLOGY TYPE I

Technology: Type I (R1-C1) No Conversion - Hand Transfer

Case 26b, 28b, 29b Wire and Tube Rolling (Mill Changes).
Case 6b Blast-Furnace Feeding I (Ore-Wagon Handling).

T4: SPATIAL CONSTRAINTS

Relation of Workers to Work Stations	Talking Distance	Shouting Distance	Seeing Distance	Beyond Seeing
Open	6b,26b, 28b,29b			
Confined to fixed place				
Confined to mobile place				

T5: FUNCTIONAL CONSTRAINTS

Differentiation Pattern	No Work Flow		Work Flow	
	Independent	Dependent	Independent	Dependent
All tasks undifferentiated				
Each differentiated task shared		6b,26b, 28b,29b		
Some exclusive and some shared tasks				
All tasks performed exclusively				

141

TABLE 17. CODING SUMMARY: TECHNOLOGY TYPE I (continued)

T6: TEMPORAL AND PERCEPTUAL CONSTRAINTS

Attention Requirements		Operation Cycles	
Low	6b,26b,28b,29b	None	26b,28b,29b
Surface		1 minute	6b
Detailed			
External focus			
Watching			

stations are actively operated by remote controls and that all of the conversion operations can be switched to "manual," that is, to steering by remote controls. Once the mill was fully in operation, the operators frequently switched to "manual." We will recognize the difference in subsequent analysis, but our data are not precise enough to suggest that an overly detailed differentiation would be useful for our analytical purposes. There seems to be a sufficient predominance of characteristics of a technology of "steered automatics" to permit inclusion of this case in Type VII together with the other cases.

Case 32 (Soaking Pit) is also a case of mixed characteristics. In the next chapter, we will classify Case 33 (Blast-Furnace Air Control) in the same category, but assign it to Type VIII. In Case 32, a large part of the operator's work involves active regulation of the process, and he observes directly a major part of the operation. The report also indicates that, at the time of the interview, the self-regulating features of the equipment were not functioning properly. By contrast, in Case 33, the operator is completely removed from the operation itself. He regulates the process by dials and preset time schedules. Here the major process in which the operator is involved is an information flow, while this component is small in Case 32. We have combined, then, eight cases in one type, characterized by a technology of remote controls, in either conversion or transfer operations, or both.

The uniformity of characteristics of technical demands in the cases of Type VII is quite evident from the summaries just given. In all of these cases, operators are confined to their work locations, although in Cases 7, 8,

TABLE 18. CODING SUMMARY: TECHNOLOGY TYPES VI AND VII

Technology: Type VI (R3-C5) Hand and Machine Tools - Live Line
Case 26a Wire Rolling.

Type VII (R5-C4) Steered Automatics - Steered Line
Case 27 Bloom Rolling. Case 28a Tube Rolling I.

Type VII (R6-C5) Steered and Self-Regulating Automatics - Live Line
Case 29a Tube Rolling II.

Type VII (R1-C4) No Conversion - Steered Line
Case 6a Blast-Furnace Feeding I. Case 7 Blast-
Furnace Batching and Feeding II. Case 8
Bridge Crane. Case 9 Coking Battery.

Type VII (R6-C4) Steered and Self-Regulating Automatics - Steered Line
Case 32 Soaking Pit.

T4: SPATIAL CONSTRAINTS

Relation of Workers to Work Stations	Talking Distance	Shouting Distance	Seeing Distance	Beyond Seeing
Open				
Confined to fixed place		26a	27,28a, 32	6a,29a, 32
Confined to mobile place			8	7,9

TABLE 18. CODING SUMMARY: TECHNOLOGY TYPES VI AND VII
(continued)

T5: FUNCTIONAL CONSTRAINTS

Differentiation Pattern	No Work Flow		Work Flow	
	Independent	Dependent	Independent	Dependent
All tasks undifferentiated				
Each differentiated task shared				
Some exclusive and some shared tasks				6a,28a
All tasks performed exclusively				7,8,9, 26a,27, 29a,32

T6: TEMPORAL AND PERCEPTUAL CONSTRAINTS

Attention Requirements		Operation Cycles	
Low		Variable	8,32
Surface		25 minutes	9
		7 and 20 minutes	7
Detailed	26a	1 minute	6a
External focus	6a,7,8,9,27,28a,29a,32	7 seconds and 2 minutes	27
Watching	29a,32	7 seconds	26a
		? seconds	28a
		21 seconds	29a

and 9, their work location is mobile. In all cases, at least some tasks are performed exclusively and are connected by work flow and functional dependence. Distances between work stations are comparatively great; only in Case 26a can workers communicate directly, at least by shouting. Case 26a differs from the other cases by requiring continuous and very detailed attention. Cases 29a and 32 have mixed attention requirements. In Case 32, the attention requirements of regulating the flow of ingots are mixed with the watching of indicators of the heating process. The use of both automatic regulation and "manual" remote controls in Case 29a produces the two requirements. The other cases combine a visual focus on the larger process with habituated movements and high concentration. Five of the cases have short and demanding operation cycles, while time requirements are more "open" in the remaining cases, being either long or variable.

Chapter IX

AUTOMATION:
Watching a Self-Regulating Process

Case 31—Auto Engines

The following four cases are the last of our analysis. The first of these is concerned with an operation using so-called transfer machines in the production of automobile engines. The remaining three cases describe various processing operations which require the control of fluid or gaseous materials.

Other operations involving the use of transfer machines have been described in the literature, particularly by Touraine and Hammer.[1] But these studies, not anticipating the uses to which we would put them, do not contain observations on both technology and workers' social behaviors. Rather, they are concerned with demonstrating a degree of parallelism between technical "evolution" and changes in the general occupational characteristics of automobile workers in Europe. While generally relevant for this study, these reports do not lend themselves as bases for specific cases as we have presented them here.

Case 31 is based on a dissertation by Faunce,[2] parts of which have been published in several articles.[3] References are all made to one chapter of the dissertation. It is the result of research conducted in two phases in 1956 and 1957 on Detroit automobile plants. Data were obtained during the first phase by interviews with staff personnel in two plants, providing

---

[1] A. Touraine, *L'Évolution du travail ouvrier aux Usines Renault* (Paris: Centre National de la Recherche Scientifique, 1955). M. Hammer, *Vergleichende Morphologie der Arbeit in der europäischen Automobilindustrie: Die Entwicklung zur Automation* (Basel: Kyklos-Verlag, and Tübingen: Mohr, 1959).

[2] W. A. Faunce, *Automation in the Automobile Industry: Some Consequences for In-Plant and Union-Management Relationships* (microfilmed Ph.D. dissertation; Detroit: Wayne State University, 1957).

[3] W. A. Faunce, "Automation in the Automobile Industry: Some Consequences for In-Plant Social Structure," *American Sociological Review*, 23 (1958), 401–407; "Automation and the Automobile Worker," *Social Problems*, 6 (1958), 68–78; "The Automobile Industry: A Case Study in Automation," and "Automation and Leisure," *Automation and Society*, ed. H. B. Jacobson and J. S. Rouček (New York: Philosophical Library, 1959), pp. 44–53, 297–308.

general information on automation in these plants. In the second phase, a sample of workers from four machining departments of one engine plant was interviewed. Most of the reported data are from these interviews. This study was concerned with the effects of automation upon job content, social interaction among workers, relations between workers and supervision, and sources of work satisfaction and dissatisfaction on an automated line. (Faunce, 94) In addition to the data about the engine plant, occasional references are made in the report to the second plant, a transmission plant, in which preliminary investigation had also been carried out. The effects of automation on the several factors mentioned were measured by asking workers, who had all worked in a nonautomated shop before, to report on conditions both in their present work place and in the one from which they had come.

It should be made clear that the description of this case is not supported by any systematic direct observations. In other studies, interviews with workers as a source of data were at least supplemented by observations at the work place itself. The use of transfer machines is an important development in the technical and social organization of production, and it is unfortunate that there are no reported observations which are more complete than this case. Inferences are made for our analysis from a very limited set of data, and data based almost entirely on precoded interview responses.

The 123 workers interviewed were employed in the four most completely automated departments of an engine plant. These shops do all the machining work on cylinder blocks, crankshafts, connecting rods, pump housings, and flywheels. The work includes the common machine-shop operations of boring, reaming, milling, drilling, broaching, honing, and tapping. Most of the handling and positioning of work pieces, the disposal of metal chips, and the controls for tool wear and quality inspection are built into an integrated transfer machine and performed automatically. Work pieces move automatically from position to position in the sequence of operations within the transfer machine, while operators watch panels of lights and gauges. The job classification of "console operator" was created when the plant was put into operation. In 1957 the output was 150 engines per hour.

Most of the workers in the new plant, and all of the workers interviewed, had come from the older, nonautomated plant. In order to obtain a description of conditions at the new plant, we will use the comparison between old and new as it is provided in the report. Some materials handling was contained in 80 per cent of the machine-operating jobs in the old plant. The materials handling mentioned as part of their new job by 44 per cent of the workers consisted primarily of feeding small parts into loaders. In the machine-shop operations of the old plant, workers exercised full control over work cycles by starting and stopping machines largely at their own discretion. This permitted them to work ahead and take a break occasionally. By contrast, only two of the interviewed workers actually operated machines in this fashion. Many jobs on the transfer machine require constant attention to the control panel, while in the old plant there were periods in the work cycle which required no attention. In addition, the effects of not paying close attention are more severe: more can go wrong on the complex and integrated machinery; damage from mistakes is more costly; and a breakdown of a transfer machine draws supervisors, engineers, and repairmen to the scene, and most workers prefer to steer clear of this kind of attention to their troubles. They generally emphasize the necessity of constantly thinking about the job.

At an average of about 20 feet, the distance between working positions is greater. There is more noise and less teamwork. In the old plants the work pace of 38 per cent of the workers was controlled by machine, and on the automated jobs it is 72 per cent. Similarly, 70 per cent of the workers claim that in the old plant they could vary their pace and take a break; whereas only 19 per cent have that opportunity now. (Faunce, 95, 96, 99, 103, 111, 115, 125, 127, 141)

No reports have been found of any production plant with extensive use of integrated and self-regulating machinery in which not at many points human "stopgaps" regulate certain parts of the operation by remote controls. This is true for this case and for the other cases in this chapter. But since self-regulating features seem to be dominant here, and work pieces move from work station to work station along a continuous line, we will classify this case as being characterized by self-regulating automatics in conversion operations and by a "live line" for work-piece transfer. (Code T3:R7-C5)

The attention requirements observed in this case have been recorded for several previous cases in which they occurred in a mixture with other demands: the weaving operation on automatic looms in Case 20; the semiautomated tubing mill of Case 29; and the work of the soaking-pit operator in Case 32. If we assume for the present case that the rate of 150 engines per hour given in the report applies to any given transfer-machine station, a precisely uniform and short cycle would be present. When work is repeated in exceedingly short cycles, time is likely to be felt as mere duration, as in the clicking room of Case 18. However, in that case and other cases, the cycle repetition is accompanied by an operator's synchronic actions. When the job demands the continuous observation of instrument panels in order to detect when something has gone wrong that is not corrected by the self-regulating features of the equipment, the conditions for attention requirements are quite different. Instead of focusing on the work under his hands or on the directly visible production process to which he contributes by remote control, the operator here must comprehend a complex operation only represented by the lights and gauges on his panel but hidden from direct perception. This probably means that he must think about the process quite continuously and that his own action has little habituation and repetition. When something goes wrong, he must be ready to do the right thing quickly; but when such an emergency will happen is a matter of chance for him. In fact, the operation is so complex that neither operators nor foremen can cope with repairs that must be made. In the event of a breakdown of any part of the setup, the whole transfer line is stopped and repairmen are called. (Faunce, 133) The console operator may in fact see a periodical lighting up indicating routine events, but these will not govern his hand movements.

With regard to connections between work stations, a similar dissolving of the determinacy of distinctions in the relationship between operator and machine seems present. There are clearly a work-flow sequence and functional interdependence of highly integrated work stations, but individual work stations are no longer manned. If we focus on the console operator, we find that he controls a whole large complex of work stations which together constitute, as the name suggests, a machine. "Stations" in the process of the operation would consist of the places in the transfer machine at which work pieces temporarily stop to be worked on by multiple tools built into a common machine head, where even at any one such "station" dozens of "operations" are performed all at once. Though each transfer machine as a whole also has a place in a more general work-flow sequence, the functional interdependency of the whole machine in that flow is perhaps of less importance to the performance of the operator than are events within it. Distances between work stations, taken as whole transfer machines or parts of them, are long. They are extended by the noise of machinery concentrated in a narrow space to what we have called seeing distance. Whether seen as parts of the transfer machine or as transfer machines, work stations are functionally interdependent and connected by work flow.

For the remainder of our classifications, the information is not entirely clear. We will assume that each operator performs a differentiated function of his own and that at least console operators are confined to their position at the console during operating times. (Code T4:7; T5:16; T6:5)

Case 33—Blast-Furnace Air Control

Material for this case appears in various small pieces in the first book by Popitz and his associates.[4] With this case we return to the blast-furnace operation with which we were occupied in several previous cases. This time we are specifically concerned with the work of the man who regulates the heating of blast air. The air is passed through the several stoves attached to each blast furnace and is directed from there to the wall of the furnace and

---

[4] H. Popitz *et al.*, *Technik und Industriearbeit* (Tübingen: Mohr, 1957).

blown into it through the tuyeres. A checkerwork system of brick inside the stoves is periodically heated with gas produced in the blast-furnace process itself. Once the brick checkerwork is sufficiently heated, the gas is redirected to another stove while cold air is blown into the heated stove and its temperature increased by passing through it. The heated air then leaves the stove to the blast furnace. Not only are several stoves required for each blast furnace to keep it in operation continuously, but gas from several blast furnaces is centrally controlled in order to assure the required supply of gas to the stoves of all blast furnaces in the same plant.[5]

Each of the blast furnaces in this plant has one operator who controls the heating of blast air in the stoves and the flow of gas into the stoves, as well as the flow of air into and out of the stoves and into the blast furnace. Each such operator sits in a room by himself, regulating the flow of gas and air by remote control and receiving relevant information by means of an armature board. This board indicates to him air temperatures and quantities of air and gas. He receives instructions from the central control of gas for all blast furnaces, from supervisors, and from the smelting crew of the blast furnace. Under certain conditions, he must coordinate requirements from these various directions and and from other blast furnaces and their blast air-control operators. The performance of the operator is regulated by several temporal requirements of the operations involved. Blast-furnace gas is utilized not only by blast furnaces but also at other places, and its distribution is regulated by an intricate time plan governing the activities of each operator as well as the temporal distribution of activities between operators. Bound by the demand for an equitable distribution of gas regulated by timetable, the operator is also tied in with the operation cycle of his blast furnace. Time is divided for the operator by the requirements of shifting gas supply from stove to stove. It is interrupted by the necessity of allowing gas to be supplied to other places. Each "heat" of the furnace is renewed every 4 hours or so, and creates an additional time unit requiring the supply of variable amounts of hot air. (Popitz 1957a, 142, 152, 154–155, 168, 170)

The conversion process in this case consists of the heating of air, and the transfer operations consist of the flow of gas and air. It is not entirely clear to what extent these processes are self-regulating and to what extent they are actively controlled by the operator. This case differs from those in the preceding chapter characterized by "steering" or remote control. In those cases, operators ordinarily could see at least a part of the operation and work pieces they controlled. In this case, the operator is completely removed from the processes he controls. Also, once turned on, the flow of

---

[5] S. S. Miller, *Manufacturing Policy: A Case Book of Major Production Problems in Six Selected Industries* (Homewood, Ill.: Irwin, 1957), p. 555; J. L. Morris, *Modern Manufacturing Processes* (Englewood Cliffs, N.J.: Prentice-Hall, 1955), p. 12.

gas and air probably continues; while in the other cases, an operation ended and had to be actively renewed with every short run. Although we will put this case into the same technical classification as Case 32 (Soaking Pit), it is the greater remoteness from operations and the continuous flow over extended periods by which we assign the case to technology Type VIII, while Case 32 was assigned to Type VII. (Code T3:R6-C4)

The different time cycles relevant for this operation are long and perhaps relatively uniform, except in the event of disturbances either in the supply of gas or in the smelting process, and have a constant work content. Popitz suggests that for the operator to vary the switching from one stove to another by half a minute is not likely to matter, but that neglect of certain crucial times in which operations are required might cause immeasurable damage and endanger human lives. Attention must be directed to the armature board only from time to time, but attention to time itself is quite continuous. The report indicates that operators glance at their watches regularly and might also have a feeling of when crucial times will occur. The attention requirements of this operation, then, seem best to fit the category of "watching," encompassing a very large space and processes in many other work stations never directly observed. One operator is involved in several kinds of work flow, that is, the flow of gas, air, and information. The control operation performed in the operator's room is functionally interdependent with gas supply centrally controlled, with the requirements of other operators of blast air controls, and with the blast furnace and its crew. This position is beyond seeing distance of all other work stations and confined to an enclosed work place. (Code T4:8; T5:16; T6:5)

Case 34—Petroleum Refinery

This case is based on a report by Whyte[6] comprising a story of events in an American aviation-gasoline plant from 1938 to 1943. No information is given on how data for this case were obtained. The purpose of the report is to describe technological change and unionization; personal adjustment of individual workers; and relationships among workers, supervisors, and engineers. We will be concerned only with a short description of the work of three control-room operators, whose performance is connected with the operations of two other parts of the plant.

This refinery has three operating units. Six large engines in the engine room generate power for the plant. The engines are watched over by one operator who is "alone with the machines and the noise" except for about two visits a shift to the control room, during one of which he joins the

---

[6] W. F. Whyte, "Engineers and Workers: A Case Study," *Human Organization*, 14, No. 4 (Winter 1956), 3–12.

three control-room operators for lunch. The engine room is connected with the control room by the technical process, by the charts in the control room referring to the operations in the engine room, and by shared supervision. The second unit is the catalyst plant near the engine room. It is not connected with the engine room and the control room except by shared supervision. This case is not concerned with the operator and his crew of about ten men in the catalyst plant.

The control room is occupied by the poly operator, the hydro-stillman, and the fractionator operator. The first of these three men is responsible for all three units, and his main interest lies in coordinating the work of the two other men. One wall of the control room is covered with automatic indicators which record changes in the production process. During periods of routine operation, the three men in the control room on each shift are required to draw product samples every hour from various pieces of equipment for testing and to watch the charts. When the process runs irregularly, constant adjustments are necessary, and changes made by the hydro-stillman immediately affect the process under control of the fractionator operator. An emergency like the breakdown of one engine demands quick activity. Unless the load on the other five engines is reduced, all the engines might stop, resulting in a very costly breakdown of the whole process. The specific observation and control is in the hands of two operators. The third, the poly operator, coordinates the work and makes hourly checks on the equipment in order to extend the life of certain parts and to prevent blowouts. The report describes an incident when a poly operator barely escaped being burned seriously from a blowout. (Whyte, 3–6)

The conversion operations looked after by these four workers are performed by self-regulating automatics, but not self-regulating to the extent that "when operations were not going quite right," the operators would not be required to make adjustments. The work flow of the production process is continuous, following an equivalent of what we have called "live line." (Code T3:R7-C5)

The three operators in the control room are within talking distance of one another when they are not in the plant for their hourly checks. The engine operator is out of sight of the control room for most of the day. Similar to the preceding two cases, we have here a "work flow" of a number of different things, including electricity, heat, gas liquid, other chemicals, and information. The four operators are interconnected by these different work-flow sequences and are functionally interdependent. Each task is performed exclusively by one man. The operators are confined to the control room or engine room most of the time, but must encompass perceptually a large work-relevant space and take into account many "work stations," all of which are represented on the automatic meters in front of them. In an operation involving a continuous flow of liquids, there are no technically determined operation cycles. The work content remains constant during regular operations and varies greatly for changes in the process. The only regular time division consists of the taking of hourly samples and the poly operator's hourly visual check of the cracking-furnace tubes. The difference in proficiency requirements between operations demanding more traditional craft skill and those of the "skilled watchmen" of automated operations is suggested in what a superintendent of this plant said: "If anything goes wrong with the meters, you just call a meter man. If anything goes wrong with the engines, you call a repairman. If anything goes wrong with operations, you call an engineer, and he tells you what to do." (Whyte, 7) This remark was resented by the operators as much as another one pointing out that the operators had nothing to do but watch the charts. The attention requirements of the job are characterized by this necessity for continuous watching. Changes in a number of indicators must be clearly recognized, and immediate and well-coordinated activity becomes necessary when something does not go as planned. While these jobs may require the aid of specialists for emergencies, repairs, and setups, quick action is demanded in emergencies in which extensive understanding of complex processes must be displayed. (Code T4:5 and 8; T5:16; T6:5)

Case 35—Power Plant

The sources of this case are reports by Mann and Hoffman[7] of a study in two American power-generating plants. Data were gathered by six months of direct observation in the two plants in the summer of 1954, and by questionnaires administered to workers in the two plants in December of 1954. One of these two plants was called "Stand" and contained both technically older and technically newer installations. The second plant was called "Advance" and contained an automated and integrated power-generating installation even more technically advanced than the newer part of "Stand." For our purposes we will focus predominantly on the second plant, but the report itself contains many comparisons between the two.

The purpose of the study is to describe the effects of technological change on workers' job interest and satisfaction, on the characteristics of jobs, on organization structure and supervision, and on problems produced by different kinds of shift schedules. The study deals predominantly with operating personnel, leaving out consideration of work other than that related to the operations performed in the control rooms. Only to a minor

---

[7] F. C. Mann and L. R. Hoffman, "Individual and Organizational Correlates of Automation," *Journal of Social Issues*, 12, No. 2 (1956), 7–17; F. C. Mann and L. R. Hoffman, *Automation and the Worker: A Study of Social Change in Power Plants* (New York: Holt, 1960).

extent was the study concerned with the observable social behavior of operators.

In simplified outline, electrical power is produced by burning pulverized coal in a furnace and converting water into steam in a boiler. Steam is transmitted to a turbine generator, and electric power goes from there through a switching system. In the newer plant at "Advance," a unit system of production is used, in contrast to the header system at "Stand." One unit includes a boiler and its furnace, a turbine generator, and an electrical switching system. Boiler and generator are directly connected. Two characteristics of the production unit distinguish its technical design from the older system: production functions are highly integrated, and the links between them are regulated by feedback control systems. Variation in steam pressure on the way from the boiler to the turbine controls the mixture of air and coal fed into the furnace and the pressure-regulating fans in the furnace. Steam dampers and an attemperator are controlled by differences in steam temperature on the way from the boiler to the turbine. The water level in the boiler drum regulates the flow of recirculated water. Each of these monitoring functions was previously performed by workers. In addition, the removal of slag and fly ash from furnace walls and heaters is performed by a programed mechanical device which is controlled by push-button from a control room. Previously, this work required manual lancing and hosing. Integration and self-regulation by feedback devices have several consequences for the organization of work. The controls for the whole process are found together in a few central locations. There are two control rooms, from each of which a pair of boiler-turbine units is monitored. Electrical switching is controlled from a third control room. All three rooms are close to one another on the third floor of the plant.

Most of the power-plant operators, in contrast to maintenance men and other personnel, monitor production from here. In the old plant, three classes of work are distinguished among operators: regulation of boilers, of turbines, and of electrical switching. In the new plant, operators must have knowledge about all three components and are only distinguished by three skill categories. An operator A is more advanced in skill than an operator B, who is always paired with an operator A. The category of helper is reserved for the few remaining dirty jobs. Each shift is manned by five pairs of A and B operators. There is one pair in each of the three control rooms. A fourth pair is divided, the A operator patrolling the plant and the B operator supervising the work of helpers in the condenser room two floors below. A fifth pair is available for special assignments. All men rotate through these five jobs.

The characteristics of the technical process require coordination among groups when, for instance, changes in the required supply of electrical power demand changes in the boiler operation. Coordination within groups is also necessary when, for instance, a turbine is taken off the line.

In addition, there is dependence of one operator on the knowledge of the others about operations with which they are more familiar through their previous more specialized experience. (Mann 1960, 16–19, 72–73, 85–87)

Conversion from coal and water takes place here by means of self-regulating automatics, and the work flow follows continuous, fixed lines. (Code T3:R7-C5) Technical demands on operator performance, similar to those of the preceding case, require continuous attention in the predominant watching of control panels. Work content is constant and there are no cycles, except for the widely spaced turning on and shutting off of sections of the plant that might not be necessary for several days, and the occasional switching for redirecting generated current to other parts of the "mat."

Workers in each of the adjacent control rooms are within talking distance of one another, while being beyond seeing distance of men on inspection tours through the plant and in relation to other centers with which information and instructions are exchanged, including telephone communication with a downtown office from which the supply of electricity is regulated. Technical work stations are highly integrated, functionally interdependent, and connected by work-flow sequences, but operators are connected to one another and with the work flow indirectly by way of observed signals representing the operations.

All functions are at least shared by two people in pairs of operators containing two job grades. Operators work in rotation, going successively through the several operating jobs, but at any one time control-room operators are confined to the control room while always a pair of men is on inspection tour through the plant and the second pair is assigned to special duties. (Code T4:5 and 8; T5:14; T6:5)

Summary

A summary of classifications of technical demands is given in Table 19. The presence of self-regulating devices is accompanied by a particular kind of technically required attention—the continuous watching of dials and the constant readiness to operate controls at unpredictable times. The short machine cycles of the transfer machine in Case 31 are not relevant for the temporal requirements of demanded attention. The long cycles of Case 33 constitute only a loose framework, breaking into meaningful units of repeated action what in the other cases would be mere duration—if operators did not have certain inspection schedules.

In all of these four cases, work stations are functionally interdependent and connected by work flow, but work-flow characteristics are much more complex in these cases than in the preceding cases. The flow of technical information becomes as important as the flow of materials. In the last three cases, all the relevant processes are represented symbolically to the

TABLE 19. CODING SUMMARY: TECHNOLOGY TYPE VIII

Technology: Type VIII (R6-C4) Steered and Self-Regulating
Automatics - Steered Line
Case 33 Blast-Furnace Air Control.

Type VIII (R7-C5) Self-Regulating Automatics -
Live Line
Case 31 Auto Engines. Case 34 Petroleum
Refinery. Case 35 Power Plant.

T4: SPATIAL CONSTRAINTS

Relation of Workers to Work Stations	Talking Distance	Shouting Distance	Seeing Distance	Beyond Seeing
Open				
Confined to fixed place	34,35		31	33,34,35
Confined to mobile place				

T5: FUNCTIONAL CONSTRAINTS

	No Work Flow		Work Flow	
Differentiation Pattern	Independent	Dependent	Independent	Dependent
All tasks undifferentiated				
Each differentiated task shared				
Some exclusive and some shared tasks				35
All tasks performed exclusively				31,33, 34

TABLE 19. CODING SUMMARY: TECHNOLOGY TYPE VIII (continued)

T6: TEMPORAL AND PERCEPTUAL CONSTRAINTS

Attention Requirements	Operation Cycles	
Low	None	31,34,35
Surface	1 and 4 hours	33
Detailed		
External focus		
Watching 31,33,34,35		

operators. Their work stations become linked with others only by information flow, and part of the information is transmitted through the process and then to another operator. Relevant only in Case 31 are both the partly visible work-piece flow and the dials indicating events inaccessible to direct perception. Operators in all of these cases are confined to a narrowly confined location. These are all jobs of high complexity, but a complexity which differs from that faced by men of whom traditional craft skills are required. Functional exclusiveness is high in all cases except Case 35, where always two men jointly perform one task.

Chapter X

TYPES OF TECHNOLOGY

The purpose of the preceding chapters of Part Two was to provide a description of industrial technology and its demands. In Part Three, we will attempt to describe the behavioral adaptations to these technical conditions. In this chapter, we summarize the descriptions of technical characteristics of industrial work as they have been classified before. Table 20 shows that the thirty-eight cases are distributed over eleven cells of the matrix of work-place technologies. In the following list these are reduced to eight types. Simpler names are given in place of the characteristics of specifically defined categories and cases assigned to them.

Type I	(R1-C1)	Handling
Type II	(R2-C1)	Hand Work
Type III	(R4-C1)	Machine Work
Type IV	(R4-C3)	Machine-Work Sequence
Type V	(R2-C5)	Assembly Line
Type VI	(R3-C5)	Hand and Machine Line
Type VII	(R1-C4)	
	(R5-C4)	
	(R6-C4)	
	(R6-C5)	Remote Controls
Type VIII	(R6-C4)	
	(R7-C5)	Automation

In Table 21 (pp. 161–162), all of the thirty-eight cases are listed by categories of technical constraints. The description of six work places has been divided into two parts. Part a contains the dominant production operation, and part b consists of a subordinate component differentiated from the first by an operation performed either at a separate time or by a separate part of the crew.

The activities of production workers are fitted into the technical design by division of the time of their involvement in the production process and by their location and movement in the space in which operations take place. Location and division of activity time are related. For different times and different locations, the exclusiveness with which tasks are performed

TABLE 20. CASE DISTRIBUTION BY TECHNOLOGY

Conversion	Transfer				
	C1 Hand Transfer	C2 Auto Transfer	C3 Dead Line	C4 Steered Line	C5 Live Line
R1 No conversion	TYPE I 1,3a,3b, 4,5,6b, 26b,28b, 29b			TYPE VII 6a,7,8,9	
R2 Hand tools	TYPE II 10,13,14, 15,21				TYPE V 11b,22, 23,24,25
R3 Hand and machine tools					TYPE VI 26a
R4 Machine tools	TYPE III 11a,16, 17,18,20		TYPE IV 19		
R5 Steered automatics				TYPE VII 27,28a	
R6 Steered and self-regulating automatics			32	TYPE VIII 33	29a
R7 Self-regulating automatics					31,34,35

might also change. In some of our cases, work time is divided into two different kinds. During one time, operators are spread over the work space, performing independent and exclusive functions. At another time, they come together in space and jointly perform functions which are now interdependent and shared. The smeltermen of Case 3 work independently when building runners, and come together for the opening of the tap hole. Rolling-mill workers in Cases 26, 28, and 29 perform exclusive functions separated in space during the running of the mills, and come together for the joint task of mill changes. In these cases, times are clearly separated during which sharply different technical demands are made on the same men. In other cases, we found a permanent functional differentiation where some workers work jointly all the time and others separately all the time. Cases in point are the steel maintenance crew of Case 1 and the dock workers of Case 4, on the one hand, and the operators in the blast-furnace feeding of Cases 6 and 7, the bridge-crane operator of Case 8, and the men on the coking battery of Case 9, on the other. In the latter cases, we find differentiation within the same case: joint performance by the men at the bottom and top of the blast-furnace elevator of Case 6, during the rolling operation among the ancillary work-station crews in tube rolling of Case 28, and within the pairs of operators on the top and one side of the coking battery.

In Types VII and VIII, cases are combined from several classifications of technical characteristics because the differences among them did not appear great enough to be of value in much of the subsequent analysis. When necessary, these internal differences will be noted without being assigned separate types.

Our first category of conversion operations—providing for situations in which no conversion takes place—does not entirely fit into the developmental sequence implied in the succession of the remaining six categories of conversion operations. But the cases of Type I involve only hand operations and constitute a first step in that sequence. Since these are simple, almost preindustrial operations, we can view them as preceding the cases in category R2-C1, in which both conversion and transfer operations are performed by hand or with the use of hand tools. In the second set of cases in question (R1-C4), materials are moved by "steering" along fixed lines. These cases have been combined with those of Type VII, where conversion machinery is also "steered" by remote control.

Table 20 shows not only that the available case reports leave large gaps in our preconstructed typology, but also that data for cases encompassing a fairly full range of technical conditions are at hand. We will be concerned only with the types of technical conditions for which we have case material, that is, the eight types of technical conditions just listed. They are listed in the sequence of development in which work components performed by men at one stage are successively conferred upon machines. Moving from one of these types to the next, we also move one or two steps down or to the right in our original typology. In order to produce generalizations about the relationship between work-place technology and workers' social behavior, we will, in the following chapters, describe variations in social behavior and then point to these eight types of technical conditions

TABLE 21. CODING SUMMARY FOR ALL CASES

T4: SPATIAL CONSTRAINTS

Relation of Workers to Work Stations	Talking Distance	Shouting Distance	Seeing Distance	Beyond Seeing
Open	1,4,6b,10, 14,16,17, 21,26b, 28b,29b	3b,5, 11a,11b, 20	3a	
Confined to fixed place	13,15,18, 19,23,24, 25,34,35	22,26a	27,28a, 31,32	6a,29a, 32,33, 34,35
Confined to mobile place			8	7,9

T5: FUNCTIONAL CONSTRAINTS

Differentiation Pattern	No Work Flow		Work Flow	
	Independent	Dependent	Independent	Dependent
All tasks undifferentiated	3a,13,18	1,3b,4	11b,23	
Each differentiated task shared	5,14,16, 17	6b,10,21, 11a,26b, 28b,29b	22	35
Some exclusive and some shared tasks	20,15			6a,19,28a
All tasks performed exclusively				7,8,9,24, 25,26a, 27,29a, 31,32,33, 34

TABLE 21. CODING SUMMARY FOR ALL CASES (continued)

T6: TEMPORAL AND PERCEPTUAL CONSTRAINTS

Attention Requirements

Low	1,3a,3b,4,5,6b,10,21,26b,28b,29b
Surface	11b,13,14,15,18,19,22,23,24,25
Detailed	11a,16,17,20,26a
External focus	6a,7,8,9,27,28a,29a,32
Watching	31,33,34,35

with which those variations might be associated. It is quite clear, however, that among the cases within any one type, there are still major variations likely to make a difference for social behavior. In order to deal with these differences, we will introduce the categories of technical constraints and attempt to demonstrate that work-place technology, *together* with these additional conditions, accounts for behavior differences.

Our data suggest five major divisions among kinds of attention demanded of workers. Differences between these kinds are characterized by different relations between operator involvement in the production process and operation times (or cycles) and work space. Differences in attention requirements are characterized by differences in the inclusion of kinds and amounts of cognitive and sensory processes and the "tightness" of their connection with movements of parts of the body. An additional difference lies in the part of the work space on which an operator must focus visually or of which he must think while doing his work.

1. A generally "low" level of attention is required in all of the Handling cases of Type I, the coal-mining Cases 10 and 11b, and joint off-line auto-assembly work of Case 21. Work pieces handled are bulky. With the exception of Case 6b (Blast-Furnace Feeding I—Handling of Ore Wagons into Elevator) and Case 11b (Coal Mining II—Filling), the division of time is not narrowly defined. Cycles are either absent, variable, or long (ranging from 6 minutes to 4 hours). In all cases but one, operators have no confined work locations. In Cases 5 and 21, operation cycles are still somewhat shorter (7 and 6 minutes), and closer attention is also required.

Cases 5, 21, 6b, and 11b (in that sequence) constitute the transition between the first two kinds of attention requirements.

2. Where "surface" attention is necessary, operators must focus visually on the work immediately before them and closely coordinate intricate and highly repetitive hand movements with · visual observation, but without thinking-through of the technical process every time it is performed. Cases in point are the stationary assembly operations of Cases 13, 14, and 15; the work in the clicking room of Case 18 and shoe-bottoming room of Case 19; and the work on assembly lines of Cases 22, 23, 24, and 25. In these nine cases, workers are confined to one location. Operation cycles are short, ranging from a few seconds to 4½ minutes. As a result of short operation cycles and the concomitant repetition of highly segmented task performance, surface attention is required continuously.

3. We now turn to situations where operation cycles are variable and where intermittently different levels of attention are technically demanded. In these cases there are distinct repeated times of "detailed" attention, requiring not only close visual observation and its coordination with skillful hand movements but also a more complete thinking-through of interconnected technical variations in the production process. Cases in point are the machine-shop operations of Cases 16 and 17 and the handling of coal-face machinery in Case 11a. Periods of required detailed attention alternate with periods of low required attention when machinery or work pieces are moved or when machines are running automatically after having been set up and started. In three additional cases, detailed attention is required in combination with other demands. In the weaving operation of Case 20, detailed attention is necessary when an operator actually works on a given loom, either connecting broken threads or changing over, while general but close "watching" over a number of looms is demanded in-between. In contrast to these four cases where operation cycles are variable, operation cycles of a few seconds are present in the wire-rolling operation of Case 26a. Here, detailed attention is also demanded, but it is demanded continuously due to the short operation cycle. In the tube-rolling operation of Case 28, a similar kind of attention is necessary for those workers not involved with the "steering" of the five major machines but with the work performed by the crews surrounding each of the work stations.

4. In the cases requiring surface and detailed attention, an operator's vision is focused directly on the work before him, controlling interconnected movements of hands and work pieces. The work in the following cases demands attention focused on the larger work space and distinctly not on the operator's hands. The machine operators in the tube and blooming mills of Cases 27, 28a, and 29a, and the operators of elevators, conveyors, cranes, ovens, and large vehicles in Cases 6a, 7, 8, 9, and 32, are "steering"

their equipment. The hand movements with which they manipulate levers and controls are habitual and consist of automatic reactions, while the operator observes in detail the movement of machinery and work pieces at a distance from him. He must follow cognitively the operation process every time it occurs. In Case 29a, this condition is only present for "manual" operation while general watching is required for the times, or by parts of the crew, of "automatic" operation. Also, the elevator operators in Cases 6a and 7 do not see much of the equipment itself but still "steer" it, orienting themselves to the observation of symbols representing equipment movement. In these last eight cases, then, certain parts of the conditions of both surface and detailed attention are present, in addition to a third condition. We find the automatic hand movements of the cases requiring surface attention, the detailed observation and thinking-through of the technical process of the cases requiring detailed attention, and in addition a focus beyond the operator's immediate location to events in a much larger work space now relevant for performance. We have called this attention requiring "external focus."

5. The characteristics of attention requirements we have called "watching" involve the continuous observation of dials and armature boards in order to detect variations from prescribed settings and to make adjustments by the manipulation of controls and switches in the event of such variation. The watching-over of the control consoles of transfer machines in Case 31, and of large numbers of dials indicating processes in the petroleum refinery of Case 34 and the power-generating plants of Case 35, is related to technical operations. These are largely self-regulating, but still require operators when "something goes wrong" or for the regulation of occasional changes in the process. It appears that none of these "automated" processes is so self-sufficient as to require no more than the mere observation of movement of the dials themselves. Rather, they demand of the operator comprehension of the technical processes represented on their armature boards. Attention, then, is focused on the dials, but at the same time the operators must think of the operations themselves. Operators are remote from operations, and must be prepared to reset their controls or push buttons when variations beyond prescribed limits are read. The time at which this latter activity is demanded is almost always unpredictable, but the activity must be a consequence of having understood interrelated sequences of events in the technical plant itself, thus "taking in" cognitively a work space much larger than the control room. Similar attention requirements are present for part of the work of the tubing-mill operators in Case 29a, the soaking-pit operator of Case 32, and the blast-furnace air-control operators of Case 33; but added are the attention requirements of actively "steering" the process. In the tube-rolling operation of Case 29a, two operators are involved only in steering all the time, while the others must "watch" during automatic runs and "steer" during nonauto-

matic running on "manual." In this case, the two kinds of demands for attention are therefore separated, and equipment and work-piece movements are also *directly* observed. Both kinds of attention requirements are combined in the work of the soaking-pit operator of Case 32. He watches dials indicating processes internal to the operation, but directly observes and steers the opening and closing of the pit for the movement of ingots. The blast air-control operator of Case 33 relies entirely on schedules and dials for the observation of processes which continue automatically for some time but require active regulation during uniformly cycled periods separated by long intervals. Finally, the work of weavers in Case 20 also requires continuous watching to detect stopping looms. Watching is combined, however, with the detailed attention required on stopped looms. In Cases 31, 34, and 35, attention requirements involve only watching, and there is also no clear division of time into operation cycles.

In the cases with mixed attention requirements, cycles of different lengths and variability are present. Cases requiring only externally focused attention, associated with steering, are also distinctly cycled. Cycle lengths vary from a few seconds in tube rolling to 25 minutes on the coking battery. They allow more or less distinct breaks of different lengths between operation cycles, but with some intermittency of demanded attention in all cases.

Table 22 suggests that attention requirements are approximately related to technical conditions. Several cases contain situations in which two kinds of attention requirements are present but clearly separated, while in some other cases two requirements are present in combination. The characteristics of operation cycles influence the kind of attention that is technically required. For Types V to VIII, the speed of machines determines cycle lengths; whereas for Types I to IV, machine speed does not. Exceptions of Type V are Cases 11b, 23, and 25: coal is shoveled onto a moving belt, or work pieces are removed from the conveyor belt and thus, temporarily, from machine-determined pace. By and large, operation cycles are relatively "open" when low attention requirements are present, but they are relatively "tight" in the presence of surface attention; variable for detailed attention, and absent for attention requirements involving continuous watching. A variety of cycling conditions is found in cases requiring an external focus of attention.

Table 23 shows the relationship between type of work-place technology and work-flow characteristics, together with the distribution of workers over tasks to be performed. Four classes of cases can be observed: (1) cases in which tasks are not connected by work flow and the work performed by operators is functionally interdependent; (2) cases without a work flow where tasks are performed independently; (3) cases in which tasks are performed independently even though they are connected by work flow;

TABLE 22. TECHNOLOGY, ATTENTION REQUIREMENTS, AND CYCLES

Technology Type	Case	Attention Requirements					Operation Cycles
		Low	Surface	Detail	External	Watch	
I	1,4	x					variable
	3a,3b	xx					4 hours
	5	x					7 minutes
	26b,28b	xx					none
	29b	x					none
	6b						1 minute
II	10	x					none
	21	x					6 minutes
	13		x				1 minute
	14		x				4 and 12 seconds
	15		x				? minutes
III	18		x				? seconds
	11a			x			variable
	16,17			xx			variable
	20			x -------- x			variable
IV	19		x				5 and 10 seconds
V	11b,23		xx				? seconds
	22		x				1½ minutes
	24		x				4½ minutes
	25		x				? minutes
VI	26a			(x)			7 seconds
VII	27				x		7 seconds, 2 minutes
	28a				x		? seconds
	6a				x		1 minute
	7				x		7 and 20 minutes
	8				x		variable
	9				x		25 minutes
	29a				x - - - x		21 seconds
	32				x - - - x		3 minutes, variable
VIII	31					x	none
	33					x	1 and 4 hours
	34,35					xx	none

and (4) cases in which work stations are functionally interdependent and connected by work flow.

Differentiation patterns have been assigned to "high" and "low" categories. Differentiation is low when all tasks are undifferentiated or when each differentiated task is shared. It is high when each task is performed exclusively by one worker. Of the five cases with some exclusive and some shared tasks, two are considered low and three high. Among the jobs in the weaving shed of Case 20 and in the assembly work of Case 15, most jobs are shared, and these are the jobs most central to the operation. In the shoe-bottoming lines of Case 19, the blast-furnace feeding of Case 6a, and the tubing mill of Case 28a, all the central operating tasks are performed exclusively.

Exclusiveness of task performance is low in the first three classes of work flow and dependence, and high in the last. There are only three cases for the third category. In Case 11b (Coal Mining II—Filling), coal is filled off onto the continuously moving conveyor. In Case 23 (Candy Wrapping), work pieces are put on the belt after work has been performed on them. In both cases, materials do not move from work station to work station for successive operations. In Case 22 (Auto Assembly II), larger sections of the line are functionally interdependent, but adjacent work stations are not.

We might consider the Type IV technology of Case 19 (Shoe Bottoming) as the line separating machine-paced operations from man-paced operations. All of the cases in the first two categories of connections between work stations are above that line, and all cases of the second two categories are below.

A review of some additional information will modify the impression given in Table 23. Cases 3b, 4, 6b, 3a, 5, and 21 are shown as having no work flow. This classification applies to the relationship of tasks performed within a work section. The section as a whole constitutes a position in a larger work-flow sequence. Work flow also occurs in Cases 14 and 20, but so infrequently that, for a large proportion of the working time, connections by work flow are not relevant. It will have to be recognized that in the cases of technology Type VIII the more important component of work flow is the flow of information transmitted as signals flowing through the production process from operator to operator at their control positions. In order to describe the dominant characteristic of these operations, we might speak of a "signal flow" instead of a work flow.

If we were to transfer the information on operation cycles from Table 22 to Table 23, and recognize in addition the difference between Types I–IV and Types V–VIII with regard to machine or operator control of cycle timing, we would notice that, with very few exceptions, the cases in the upper half of Table 23 show an absence of work flow and at the same time a relative openness or indeterminacy of operation cycles. With the excep-

TABLE 23. TECHNOLOGY, WORK FLOW, FUNCTIONAL DEPENDENCE,
AND TASK DIFFERENTIATION

Tech- nology Type	Case	No Work Flow				Work Flow			
		Dependent		Independent		Dependent		Independent	
		Differentiation of Tasks							
		Low	High	Low	High	Low	High	Low	High
I	1,3b,4,6b	xxxx							
	26b,28b,29b	xxx							
	3a,5			xx					
II	10,21	xx							
	13,14,15			xxx					
III	11a	x							
	16,17,18,20			xxxx					
IV	19						x		
V	11b,22,23								xxx
	24,25						xx		
VI	26a						x		
VII	6a,7,8,9						xxxx		
	27,28a,29a						xxx		
	32					x			
VIII	31,33,34						xxx		
	35					x			

tion of Type VIII, we find quite clearly defined operation cycles in the lower half.

The information brought together in Table 24 is in part precipitated by the data summarized in the preceding tables on attention focus, functional interdependence, and exclusiveness. We are now looking at our cases with regard to the distances perceptually separating the places at which work

TABLE 24. TECHNOLOGY, DISTANCE, AND SPATIAL CONFINEMENT

Technology Type	Case	Talking Distance		Shouting Distance		Seeing Distance		Beyond Seeing	
		Open	Con-fined	Open	Con-fined	Open	Con-fined	Open	Con fined
I	1,4,6b	xxx							
	26b,28b	xx							
	29b	x							
	3b,5			xx					
	3a				x				
II	10,21,14	xxx							
	13,15		xx						
III	16,17	xx							
	18		x						
	11a,20			xx					
IV	19		x						
V	23,24,25	xxx							
	11b		x						
	22			x					
VI	26a			x					
VII	8,27,28a						xxx		
	6a,7,9								xxx
	29a								x
	32						x - - - - - -		x
VIII	31						x		
	33								x
	34,35		xx - - - - - - - - - - - - - - - -						xx

tasks are performed and the extent to which operators are confined to work locations.

Listed in the table under "confined" are the three cases in which operators are confined to fixed positions on mobile equipment. In all but one of the cases where positions are separated by distances beyond verbal contact, operators are in fixed locations. In cases where operators are ordinarily beyond talking distance but are in "open" locations, the distance can be overcome when workers move about in the course of their work and come closer to the positions of other workers at least from time to time.

By and large, distances become more extended as we move down the list of types of technology. Dual conditions of distance between working positions are present in three cases. In Case 35, for instance, two operators in the power plant share a control room, while other operators are in locations far removed from them—in another part of the plant.

In this chapter we listed cases by type of technology and by categories of technical constraints. We have reviewed the decisions for inclusion of certain cases in one classification rather than in another. We have, then, summarized the material of Part Two by bringing clusters of cases together in eight types of technology. Relationships between levels of technology and variations in technical constraints were plotted in a number of tables. The differences between cases thus described will be taken up again in the analysis of workers' behaviors in Part Three.

Part Three

BEHAVIORAL ADAPTATIONS

Chapter XI

COOPERATION AND INFLUENCE

In this chapter we begin our attempt to generate statements of relationship between the technical and social properties of units of production organizations. We will introduce cases which reveal the same or similar behavior characteristics; then we will turn to the technical conditions and their demands with which these behaviors were found together. Much of the material required for the discussion of technically demanded cooperation and technically determined influence is already contained in the data presented in the preceding chapter. These data have not come to us in the neat analytical divisions in which they would have been desired. Frequent references will therefore be made to that material, and additional evidence will be added here.

It will be necessary to discuss relationships called *influence* and relationships called *cooperation* at least to some extent together. But there is a difference in the focus on the outcome of observed behavior. When we speak about cooperation, we imply that the joint behaviors of the men said to cooperate result in a joint product. When we speak about influence, we mean that a behavior change of the first man in a behavior sequence produces a behavior change on the part of the second man. Anticipating an argument to be made later on empirical grounds, we might expect that technical influence and necessary cooperation in the *same* set of behaviors are found under particularly compelling technical conditions. In a technically more open situation, influence is observed which does not have its basis in the technical design and its demands. It lies rather within the range of what is technically permitted but beyond what is technically demanded.

We might view social behavior as being ordered by the intersection of choices and restraints. We would then see the technical design of a work place, together with the demands it makes on workers' activities, as a variable restraint on the choices which production workers have for associating with their fellow workers. We will begin with a number of cases in which it is necessary that several workers cooperate in order to produce the technically designed outcome and in which the influence relations created by the technically required cooperation are of an almost instantaneous reversibility. They allow a limited range of choices of behavior changes on the part of the second man following a behavior change on the part of the first man. Then a number of cases will follow in which technically required cooperation is absent and influence is nontechnical. Subsequently, we will deal with cases in which behavior choices are severely restricted and reversibility of influence in cooperative relationships is delayed, making for irreversibility within a given operation cycle. In the remainder of cases, cooperation encompasses fewer behavior items and is less determinate than in the others, but influence is irreversible within specified time spans and occurs less frequently.

We will look at these cases with regard to the cooperation that is technically necessary, and at the differences in influence relations based on the use of technical resources. We will also compare cases in terms of the kind and amount of cooperation which is not technically required, but permitted and limited by technical conditions, and of influence based on nontechnical resources.

1. Level A—Heavy Hauling: Simultaneous Cooperation and Reversible Influence

In the description of the work of the steel-plant maintenance crew in Case 1, we find several men simultaneously working together with heavy bars, hammers, and ropes in the repair of parts of the cooling system on the outside of the blast furnace. These men share tools and work pieces at the same time, a condition for the presence of technically required cooperation. The technical outcome for which this operation is "designed" is attained only as a result of a distinct sum of the activities of several workers. When one man decreases his effort, the effort of the other men must increase in order, for instance, to remove or install a piece of pipe. In other operations described in this case, cinder is removed jointly by several men who do not share the particular tools used, but do share the same part of the blast-furnace stove worked on. Here again we find clearly described the requirement of one man taking over a part of another man's performance in order to make up for the sum of activities necessary for reaching the required outcome.

Two major kinds of job requirements are found in the work of the smeltermen in Case 3. For part of the time these men individually build up the runners in which slag and molten metal flow during a tap; during other times they jointly open the tap hole and also, once a week, rebuild the "fox" together. The same type of work-place technology is present in both cases, but the manner in which worker activities are channeled differs. The building of runners of Case 3a will be dealt with later. The remaining operations of Case 3b are relevant to our present discussion. These men share the same air hammer and the same tap hole to be opened with the same simultaneous distribution of effort as was described in Case 1.

The description of the job of the dock workers in Case 4 suggests that for the work in the hold of a ship two men together "work a corner," again jointly and simultaneously moving pieces of cargo to pallets or slings by which the crane is to lift the cargo out.

The pair of colliers in the hand-got system of coal mining of Case 10 jointly work a stall, hewing and shoveling the coal together. As the report suggests, there may be a division of labor between the two men, but they are usually interchangeable and they share the coal-face section and loose coal. Simultaneity of activities is not as clear-cut here as in preceding cases. But there is certainly not the sharp temporal division of steps in the process—associated with functionally differentiated tasks—that is present in cases to be discussed later, in which cooperation is unequivocally sequential. There is still a distribution of activities for a joint sum such that one man must take over a part of the other man's performance in order to attain the common outcome.

Automobile assemblers of Case 21 work on "bucks" just off the main assembly line. As a unit their work is built into a sequence of work stations technically connected by overhead conveyors. Pieces to be worked on are taken off the overhead conveyor and put on the main line after the assembly operation. As in Case 3b, activities are bounded by an outer temporal framework determined by the sequence of operations of which all of the crew is a part. Like Case 10 this is a case of technology Type II, involving hand work and hand tools in both conversion and transfer operations. Focusing particularly on the front-end assembly presented as a prototype in the original report, we find several men jointly and simultaneously contributing activities to the designed total product of this kind of work station.

We can visualize the instantaneous reversibility in direction of influence in these cases by an example of two men together lifting an automobile fender or grille. A shift in one man's movements in putting on the work piece must be responded to instantly by a corresponding shift in the movements of the other. If the other does not change his behavior or if he makes up for the variations only partially, this condition in turn makes it necessary for the first man to change his behavior again. Each man has, as it were, a comeback on the other, and failure to attain the designed outcome is a joint failure of both, up to the point at which one man entirely ceases to perform and, in a pair, is likely to stop the operation altogether. In teams comprising more than two men, it might be possible to cope with the dropping out of one man by a redistribution of activities and effort as long as each of the others takes over a part of the first man's performance.

We will now turn to three cases taken together where we will be concerned with only a distinct part of the rolling-mill operations in Cases 26, 28, and 29. At certain times in the operations described in these cases, so-called mill changes become necessary, requiring adjustments or exchange of rolls and other parts of the equipment for a change-over in product size and type of material. During these periods of setup operations, the work-place technology changes radically from the dominant and technically more advanced condition to a situation of moving, by hand and with the use of hand tools, pieces of equipment which now become work pieces. We have numbered these case parts 26b, 28b, and 29b. They have a technology of Type I and are characterized by the sharing of work pieces and equipment by two or more men in relationships of simultaneous cooperation and reversible influence.

Cases 1, 4, and 10, with the somewhat arbitrary boundaries inherited from the original studies, involve operations relatively uniform in type of technology as well as characteristics of cooperation and influence. In Cases 3b, 21, 26b, 28b, and 29b, the same technical conditions and associated forms of cooperation and influence were found as in the first-mentioned three cases. But this time they are temporally embedded in a larger operation of which the one under focus is only a part, and where the same operators also perform other operations under different technological conditions. But in all of these latter cases the two kinds of conditions are clearly separated in time and also involve, with the exception of Case 21, workers' movements in space making previously inaccessible "work-relevant environment" the immediate "work space."[1] The Type II technology of off-line auto assembly in Case 21 is only present after work pieces have arrived and before they leave again by way of a different type of technology. This operation is distinguished from the remaining continuous line of operations by the fact that the temporal distribution of activities between the arrival and departure of work pieces and completed subassemblies is independent of line-determined cycling. In the other four operations there are even more pronounced time divisions between the dominant regular production operations and the operations under focus here.

In the following three cases the divisions between types of technology and forms of cooperation and influence are not signified by different times, but by different functions performed in the sequence of operations and by involving some operators but not others. Case 6 described the work of seven men moving filled ore wagons into an elevator, moving them up to the top of the blast furnace, taking them out of the elevator, and dumping the material into a hopper above the blast furnace. Empty wagons are moved simultaneously into and out of the elevator at the top and bottom. Filled wagons move up in the elevator at the same time that empty ones move down. We will leave for later discussion the technical and behavioral system surrounding the elevator operator in Case 6a—a system which includes him and the crews at the top and at the bottom.

---

[1] For this distinction, see H. Popitz et al., *Technik und Industriearbeit* (Tübingen: Mohr, 1957), p. 171.

We now focus on the technical connections and behavioral relations in Case 6b between the two men at the bottom, and among the four men at the top. Within the limits of this particular focus there is a technology of hand movement of materials. The two workers at the bottom share the same elevator basket, but not the ore wagons which each moves in and out of the elevator. As the elevator basket is shared, and is present only during distinct, short, and frequently repeated times, these two workers cooperate simultaneously in the sense that the two empty wagons must be moved out, and the two full wagons moved in, at almost precisely the same time, and that the elevator cannot be put in motion unless both have completed the operation. The same is true among the four workers at the top, but their work involves more intricate relations. Two workers share the same elevator basket. For part of the cycle, each of these shares with another man two wagons, one full and one empty, which are repeatedly exchanged between the man at the elevator and the man who moves between elevator and hopper. In this case the joint product made up of the sum of activities of the two or four workers is a unit of time within which simultaneously moved wagons must change positions. There is therefore a less ready relation of reversibility of influence, but still the simultaneous taking over (this time regarding differences in the speed rather than the effort of performance) that makes for the joint outcome. There is also the fact that failure to accomplish the designed outcome, that is, a temporal delay, can be the product of any one man's behavior, and affects all others within the temporal boundaries of the same operation cycle.

Coal-cutting and coal-boring machines are shared by pairs of operators in Case 11a, and simultaneous cooperation is required in moving and operating the equipment. While the case was classified in the Machine Work technology of Type III, the reason for the observed kind of cooperation and influence would lie in the fact that the largest part of the work requires the moving of heavy equipment by hand. The requirements of moving heavy objects by hand is common to all of these ten cases. Entirely or in part, they all display a technology dominated by heavy muscle work. Technical demands are characterized by an absence of work flow between workers, functional interdependence, low exclusiveness of task performance, and the sharing of technical resources.

We can now refer to the discussion of cooperation and influence in Chapter II. In all of these cases, technically required cooperation consists of the simultaneous distribution and redistribution of the activities of the cooperators. "Simultaneous" means that this distribution and redistribution takes place within the temporal limitations of one given unit in the sequence of operations, that is, one cycle. We would also observe reversible technical influence.

It is characteristic of these cases that cooperation and influence are not wholly defined technically. For instance, when two operators jointly lift a work piece or equipment part, they are technically bound together by a work piece that cannot be moved by only one man, and for the movement of which there are no other technical means. This is the technically delimited characteristic of this form of cooperation. But the distribution of effort or activities within the operation is a matter of some choice by the operators. This choice, in turn, is regulated by the constant reversibility of influence between the two.

While this influence relationship is made possible by the technical fact of sharing a work piece and the task performed on it, it allows a choice of responding in several different ways to a change in activity or effort expended by one's partner: (1) to make up fully for the other's variation; (2) not to change one's behavior at all and thus to force the other to change his behavior again; (3) to change one's behavior to make up only a part of the other's variation; or (4) to change one's behavior in the direction opposite to making up the other's variation and thus force the other to change his behavior accordingly. A chain of these interrelated variations is possible within a given operation. It might also be carried into

TABLE 25. REQUIRED COOPERATION AND INFLUENCE - LEVEL A

Technology Type and Functional Constraints	Required Cooperation			
	Absent	Simult- aneous	Sequential	Sporadic Symbolic
Type I,II,III, no flow, depen- dence, low dif- ferentiation		I: 1,3b,4, 6b,26b, 28b,29b II: 10,21 III: 11a		

Technology Type and Functional Constraints	Influence			
	Reversible	Irre- versible	Semi- technical	Extra- technical
Type I,II,III, no flow, depen- dence, low dif- ferentiation	I: 1,3b,4, 6b,26b, 28b,29b II: 10,21 III: 11a			

the next cycle, but a carry-over is not technically required and would have its source in nontechnical behavior rules. The possibility of carry-over from one cycle to another, that is, an exchange of greater effort expended by the first man during operation 1, for greater effort expended by the second man during operation 2, is severely restricted in all of these cases. It cannot find full-fledged expression when the activities of operators are bound together, and their cooperation mediated, by a shared work piece or equipment part.

Seven of these cases, then, displayed the characteristics of technically required simultaneous cooperation, and of reversible influence based on technical resources and affecting technical performance, in the presence of a Handling technology of Type I. The same behaviors were observed in two cases with a Hand Work technology of Type II, and in one case of Type III Machine Work technology. The latter cases contain a dominant element of a Handling technology.

There is no work flow between the tasks performed by the operators on whom we have focused, but the men are functionally interdependent and perform tasks of low exclusiveness. In most of these cases the time limits of operation cycles for performance are relatively open, involving either variable cycles, no cycles, or cycles of such length as to constitute only a loose temporal framework. The exception is Case 6b with a 1-minute cycle.

Similar conditions can be seen in certain uncoded parts of Cases 9 and 28. Some of the work of the crews around each major conversion machine in Tube Rolling I, and of the pairs of workers on the top and one side of the Coking Battery, display both technical and behavioral characteristics similar to those of the cases just discussed.

The partial summary given in Table 25 describes the relation of level of technology (and connections between tasks) with kinds of influence and technically required cooperation.

2. Level B—Hand Work: No Technically Required Cooperation and Nontechnical Influence

We will now deal with cases in which no technically required cooperation is observed and only nontechnical influence of different kinds is operative. None of these cases display the technological characteristics of Types VI, VII, and VIII and are in that respect clearly distinguished from the cases of the following sections. But they do contain cases of technology Types I, II, and III and must be distinguished from cases with the same level of technology in the first section. This distinction lies in the difference between technically defined functional dependence in the first cases and functional independence in the present cases. In contrast, all cases of technology Types IV and V are included in this section and require no further distinction from cases in other sections. Internal relations of technical constraints with behavior will suggest additional differences.

We now return to the work of the smeltermen and deal in Case 3a with that part of the operation during which the men build up the runners in preparation for the next tap. Each man works independently on his part of the system of runners, and no cooperation between them is required. We also find that one man might help another in removing a heavy lump of slag and that men who have finished earlier with building their runners will help others so that all finish together. This is what we have called technically permitted but not required cooperation, accompanied by semi-technical influence. Chapter II specified exchanges of work pieces, equipment, or task as forms of technically permitted cooperation. Our data indicate only that one man takes over a part of what is equivalent to "work piece" in this case, the runners, and a part of another man's task. We can only assume that an exchange is present in the sense that one man is not likely to continue helping the other unless he receives a return in the form of help of the same kind at some other time, or in the form of prestige or gratitude.

An influence relation is present in the sense that one man's helping or not helping results in the other man's having to do more or less work. But the· bases of influence are mutually felt obligations, and not technical resources. Tasks are technically independent, and influence is not related to technical connections between them. We observe, then, in this case no technically required cooperation. There is technically permitted cooperation consisting of exchanges of work pieces and tasks, and semitechnical influence (that is, the use of nontechnical resources influencing technical performance). At the same time, we find a Handling technology of Type I, no work-flow sequence between operators, functional *in*dependence, and low functional exclusiveness. No technical resources are shared by design, but become shared from time to time by choice when operators help each other. (Popitz 1957a, 62, 65, 178).

Among the handlers of ore and coke wagons on the batching floor of the blast furnace of older construction in Case 5, each man has his own area under the bunkers and moves ore wagons independently from other ore handlers. No cooperation is technically required, except in cases of emergency where the operators must help each other in order to prevent an interruption in the feeding of the blast furnace. (Popitz 1957a, 61) But technically permitted cooperation is extensively practiced, as indicated in the following quotation from the report which also suggests that the basis for the observed relationships of cooperation and influence is not the technical setting but mutual obligation.

> . . . the extent of mutual support depends to a great extent on the relation-
> ship of individual ore handlers to each other. There is much room in this
> form of cooperation for *Kollegialität*.[2] To a certain extent it is enforced: as

---

[2] German workers presumably refer to a fellow worker as *Kollege* (colleague), unless they think of him as *Genosse* (comrade). What seems involved are occupational ties exceeding formal work requirements, but falling short of the feelings and conduct of friendship.

mentioned, there are some cases of disturbances in which help *must* be given if the feeding of the blast furnace is not to be delayed. For the same reason the dropping out of one man means a greater load for all others. Finally, a moral force is derived from the mutuality of giving help. Each can expect help only so long as he is willing to help. But *Kollegialität* can be further intensified. For instance, when the wagon is especially heavy or when it becomes stuck between two floor plates, aid can be given and the wagon put into motion again by a push. A man can pay attention to another and not run into his way. When a man has a bad day, another can from time to time take over his wagon and thereby ease his work. And finally the fact that mutual help is given as a matter of course depends on the intensity of the collegial relationship. In that respect this form of cooperation offers the possibility of informal association of all shades. (Popitz 1957a, 51–52)

An interview with a scale man also indicates helping among workers. (Popitz 1957b, 35) This operation is so designed as to accomplish its required outcome—the regular feeding of the blast furance—by the performance of independent tasks by the ore handlers. But by exchanging tasks and ore wagons, or parts of tasks, operators display technically permitted cooperation and semitechnical influence. These behaviors have their source in the rules of mutual obligation and exchange rather than in the technical design, although they are both limited and facilitated by it. As in the preceding case, this form of cooperation and influence is found in the presence of a Handling technology of Type I. There are functionally independent tasks of low exclusiveness, not connected by work-flow sequence and with no technical resources shared. When we speak here about the absence of a work flow, we do so only when focusing on the internal relations among ore handlers; their work as a whole is part of a larger work-flow sequence.

Neither technically required nor other forms of cooperation are observed among the relay assemblers of Case 13. Each assembler performs her work technically independent of the others, neither sharing nor exchanging any of the technical resources. But we find clear manifestations of semitechnical influence, of which two particular forms are recorded in the original report. One operator, at times joined by others, was particularly preoccupied with increasing the output of the five assemblers and thus their output-based pay. More interesting is the fact that over long periods during the five years of observation, fluctuations in the rate of output of some pairs, and particularly of one pair of operators, were very highly related. The average hourly rates of output for each week of two assemblers maintained a correlation coefficient of .97 for a period of almost four months. These relationships disappeared almost entirely for some time after the replacement of an operator by a substitute. (Whitehead I, 157, 197–218; Whitehead II, D17-D26, F34-F37)

The data indicate that these relationships in output rate are connected with the influence exercised by one particular operator. The pair relationship in associated output rates does in fact shift from one pair to another after a change in seating arrangements with each pair containing the one "influential" assembler as a member. In this case, then, we observe the absence of both technically required and permitted cooperation but the exercise of semitechnical influence, in the presence of a Hand Work technology of Type II. There is no work flow between operators who perform functionally independent tasks of low exclusiveness and who share no technical resources.

The workers in the two assembly sections of Case 15 are also not technically required to cooperate, and the report gives no indication of technically permitted cooperation in the form of exchange of technical resources. Anything approaching a form of cooperation lies only in what the report calls "small job accommodations which worked toward making the overall work easier and more pleasant for the sub-group" in one of the two sections. These accommodations consisted of the group leader preparing work assignments for one assembler so that she would not have to walk to the storage bins; another assembler pushing semicompleted units into a favorable work position for another assembler; and one assembler fixing lead wires so that another would not have to check her end of the test board. Although the report lacks directly relevant data, we might infer that technical behavior has in this case no part in influence relationships. This might be related to the fact that, as the report indicates, each worker works her own batch in the job-lot production. Direct influence by one worker, on the pace with which another works, seems unlikely although not entirely impossible. The report does contain many observations of extratechnical influence exercised by dominant members of various interlocked sub-groups, involving such things as where and with whom to take coffee breaks, what to contribute to money collections for charitable purposes, and what part to play in games. We find, then, the same types of behavior and technical conditions as in the preceding case. In the previous case, however, semitechnical influence was pronounced and appears less likely in this case.

No technical resources are shared among the workers in the bank-wiring room of Case 14, and no technically required cooperation is found. But technically permitted cooperation occurs frequently when certain inspectors, wiremen, and soldermen exchange tasks, work pieces, and equipment with each other, and when for instance one wireman helps another by taking over a part of his task and work piece, either in exchange for the same kind of help at another time or in exchange for recognition. (Roethlisberger, 460, 462–464, 467, 468, 470, 472, 474, 477, 482, 483, 496, 504, 505–507) The report also indicates that both job trading and job helping were actually forbidden and there were very few occasions when helping one another was "technically justified." (Roethlisberger, 505)

In addition, semitechnical influence is revealed. Some wiremen would

speed up their work and thus frequently make it necessary for the soldermen to speed up as well when performing the next step of the operation on
the same work piece. Similarly a solderman could at times prevent a
wireman from immediately continuing his work by taking more time. The
same absence of technically required cooperation as in the preceding four
cases, the presence of technically permitted cooperation as found in the
first two cases of this section, and the presence of semitechnical influence
as in all of these last cases except Case 15 are here found together with a
Hand Work technology of Type II. We should also notice that work flow
connects only certain sets of workers. It does not consist of the movement
of work pieces but of the movement of workers. Work flow is not connected with the very short cycle of the work on one connection but only
with the shift between banks which occurs only a few times each day. All
tasks are shared.

There is no technically required cooperation among the workers in the
two machine-shop subsystems of Case 16. Also the report does not mention any observation of technically permitted cooperation consisting of the
exchange of work between operators either in the form of helping or job
trading. But there is also no positive statement about the absence of such
forms of cooperation. A variety of relationships of extratechnical influence
can be seen in much of the report. We can now record for this case the
absence of technically required cooperation, the possible presence of technically permitted cooperation, and the proliferation of nontechnical relationships of influence on nontechnical behavior. This is a case with a
Machine Work technology of Type III, no work-flow connections between
work stations, functional independence, and low exclusiveness of tasks
performed, as well as no shared technical resources.

Among the workers in the machine shop of Case 17, "no one person
depended on another to meet the management's requirements of accepta-
ble job performance. " (Zaleznik 1956, 27) Technically permitted cooperation consists in this case of the exchange of tools in return for prestige; in
one man's helping another to lift a heavy part; the exchange of advice; and
a man actually doing a part of the work of another. (Zaleznik 1956, 33–37)
That the exchange of tools, for instance, is not technically required is
indicated by the observation that workers could have obtained required
tools from the company's tool crib. (Zaleznik 1956, 36) Semitechnical
influence can be seen in the change of the behavior of a man receiving
help, as a consequence of another man's behavior change consisting of
leaving his own work and turning his attention and activity to the work of
the man whom he is helping. These types of behavior are here related to a
Machine Work technology of Type III, where no technical resources are
shared by design, and where tasks of low exclusiveness are functionally
independent and not connected by work-flow sequence.

The four operators in the clicking room of Case 18 are clearly not engaged in any form of cooperation, neither technically required nor permitted. The work is technically entirely independent and separate and does not make any form of helping possible. Although the superior output record of a night-shift worker is frequently pointed out by one man to another, this fact appears to have no consequences for the latter's technical behavior. Influence relations are therefore confined to the nontechnical influence of nontechnical behavior involved in a repeated series of alimentary and conversational rituals. Regularized peach time, banana time, fish time, coke time, and coffee or lunch time are predictably introduced by one of the men every day, through behaviors followed by the corresponding conduct on the part of others. This case displays the same characteristics of work-place technology and its demands as the preceding two cases. There are no relationships of technically required or permitted cooperation. Influence relations are confined to nontechnical behaviors.

In Case 20, workers almost never share the same equipment and work piece at the same time when working on looms in regular production operation. There is no technically required cooperation. Whether any form of technically permitted cooperation takes place, is not reported, but seems quite unlikely. Such cooperation might take place after machine breakdowns or during change-overs. There is also no observation of any form of influence relationship. On jobs which require either the continuous watching of a large number of looms or the simple replacing of yarn spools, any influence on technical behavior might be confined to a call for any of the several men performing specialized tasks. Although a work flow is present in this situation, the connection by work flow is very loose. It consists only of the supplying of yarn and the moving away of completed cloth over extended intervals. Workers called "weavers" are among themselves as little connected by work-flow sequence or functional dependence as are the battery fillers who, together with the weavers, constitute the largest number of workers in the weaving shed. We record an absence of technically required and permitted cooperation, and barely any influence relations involving technical behavior. This is a case of Machine Work technology of Type III, where only some tasks are occasionally connected by a loose work flow and by functional dependence, and tasks are of low exclusiveness.

So far in this section we have dealt with nine cases encompassing work-place technologies of Types I, II, and III. In the ten cases of the first section, we also discussed cases of technology Types I, II, and III, but observed different forms of cooperation and influence. We therefore need to show how we will distinguish between the technical characteristics of these cases in order to explain observed differences in the social behavior of workers. All the cases in the first section were either clearly of a Type I technology, in whole or during distinctly separate times, or they contained a dominant component of a Handling technology. The operating of coal-cutting and coal-face-boring machines of Case 11a had been classified as involving a Type III technology. In fact, the case contains a large component of the manual moving and directing of machines. Working these machines does not have the characteristics of the operation of stationary machine tools which will be dealt with in the third section of this chapter. With the exception of Cases 14 and 20 in the second section, all cases in both the first and the second sections have no work-flow connection between work stations manned by the operators under focus. The work flow in these two exceptions is weak and unconnected with operation cycles. Exclusiveness of task performance is low in all cases of both sections.

The difference between the two sections, then, is that in the first section, tasks are functionally interdependent and operators share technical resources at the same time, while in the second section, tasks are independent and no technical resources are shared.

In general, we have dealt in the first section with the handling of heavy work pieces or equipment parts by hand, where operators are not connected by work flow but are functionally dependent and perform the same or similar tasks jointly and simultaneously. The cases of the second section so far dealt with involved Types I, II, and III technologies and are distinguished from the cases in the first section by independence of functions. In none of these cases was technically required cooperation observed.

The remainder of this section will deal with the one case of technology Type IV and all five cases of technology Type V. In all of these, technically required cooperation is absent. But technology and technical demands differ from the cases in the first section and from the preceding cases of this second section. They share certain similarities with the third section from which they are primarily and clearly distinguished by type of technology.

Workers on the four production lines in the shoe-bottoming room of Case 19 do not share technical resources at the same time. (An exception might be the space on the workbenches adjacent to machines on which work pieces are successively put to be picked up by the next man.) There is no technically required cooperation. Also, no technically permitted cooperation is observed, in the sense that no exchange of jobs, work pieces, or equipment takes place. But semitechnical influence occurs when one operator playfully tosses shoes—on which he has completed his work—directly to the next man instead of placing them on the bench for the next man to take. Here the behavior of the receiver changes as a consequence of the change in behavior of the thrower. Other forms of semitechnical influence are found in a striking arrangement for the redistribution of workloads. A complex system of exchange of symbolic objects for racks of shoes equalizes the take-home pay of all four sections. It regulates both work speed and type of shoe worked on, on the basis not of technical requirements but of the rules of mutual obligation agreed upon by the workers. In this case we find a technology of Machine-Work Sequence of Type IV, with work stations connected by work flow and functional dependence. Although coded as high, exclusiveness of task performance is mixed as two functions on each line are performed by a pair of operators, while the remaining work stations are exclusively occupied by one person.

Each of the fillers during the filling shift of mechanized longwall coal mining of Case 11b has his own section of the coal face and there is no technically required cooperation between fillers. (Trist, 24) But there is a distinct form of technically permitted cooperation among neighboring fillers who help each other out in groups of two, three, or four and who often work together over periods of many years. While by technical design fillers are meant to work their stints separately and individually, under certain conditions fillers might not only help each other on difficult parts of the work but in fact work their stints jointly. (Trist, 30; Dennis, 44-45) Under the dangerous underground conditions, the cooperative groups seem to become highly interdependent and their relationship to one another would involve semitechnical influence based on rules of mutual obligation, exercised by sanctions including the possibility of permanent exclusion of a member from the system of mutual help. There is a work flow away from each filler on the continuously moving conveyor belt passing all of the fillers on the same coal face. But one filler is not connected with the next by this work flow. Fillers are functionally independent and perform tasks of low exclusiveness in the presence of an Assembly Line technology of Type V.

In Case 23 the work on four production lines was described, where workers wrap or decorate chocolates on a continuously moving conveyor. On the first of the lines, workers take "centers" from a supply beside them, dip them in chocolate, mark them with a decorative design, and then place them on the belt. On the other three lines, workers receive chocolates on the belt, place them in boxes or wrap them, and put them back on the belt. The first of these lines is similar to the last case. Work is independent from the belt speed. The conveyor runs past the operators, but they are not connected by the work flow in the sense that one worker would work on a "work piece" worked on by a preceding worker. In the other three lines, workers are paced, but not connected functionally, by the belt. There is neither technically required nor technically permitted cooperation. We have no information on influence relationships. We can only say that there is no technical influence between the workers, while it is possible that work speed within the limits of the pace at which work pieces move down the line is influenced on a nontechnical basis. This is a case of Assembly Line technology of Type V, with a work-flow sequence, functional independence, and low functional exclusiveness.

By far the majority of auto-assembly jobs described in Case 22 involve

no technically required cooperation and no technically permitted cooperation. There also seem to be no influence relations among workers, particularly of the kind that would affect the speed or distribution of activities in
any worker's task. On a line where work elements are segmented and
balanced and workers can barely keep up with the line, any form of
helping among workers is very unlikely indeed. In fact, we find that when a
worker "gets in the hole," it takes a relief man or the foreman to take over
parts of that man's work to get him back into line. There is an Assembly
Line technology of Type V, with work flow, functional independence, and
low exclusiveness.

In Case 24, workers assemble electrical equipment on an assembly line.
The conditions of work are similar to those of the last case in most
respects. There is an Assembly Line technology of Type V, and cooperation is neither technically required nor permitted. Work stations are
connected by work flow. In contrast to the last case, we find semitechnical
influence. It happened frequently during the period of observation that a
man did not keep up with line pace and got in other workers' way. This
affected the working speed and distribution of activities of other workers
and eventually the whole line. Influence is here not related to cooperation
but to conflict. Conflict results from the impossibility of sharing the same
working space at the same time, and from the fact that tasks are functionally dependent and performed with high exclusiveness. When variations in
the performance of one worker exceed the capacity of the space allotted to
him, they cannot be made up by behavior changes of other workers. When
variations become extreme, they result in shutting down the whole line.
Shutting down the line is also found in the preceding case. But there it was
the result of functional interdependence between whole sections, and not
between individual work stations. It was ordinarily prevented by the use of
spell-off men.

The garment workers of Case 25 perform their tasks on a continuously
moving belt. As in the last case, there is an Assembly Line technology of
Type V, work flow, functional dependence, and high exclusiveness of
tasks performed. Cooperation is also neither technically required nor permitted, and technical behavior is affected by nontechnical influence. But
this time influence relations are based on the fact that workers remove
work pieces from the belt and thus have a choice over the distribution of
work in time. This choice results in variations of the speed with which
work pieces are put back on the belt and affects other workers particularly
at the end of the line. They in turn will urge the preceding workers not to
"foul up" the regular pace by delays which cause periodic accumulations of
work pieces toward the end of the line.

Technical demands in the preceding five cases are similar to the cases of
the next section. But there is no technically required cooperation in these
five cases, while in the next cases sequential cooperation is a distinct

technical requirement. The explanation of the difference in behavioral outcomes lies in the interaction of technology with certain technical constraints. In the nine cases of the third section, workers do have control over, and in fact regulate by "steering," variations in the pace with which work pieces move through the work-flow sequence. The same characteristics of work flow and functional dependency and exclusiveness interact with a different type of technology for different behavioral results than in the preceding several cases where workers have no control over the moving line. In the sense that they do not control the line, we would also say that the part of the technical resources consisting of the line is shared by them only nominally. No other aspects—work pieces or tasks—are shared. A partial summary of this section is given in Table 26. Further refinements are added in the comparative summaries at the end of the chapter.

3. Level C—Machine Line: Sequential Cooperation and Irreversible Influence

In the following nine cases, we find technically required cooperation which is sequential and relations of irreversible technical influence between the behaviors of operators. Within a given operation cycle a behavior variation of the first man must be followed by a change in behavior of the second man that makes up the first man's variation. There is no such behavior control in the other direction.

Any given wire-return man in the hot-wire rolling operation of Case 26 must grasp a wire shooting out of a roll stand at a sharply defined point in time. This point is determined by the time at which the preceding man has stuck the same wire into his second roll stand. In contrast to the times of mill changes already dealt with, the actual rolling part of the operation is called Case 26a. It was observed that each wire-return man, once he has grasped the outcoming wire, can vary slightly the time of sticking it into the next stand. During that time he might in fact have to cut off the deformed head of the wire with foot-operated shears. The following man must make up for this variation in time by grasping the wire slightly earlier or later. Rather than "taking over" a part of the task of the other, as was the case in the simultaneous cooperation of the ten cases discussed first, he can only "take up" the variation in the first man's movements by a change in the timing of his own. This successive taking up of variation we call technically required sequential cooperation. The first man of any pair along the line has a degree of choice in varying the time of sticking the wire in. The second man shares with the first a part of the equipment, consisting of a pair of roll stands mechanically connected on the other side. He has no such choice in his relation to the first man. This is technical influence without the reciprocity present in the ten cases of the first section. A degree of influence in the opposite direction extends over two

TABLE 26. REQUIRED COOPERATION AND INFLUENCE - LEVEL B

Technology Type and Functional Constraints	Required Cooperation			
	Absent	Simult- aneous	Sequential	Sporadic- Symbolic
Type I,II,III, no flow, indepen- dence, low dif- ferentiation	I: 3a,5 II: 13,14, 15 III: 16, 17,18,20			
Type IV,V, flow, dependence, high differentiation	IV: 19 V: 24,25			
Type V, flow, in- dependence, low differentiation	V: 11b,22, 23			

- -

Technology Type and Functional Constraints	Influence			
	Reversible	Irre- versible	Semi- technical	Extra- technical
Type I,II,III, no flow, indepen- dence, low dif- ferentiation			I: 3a,5 II: 13,14 III: 17	II: 15 III: 16, 18,20
Type IV,V, flow, dependence, high differentiation			IV: 19 V: 24,25	
Type V, flow, in- dependence, low differentiation			V: 11b	V: 22,23

operation cycles: the first man can hold for a moment when he sees the second man is not ready. We infer from the report that there is no technically permitted cooperation.

This is a case of Hand and Machine Line technology of Type VI. Worker activities are affected by a work-flow sequence, functional dependence, high exclusiveness of task performance, and a sharply defined operation cycle of about 7 seconds.

We will now look again at the workers involved in moving materials from the batching floor to the top of the blast furnace. Case 6a is the operation in which two men at the bottom, the elevator operator in the middle, and four men at the top are connected by the work-flow sequence of ore wagons moved up and down in the elevator, and in and out of the elevator. The elevator operator cannot put the elevator into motion unless he has received a signal from below and above, indicating that ore wagons are in place and ready to go. Similarly, the ore-wagon handlers cannot take wagons out until the elevator basket has arrived. The recorded observations emphasize how crucial the temporal connection between the three work stations is in a short cycle of about 1 minute. A temporal variation of activities at one station must be taken up by a temporal adjustment at the others. But this case differs from the preceding case by the fact that, there, a man must take on an outcoming wire, but also cannot grasp it before it arrives. In this case a man at one work station also cannot act before a certain time, which is determined by acts performed at other stations, but he need not take on the ore wagons for a new operation cycle with the same precise immediacy of the preceding case. This difference is related to a difference in technology. In Case 26a (Wire Rolling) there is a continuously moving line not controlled by operators, while in this case the "line" is regulated by the elevator operator. Focusing on the combined operation of the three work stations with the elevator operator at its crucial center, we have, in addition to the technology of Remote Controls, a work-flow sequence, functional dependence, high exclusiveness of task performance, and a clearly defined short operation cycle.

It will not be necessary to describe again in detail the relevant characteristics of the remaining seven cases to be discussed in this section. In Case 9 we will deal with the operation at the coking battery as a whole with its four distinct work stations rather than with the internal relationships in the subcrews. In Cases 28a and 29a we will be concerned with the total operation of the mill during the actual tube rolling rather than with the mill changes dealt with in Cases 28b and 29b. Time cycles in Cases 8, 9, and 32 are longer and less sharply defined than in the other cases, where operation cycles take from a few seconds to 1 minute. Lines of sequential cooperation and irreversible technical influence in Cases 9 and 27 vary with different times of a given larger operation cycle in which sequential relationships are successively redistributed. But when we focus at any one of these sequences, we find the same characteristics of cooperation and influence already described for the preceding two cases. In addition, we should notice that this type of cooperation and influence is present in Case 29a only with regard to the two *operators* whose machines are not self-regulating and to those *times* at which all operators actively regulate the operation after having switched off the self-regulating mechanisms. Similarly, in Case 32 we are concerned with the work flow from train operator to soaking-pit operator to crane operator and with the concomitant cooperative and influence behavior.

In summary, we have just dealt with nine cases in which a sequential form of technically required cooperation and irreversible influence are observed in the presence of the Hand and Machine Line technology of Type VI for Case 26a, and of a Remote Controls technology of Type VII, for Cases 6a, 7, 8, 9, 27, 28a, 29a, and 32. All of these are characterized by the presence of a work-flow sequence between work stations, functional dependence, high functional exclusiveness, and (with few exceptions) sharply defined and short operation cycles. We must also notice that, in the ten cases of the first section, there is a sharing of work pieces or of equipment parts which had become the equivalent of work pieces. In the cases of this section, distinct and usually large parts of the operating equipment are shared. Only in Cases 9, 27, 8, and 32, we also find shared materials or work pieces the condition for cooperation. It so happens that in these four cases we also find minor elements of simultaneous cooperation. Also common to all of these nine cases is the fact that technically permitted cooperation is absent: no exchange of tasks, work pieces, or equipment parts can be observed in any of these cases. An added characteristic of influence relations in Cases 26a and 28a is physical danger as a penalty. Table 27 is a summary of the data of this section.

4. Level D—Automation: Sporadic and Symbolic Cooperation and Irreversible Influence

In the first section of this chapter, workers were bound together by shared work pieces in relationships of simultaneous cooperation and reversible influence. In the second section, workers did not, in a meaningful sense, share any of the technical resources of their work place. They were in fact separated either by the characteristics of their task or by the technology, and they were not connected in relationships of technically required cooperation. But they had varying choices of behavior variations in nontechnical forms of influence relations, and choices of being engaged in relationships of technically permitted cooperation. In the third section, workers were bound together by shared equipment which they regulated in relationships of sequential cooperation and irreversible influence.

In the four cases to be dealt with in this last section workers are rather

TABLE 27. REQUIRED COOPERATION AND INFLUENCE – LEVEL C

Technology Type and Functional Constraints	Required Cooperation			
	Absent	Simult-aneous	Sequential	Sporadic-Symbolic
Type VI,VII, flow, dependence, high differentiation			VI: 26a VII: 6a,7, 8,9,27, 28a,29a, 32	

- -

Technology Type and Functional Constraints	Influence			
	Reversible	Irre-versible	Semi-technical	Extra-technical
Type VI,VII, flow, dependence, high differentiation		VI: 26a VII: 6a,7, 8,9,27, 28a,29a, 32		

loosely bound together, not by distinct work pieces or equipment parts, but (1) by the flow of signals, and (2) indirectly by the integrated but remote operations represented by these signals. Technical resources are loosely shared in the sense that in a closely integrated process the buttons pushed or levers pulled by one operator are likely to have effect on what other operators observe on their dials and occasionally perhaps on which buttons or levers they have to push or pull. But the actual physical movements of operators are not directly related to those of others, to form a close cooperative relationship. The nearly continuous observation of dials seems the major component of the task of operators in these cases. It is subjected to variations whose interconnections are loose and indirect. This is technically required cooperation which, for lack of a better label, we might call sporadic and symbolic.

The work of the operators of blast-furnace air control in Case 33 constitutes a borderline instance between the cases of this section and those in the third section. It is a case of semiautomation, as were Cases 29a and 32 in the preceding section. All of these three cases contain a mixture of self-regulating technical features combined with active steering of parts of the operation. The difference between Case 33, on the one hand, and Cases 29a and 32, on the other, lies in the fact that the operators in the latter two cases directly observe the processes which they steer, while the operator in Case 33 relies on time schedules and dials for the timing of his performances. Operation cycles in Case 33 are long and therefore relatively "open," but short and distinct in Cases 29a and 32. The operator of blast air control shares flow processes with the operators on other blast furnaces, with the general control of gas supply, and with other gas users. He cooperates with other control operators in the sense that variations in the regulation of gas flow on their part must be followed by variations in his own performance.

The same kind of relationship exists between him and the smelting crew on his blast furnace. In this case irregularities in the blast-furnace process itself become expressed in behavior changes of the smelting crew and of the blast air-control operator. This required change is indicated to him by communication from the smelting crew. In the absence of irregularities in the operation of one or more blast furnaces, cooperation between the different work stations in this network is formally regulated by a written or memorized time schedule. In all cases cooperation is indirect; that is, it is mediated either by shared communication channels, shared time schedules, or shared flow processes. A part of this form of technically required cooperation is the technical influence exercised from one work station to another which at any one time is unidirectional and consists of a sequence of related behavior changes. Technically permitted cooperation is not reported. Here the sharing of technical resources is not a matter of choice; and sharing, by choice, of information and advice as a resource is technically restricted by dependency on signals for communication between isolated work stations.

Data are insufficient to classify fully the relationships among workers on transfer machines in Case 31. The only information about worker cooperation lies in the statement that "there were significantly fewer jobs involving team work in the automated plant." (Faunce, 125) But also indicated is the fact that the few workers stationed at one transfer machine are widely spaced and that the major features of the operation are self-regulating. These two facts together might indicate that neither simultaneous nor sequential cooperation is present. We might assume that in this case, as in the other cases of this section, cooperation among workers on the transfer line is mediated by the channels through which signals are transmitted. Variations in the technical behavior of one worker are eventually made up by variations in that of another, at least to the extent that in extreme cases a transfer line might have to be stopped. In the same sense there is likely to be technical influence. This is a case of an Automation technology of Type VIII, with a work flow, functional interdependence, and high functional exclusiveness. These characteristics connect workers only indirectly through communication channels, making for loosely defined relationships.

The report on the gasoline-refinery workers of Case 34 indicates loosely defined, sporadic, and symbolic cooperation. It is almost dormant during some periods and becomes active during emergency-like conditions. The report describes that "since any adjustment made by the fractionator operator affected operations in the area of the hydro-stillman (and vice versa), this would be a period of accelerated communication between them and with the poly operator." (Whyte, 4) Technical variations to which one operator responds by behavior variations on his part are followed by succeeding and related variations on the part of another operator. The indication for required behavior variation comes first from the dials watched by the operators, and is then extended to direct communication between them. A behavior variation on the part of one man is not directly carried to the other through a specific work piece or equipment part. It is first expressed in changes in the integrated production process from which automatic signals reach another operator who then responds. Any given sequence of behavior variations constitutes technically required cooperation. It results in designed outcomes as a consequence of the sum of the activities of two or more operators. It is also a relationship of technical influence.

We have previously distinguished a type of influence in which the direction of behavioral control is reversible within a given operation cycle, from another type where direction is irreversible within a cycle. We are now considering an operation without any clearly defined cycles. A performance change of one man is carried through the actual production process and then reaches the dials of another man. It takes a distinct time for the second man to be affected by the performance change of the first man; and once the first man has made his move, the second man must respond. We can view the time it takes for a change to be carried through the process as equivalent to an operation cycle, and then readily speak of an irreversible-influence relationship. This characteristic of the relationship is not changed by the possibility that the first man might tell his neighbor what he has done, thus allowing the second man to anticipate the next move. Furthermore, an influence sequence with one direction is distinguished in time from one in the other direction. The technical characteristics of this case are those of an Automation technology of Type VIII and indirect technical connections between work stations by work flow, functional dependence, and high exclusiveness of tasks.

Among the men of the "operating personnel" of the power plant described in Case 35, we find the same types of relationship as in the preceding case. The report speaks of "enforced contact" (Mann 1960, 63), indicating the presence of cooperation mediated by the technical design of the integrated operations of the power plant. Cooperation is the "making up" of variations in technical performance of one operator by another for designed joint outcomes. It takes place here by means of information channels through which signals are transmitted. Changes in the actual production process caused by one operator's activity are indicated to other operators on their dials, thus inserting the time taken for this sequence between two associated behavior variations. As in the preceding case, it is indicated here that this type of connection is supplemented by direct verbal exchange of information and advice. The relationship of indirect symbolic cooperation is dormant for extended periods of time and becomes active between men of one operating section. This occurs, for instance, when a turbine is shut down. It takes place between men in control of generating equipment and men in control of the switching section when current is redirected to different lines. This cooperation also constitutes temporally irreversible technical influence: one operator's behavior change is followed, after its transmission through the technical process and signal channels, by a change of the behavior of another operator. The technical characteristics of this case are the same as in Case 34, with the exception that functional exclusiveness is lower in the sense that always two operators in a pair perform a given function. The material of this section is summarized in Table 28.

5. Cooperation, Influence, and Technology

We can now summarize the relationships of technology and technical constraints with variations in types of cooperation and influence. In the first section, we discussed ten cases in which the technology was of Types I, II, and III. Technical conditions exhibited either a dominant hand-work component or temporally or functionally separated parts consisting of manual handling of work pieces or equipment parts. In all of these cases there is no work flow between operators who are nevertheless functionally dependent on each other and perform tasks of low exclusiveness. Under these conditions we find what we have called *simultaneous cooperation* and *reversible influence*. This type of cooperation is required for the attainment of technically designed outcomes. It does not allow a distinction between technically required and technically permitted cooperation as previously defined, since the availability of choices is a part of the behavior possibilities which make the design work. We might say that under these conditions "voluntary" behaviors are "necessary." Similarly, we have found that relationships of reversible influence permit a number of choices among behavior changes, in response to another operator's change of behavior.

All fifteen cases of the second section have in common only the absence

TABLE 28. REQUIRED COOPERATION AND INFLUENCE - LEVEL D

Technology Type and Functional Constraints	Required Cooperation			
	Absent	Simult-aneous	Sequential	Sporadic-Symbolic
Type VIII, signal flow, dependence, high different-iation				VIII: 31, 33,34,35

- -

Technology Type and Functional Constraints	Influence			
	Reversible	Irre-versible	Semi-technical	Extra-technical
Type VIII, signal flow, dependence, high different-iation	VIII: 31, 33,34,35			

of technically required cooperation. In the preceding detailed discussion of this section, we have claimed that this absence can be explained by differences in the combination of both technology and technical constraints even though this section contains cases with either a type of technology or types of constraints which occur in other sections, but in different combinations. The first section contained cases of a technology of Type I, II, or III, with a dominant Handling component. In the second section, there were also cases with technologies of these three types, but these cases are differentiated from the first by the fact that work stations and their operators are functionally independent.

We proposed that in the cases of the first section, technically permitted cooperation is part of the technical design. In the third section, technically permitted cooperation is absent and hardly possible. But in the second section, we find some cases in which technically permitted cooperation has been observed and others in which it has not. We also find in the second section some cases in which influence relations are independent of relationships of cooperation. We have positive information that in Cases 3a, 5, 14, 17, and 11b, technically permitted cooperation takes place, taking the form of helping or job trading, that is, partial or total exchanges of tasks or technical resources. In the remaining cases we have no information that in fact these kinds of exchanges did not occur, and we can only tentatively argue that, with few exceptions, technically permitted cooperation is rather unlikely.

We will now attempt to account for the occurrence of technically permitted cooperation by the relative confinement of operators to work locations. In Part Two we have coded our cases by indicating whether the operator's location while working was fixed in space; mobile but confined to equipment regulated by the operator; or open, that is, requiring operators to move about in their work space in the course of carrying out their work. The smelting workers of Case 3a, the ore handlers of Case 5, and the machine-shop workers of Case 17 are required to walk around among different and relatively distant parts of their work space in order to do their work. Movement among the workers in the bank-wiring room of Case 14 is somewhat more restricted, but they are still required to move between a distinct number of work stations. Coal-face workers during the filling shift of Case 11b are more confined still, to their individual sections of the coal face, but must move around in the 10 feet of the section to which they are allotted and are in fact free to move to the sections of their neighbors. In all of these cases we observe an open work location of operators. At the same time we have recorded the occurrence of technically permitted cooperation. The exchange of tasks or task components, and of technical resources, constituting technically permitted cooperation, is accompanied by influence relations with nontechnical bases of influence where the behavior influenced is technical performance.[3]

In six other cases there is semitechnical influence and no permitted cooperation. The work locations of operators are confined to one distinct place, except that automobile-assembly workers travel with the main line for a short stretch, but are then also confined to distinct locations around the assembly worked on. It can be argued that technically permitted

---

[3] A note is necessary to clarify the relation between the categories of influence relations and the quality of the data to match them. We have called *extratechnical influence* the relationship in which nontechnical resources are the basis of influencing nontechnical behavior. As the data sources are often unclear about this, we will have to include in this category cases in which there may be no influence at all. On the other hand, the use of the term "extratechnical influence" precludes the occurrence of *semitechnical influence* and of *technical influence*. Similarly, when we record semitechnical influence (that is, nontechnical resources are the basis of influencing technical performance), extratechnical influence may also occur, but technical influence is precluded. Where *reversible technical influence* is noted, the occurrence of *nontechnical influence* is likely. It seems less probable that there is nontechnical influence where there is *irreversible technical influence*. We do not have the full range of data for each case to support these assumed relationships.

cooperation is highly unlikely among the relay-assembly workers of Case 13, the workers on the equipment-assembly line of Case 24, and the garment workers of Case 25. At the same time we find the semitechnical influence previously described for these cases. Among the clicking-machine operators of Case 18, the chocolate wrappers of Case 23, and the automobile workers of Case 22, technically permitted cooperation is equally unlikely, but it is also unlikely that there are influence relations affecting technical behavior. Whether in these last three cases there are any extra-technical-influence relationships, we cannot tell with the data available.

The work locations of the machine-shop workers of Case 16 and the weaving-loom operators of Case 20 are open, and one would expect to find technically permitted cooperation as in the other cases with that same characteristic. Workers in the equipment-assembly shop of Case 15 and in the shoe-bottoming room of Case 19 are reported to leave their work places occasionally but are not technically required to do so in contrast to the last two cases. The report on Case 15 in fact indicates "small job accommodations," a very restricted form of technically permitted cooperation presumably related to the limited degree of mobility possible. The data are again insufficient for a full classification. For these last four cases, then, we can only note the absence of technically required cooperation, but we are less certain in making further distinctions with regard to technically permitted cooperation and different kinds of influence relations.

We can now briefly review our argument concerning the cases of the second section. A part of the cases in this section involve work-place technologies of Types I, II, and III, and in all of these cases work stations are functionally independent, are occupied by workers performing shared tasks of low exclusiveness, and are not connected by work flow. The limited work flow and functional dependency noted in Cases 14 and 20 involve only parts of the operation and small proportions of working time. During the remainder of time and performance the same conditions hold as in the majority of cases. In the second part of that section, we dealt with cases of technology Types IV and V, with a work flow between stations in all cases. But in these six cases we find various combinations of functional dependency and exclusiveness. These cases are distinguished from others by either technology or technical constraints or both, and in all of these cases technically required cooperation is absent. In seven cases the work location of operators is relatively open, and we find technically permitted cooperation and the technical behavior of operators influenced by the behavior of other workers on nontechnical grounds. In eight cases work locations are confined, and the occurrence of technically permitted cooperation was argued to be implausible. In half of these cases semitechnical influence was observed which was less likely in the remaining half. Data are insufficient for an explanation of this latter difference. The differences internal to the second section are shown in the tables at the end of this chapter, in comparison with data from the other sections.

In the first section, functional dependence, no work flow, and undifferentiated tasks were found together with technologies of Types I, II, and III, with a dominance of Handling as a technical condition. In nine of the fifteen cases of the second section, Types I, II, and III technologies were associated with functionally independent and undifferentiated tasks without work flow. Here, transfer operations were always performed by hand, while conversion operations consisted either of hand work or machine work. Other cases of the second section had an Assembly Line technology of Type V, with all conversion operations performed by hand and all transfer operations by machine. While there was a work flow in all of the remaining cases of the section, half displayed functional dependence and differentiation and half low differentiation of independent tasks.

Machinery is heavily used for both conversion and transfer in the cases of the third section to be reviewed now. In a total of nine cases with either a Hand and Machine Line technology of Type VI or a Remote Controls technology of Type VII, work stations are occupied by workers performing exclusive tasks, and are connected by a work-flow sequence and functional interdependence. Under these conditions we have observed sequential cooperation and irreversible influence. As in the first section, we find that influence relationships are the other side, as it were, of relationships of cooperation. In the first section, cooperation consisted of the taking over of a part of another man's performance to make up for variations in the other man's behavior in order to attain the technically designed outcome. The outcome is produced as a consequence of a fixed sum of activities of several workers. In this section the taking over of another man's performance is technically not possible. A second man can only take up the first man's variation by a change in the performance of his own task. In the presence of exclusively performed tasks connected by work flow and functional dependency, the taking up is separated in time from the first man's behavior change. It is this characteristic which we have labeled *sequential cooperation*. The sequence of behavior variations can take place in both directions in relation to the flow of the line. A sequence in one direction is clearly separated from a sequence in the other direction. During the first part of an operation cycle, a man is dependent on the operator preceding him in the flow. In the second part, he turns his attention to the man following him. He might change his performance in anticipation by observing, for instance, that the other is not yet ready. In that sense his behavior change follows the next man's performance variation. In all of these nine cases there are at least three work stations with their operators connected by work flow, and during each operation cycle shifting pairs of operators become successively engaged in the relationship of sequential cooperation.

We have called the relationship of influence between operators in these cases *irreversible*: during one operation cycle the second man must follow a performance variation of the first man by a variation in his own performance. His behavior change during that operation cycle and on the particular work piece does not affect the performance of the first man. The technical design in these cases is such that any second man can *not* take up the first man's variation only at the expense of causing a breakdown in the whole operation. It is only over more than one operation cycle that influence can be reciprocated by an anticipatory performance change straddling two operation cycles. For the sake of clarity, we have tended to focus on pairs of operators. But at least three stations are involved in any two connected interaction sequences. The fact that failure by an operator to play his part in the relationship of sequential cooperation has radical consequences for all stations and their operators in the line indicates the difference between irreversible influence and reversible influence. The reversible influence observed in the first section involved no such rigid tying together of specific operators. Failure to make up for another's performance variation did not result in the breakdown of the whole operation and could be made up again by a new variation in the performance of the first man for the attainment of technically designed outcomes.

Within the specified boundaries of the cases of the third section, there is no technically permitted cooperation. Its absence can be explained by indicating that operators perform interdependent tasks exclusively in a work flow and thus are unlikely to be able to exchange technical resources. In addition to being rigidly tied to the operation, operators are comparatively remote from work pieces or equipment, or both, and they are confined to their work stations. Even though in some cases operators move around with machines they control, they are still in a relatively confined location on these machines. In the second section, confined locations also accounted for the absence of technically permitted cooperation.

We are now left with the four cases of the fourth section, with a technology of Type VIII not observed in the other sections. These cases are differentiated from others by a technology of self-regulating automatics. There is a work flow (of which the flow of signals is particularly relevant), and functional interdependence and exclusiveness. It was argued that these connections between operators are indirect in comparison to the cases of the third section, where work pieces and equipment can be directly observed. Tasks are connected by technical operations which are spatially removed and out of sight of operators. Operators are linked with these operations and with each other by way of signal channels which only *represent* actual technical events. They are involved in sporadic-symbolic cooperation while performing their work, but only during certain widely and irregularly spaced periods when technically required cooperation becomes manifest. At the same time, we find the irreversible-influence relations between operators observed in the third section. This time the irreversibility in the sequence of behavior variations does not lie in the restrictions of an operation cycle and a moving work piece, but in the temporal delay between associated behavior variations. This is due to the fact that a performance change by one operator is not immediately transmitted to a work piece and cannot be taken up by the next operator. It must first find its way through the integrated process, and only then can it come back to another operator as a changed signal.

The characteristics of communication between operators will be explicitly dealt with in the next chapter. We mention here that in these four cases cooperation and influence are directly related only to communication flow and indirectly to the flow of materials. In the first and third sections, technically required cooperation and technically determined influence relations are based, instead, directly on the movements of materials or work pieces. Whatever communication is necessary to accomplish common technical outcomes is incidental to these work-piece movements.

Table 29 shows how technology, modified by different connections between work stations, is related to required cooperation. The table has four major divisions, corresponding to the four sections of this chapter. We will speak about "levels" of technical conditions when we refer to the types of technology and characteristics of technical constraints (for example, connections between work stations, operator location, attention requirements, and the like) which have been combined in each section. In sequence, Levels A to D correspond to Sections 1 to 4. Internal subdivisions, particularly of Level B, will be read as Levels B1, B2, and so on, in the sequence given in each table.

Required cooperation is *simultaneous* at Level A; *absent* at Level B; *sequential* at Level C; and *sporadic-symbolic* at Level D. Levels A, C, and D, and the parts of Level B with a Type IV and V technology, are clearly distinguished from each other by type of technology. The remainder of Level B is distinguished from Level A by the difference in functional dependence.

The technical conditions for permitted cooperation are stated in Table 30. Except at Level D, the condition for technically permitted cooperation is an open work location of operators. Permitted cooperation is observed or claimed to be likely in all cases of Level A, and in those of Level B where workers move about in their working area in the course of their work (B1a, B3a). There is no permitted cooperation at Level C and in the cases of Level B where workers are confined to fixed positions (B1b, B2, B3b). At Level D, workers appear to be confined to their work stations, and in at least two of the four cases observations are reported of technically permitted cooperation. Level D is distinguished from others by its different technology. In addition, the loosely defined performance requirements at this level make spatial confinement less compelling. At both Level A and Level D, permitted cooperation is part of the technical design; that is, the range of choices necessary to get the work done is greater than at the other levels.

TABLE 29. TECHNOLOGY AND REQUIRED COOPERATION

Technology Type and Functional Constraints	Level	Required Cooperation			
		Absent	Simultaneous	Sequential	Sporadic-Symbolic
Type I,II,III, no flow, dependence, low differentiation	A		I: 1,3b,4, 6b,26b, 28b,29b II: 10,21 III: 11a		
Type I,II,III, no flow, independence, low differentiation	B1	I: 3a,5 II: 13, 14,15 III: 16, 17,18, 20			
Type IV,V,flow, dependence, high differentiation	B2	IV: 19 V: 24,25			
Type V, flow, independence, low differentiation	B3	V: 11b, 22,23			
Type VI,VII, flow, dependence, high differentiation	C			VI: 26a VII: 6a,7, 8,9,27, 28a,29a, 32	
Type VIII, signal flow, dependence, high differentiation	D				VIII: 31, 33,34,35

TABLE 30. TECHNOLOGY AND PERMITTED COOPERATION

Technology Type and Constraints			Permitted Cooperation		
Function	Space	Level	Absent	Incorporated in Required Cooperation	Independent of Required Cooperation
Type I,II,III, no flow, dependence, low differentiation	open	A		I: 1,3b,4, 6b,26b, 28b,29b II: 10,21 III: 11a	
Type I,II,III, no flow, independence, low differentiation	open	B1a			I: 3a,5 II: 14 III: 16,17, 20
	confined	B1b	II: 13,15 III: 18		
Type IV,V,flow, dependence, high differentiation	confined	B2	IV: 19 V: 24,25		
Type V, flow, independence, low differentiation	open	B3a			V: 11b
	confined	B3b	V: 22,23		
Type VI,VII, flow, dependence, high differentiation	confined	C	VI: 26a VII: 6a, 7,8,9, 27,28a, 29a,32		
Type VIII, signal flow, dependence, high differentiation	confined	D		VIII: 31, 33,34,35	

TABLE 31. TECHNOLOGY AND INFLUENCE

Technology Type and Functional Constraints	Level	Influence			
		Reversible	Irreversible	Semitechnical	Extratechnical
Type I,II,III, no flow, dependence, low differentiation	A	I: 1,3b, 4,6b, 26b,28b, 29b II: 10,21 III: 11a			
Type I,II,III, no flow, independence, low differentiation	B1			I: 3a,5 II: 13,14 III: 17	II: 15 III: 16, 18,20
Type IV,V,flow, dependence, high differentiation	B2			IV: 19 V: 24,25	
Type V, flow, independence, low differentiation	B3			V: 11b	V: 22,23
Type VI,VII, flow, dependence, high differentiation	C		VI: 26a VII: 6a, 7,8,9, 27,28a, 29a,32		
Type VIII, signal flow, dependence, high differentiation	D		VIII: 31, 33,34, 35		

TABLE 32. REQUIRED COOPERATION AND INFLUENCE

Required Cooperation	Influence			
	Technical		Nontechnical	
	Reversible	Irre-versible	Semi-technical	Extra-technical
Absent			Level B	
			I: 3a,5	
			II: 13,14	II: 15
			III: 17	III: 16, 18,20
			IV: 19	
			V: 11b, 24,25	V: 22,23
Simultaneous	Level A			
	I: 1,3b,4, 6b,26b, 28b,29b			
	II: 10,21			
	III: 11a			
Sequential	Level C			
	VI: 26a			
	VII: 6a, 7,8,9, 27,28a, 29a,32			
Sporadic-Symbolic	Level D			
	VIII: 31, 33,34, 35			

Table 31 shows that workers exercise influence over the technical performance of other workers by the use of technical resources at Levels A, C, and D. The direction of this technical influence is reversible at Level A, and irreversible at Level C, within the boundaries of an operation cycle. There are no operation cycles at Level D, and influence is irreversible within the time span of the technical consequences of a change on operating controls made by an operator. The incidence of technical influence at Level D is less than at Levels A and C where it is in most cases a function of operation cycles. Influence observed in the cases of Level B does not have technical resources as a base. The differences in the occurrence of semitechnical influence and extratechnical influence (and possibly of no influence at all) cannot be fully acounted for with the available data.

In Tables 29, 30, and 31, we have looked separately at the relationship between technical conditions and each of three kinds of behavior variations. We will now consider the relations among these three behavioral categories: technically required cooperation, technically permitted cooperation, and influence. Table 32 deals with required cooperation and influence. Simultaneous cooperation occurs together with reversible influence at Level A. Sequential cooperation is accompanied by irreversible influence at Level C. Sporadic-symbolic cooperation is related to the less frequent incidence of irreversible influence at Level D. At Level B, there is nontechnical influence in the absence of technically required cooperation. Throughout, technically required cooperation is a condition for influence based on the use of technical resources and for affecting technical performance.

Table 33 relates required and permitted cooperation. At Level B, required cooperation is absent, and the incidence of permitted cooperation depends on whether opreator locations are confined or open. Permitted and required cooperation occur together at Levels A and D, where permitted cooperation is incorporated in technical requirements. At Level C, there is sequential cooperation in the absence of technically permitted cooperation.

The three behavioral variables are shown together in Table 34. At Level A, there is simultaneous required cooperation, permitted cooperation, and reversible influence. At Level B, we find no required cooperation, and nontechnical influence, in both the presence and absence of permitted cooperation. At Level C, sequential cooperation is related to irreversible influence, in the absence of permitted cooperation. At Level D, required and permitted cooperation again occur together, and sporadic-symbolic cooperation is related to irreversible influence.

In this chapter we have combined certain functional and spatial constraints with types of technology in a number of levels of technical conditions. We have distinguished several characteristics of cooperation and influence in industrial work. By ordering the data on these technical and behavioral dimensions, we have attempted to demonstrate how variations in industrial technology can account for differences in the social conduct of workers.

TABLE 33. REQUIRED AND PERMITTED COOPERATION

Required Cooperation	Permitted Cooperation	
	Present	Absent
Absent	Level B	Level B
	I: 3a,5 II: 14 III: 16,17,20 V: 11b	II: 13,15 III: 18 IV: 19 V: 22,23,24,25
Simultaneous	Level A	
	I: 1,3b,4,6b,26b, 28b,29b II: 10,21 III: 11a	
Sequential		Level C
		VI: 26a VII: 6a,7,8,9,27, 28a,29a,32
Sporadic- Symbolic	Level D	
	VIII: 31,33,34,35	

TABLE 34. COOPERATION AND INFLUENCE

| | | Influence | | | |
| | | Technical | | Nontechnical | |
Required Coop- eration	Permitted Coop- eration	Re- versible	Irre- versible	Semi- technical	Extra- technica?
				Level B	
Absent	Present			I: 3a,5 II: 14 III: 17 V: 11b	III:16,2(
	Absent			II: 13 IV: 19 V: 24,25	II: 15 III: 18 V: 22,23
Simult- aneous	Present	Level A			
	Absent				
Sequential	Present				
	Absent		Level C		
Sporadic- Symbolic	Present		Level D		
	Absent				

Chapter XII

COMMUNICATION

This chapter will attempt to discover whether and in what way social behavior as communication is directed and limited by work-place technology and its demands. We will again discuss the cases in sections which display the same or similar behavioral characteristics and then relate these characteristics to the technical conditions in which they were found. In each section we begin with the cases where positive statements of observation can be found in the source. However, several cases lack positively reported observations of the behaviors to be considered. By loose inference and hunch, we will then attempt to classify the remaining cases at least to some extent. The sections in this chapter correspond to those in Chapter XI.

Only extremely rarely are references made in our data sources to situations in which production workers, during their work time, never communicate in some way or other with someone else. But we can find very distinct differences in the incidence of either technically required or technically permitted communication. To begin with, we will ask which one of these two kinds of communication has been observed, and then attempt to answer the question: Why are both kinds found in some cases, and in other cases only one kind? Once we have seen that either required or permitted communication, or both, are present, we want to know with what frequency and regularity communication occurs. We are thus returning to the question of how behaviors are distributed over time and whether and how "times" divide communicative behaviors. Having separated required from permitted communication, we will ask the double question: What means of communication are available and used, and how are workers linked by these means in different communication systems? These linkages which connect people in technically permitted communication are the "interaction systems" referred to in the literature. We will also ask to what degree permitted communication fulfills expectations of the "sufficiency" of available means of expression.

1. Level A—Heavy Hauling: Full Communication in Teams

Walker's diary record of his experience with the men in the steel-plant maintenance crew of Case 1 actually quotes their conversations. Shouted-out orders for tools and actions indicate technically required communication. Conversations among men, and advice given to those unfamiliar with the work, take place during most of the working day, and constitute technically permitted communication. These exchanges of messages are comparatively frequent and irregularly distributed over time. This irregularity is related to the variability of work cycles. Messages are verbal and transmitted directly from person to person. This is what we call communication by *words*. But there is also required communication by means of *objects*, where messages sent constitute a simple object language.[1]

In the previous chapter we imputed simultaneous cooperation to this case. We can now add that cooperating workers observe and manipulate technical objects and thus give and receive cues. These cues facilitate the distribution and redistribution of activities among the several workers which we have noticed in cases of simultaneous cooperation. The cues may be felt by one's hands or may be visually perceived; wordless communication by objects is the continual accompaniment of this form of cooperation. One might even assume that technically required and object-mediated communication is more frequent than is technically required communication by words. The latter parallels the first and might be seen as a stopgap for faults in object communication when it occasionally fails to facilitate the attainment of technically designed outcomes. The required object communication among cooperating workers links each man with all the other men who share the same technical resource at the same time. It is multidirectional; that is, cues are transmitted through the object to everyone. But communication by words more often links only two men and consists of one-way messages from one man to another, who then responds by a change in his nonverbal work behavior. For example, one man might shout, "Bar," and another man hands it to him; or one man shouts, "Now," and, together with four other men, rams a heavy rod against a cooler to be replaced on the blast furnace. In the latter example, communication links one man simultaneously with four other men.

Chapter II specified as a measure of *culturally defined sufficiency* of technically permitted communication a count of the number of the following five properties of person-to-person communication present or plausibly possible in a given case: gestures, facework, literacy, completion of unit of discourse, and choice of partners. The reported conversations among the men of the maintenance crew in this case refer to the work at hand and consist of pieces of advice given. A variety of stories, unrelated to work, are told for the entertainment of one's fellows. All of the five sufficiency

---

[1] This term is used in J. Ruesch and W. Kees, *Nonverbal Communication* (Berkeley and Los Angeles: University of California Press, 1959), pp. 96, 148–158. These writers define the term narrowly, referring to things which speak for themselves and not, as we do, to things which are made to speak by manipulation.

factors can be observed in these conversations. Although a story might be interrupted by orders to the crew to begin another job, these interruptions do not have a machine-imposed regularity. When hands are occupied and faces are directed toward the focus of technically required attention, the possibility of gestures and facework will at times be restricted, but stories can be continued through at least some of the work activities.

In this case we have observed both required and permitted communication. Technically required communication by words occurs irregularly and links participants in systems of technically required cooperation unidirectionally. It is less frequent than required communication by objects, which links participants multidirectionally. All of the five factors indicating sufficiency of permitted communication are present. The participants in the two systems of required and permitted communication are identical. These behavior characteristics are found in the presence of a Hand Work technology of Type I, low attention requirements, talking distance between operators, and open work location. Tasks are relatively undifferentiated, functionally interdependent, and not linked by work flow.

The following material is relevant for Case 21 (Off-Line Auto Assembly). It is of interest for the discussion in both this chapter and the preceding one.

Each worker can and does interchange operations with the others. The pattern of interaction for such a group is shown in Figure [26].

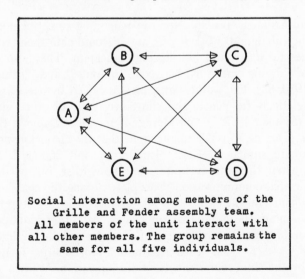

Social interaction among members of the
Grille and Fender assembly team.
All members of the unit interact with
all other members. The group remains the
same for all five individuals.

Figure 26. **Case 21—Off-Line Automobile Assembly** (Reprinted by permission of the publishers from C. R. Walker and R. H. Guest, *The Man on the Assembly Line*, Cambridge, Mass.: Harvard University Press, Copyright, 1952, by the President and Fellows of Harvard College, p. 75. Redrawn for this book.)

This team is not only a functional and spatial unit. Each member can talk with every other member, and interaction is fairly equal and constant. Subjectively these men feel that they are an identifiable social, as well as work, group. Contrast this pattern with that of the polishers where no two men had the same group. The significance of this distinction in pattern of interaction is brought out below in the evaluations of the workers.

.   .   .   .

"I'm in a team of six. One man works inside the car body right with me. We're good friends. So are the others in my group. We talk and kid all day long. Makes the job sort of fun. I'd much prefer working with others than alone."

"I work off the line making bumper guards. I have a partner. The two of us work as a team. We talk all the time . . . ."

"I work with another fellow. He pulls the fender back and I tighten it with bolts. If we do it wrong, it costs a lot of money. We have a lot of fun and talk all the time."

"There are about a dozen hood fitters where I am. Everybody helps the other out. I work especially with one other. We cooperate together. I'm not a great talker, but it's nice to have somebody else around, kid around once in a while . . . ."

"I have one partner in a group of five fellows. We all help one another and change jobs for variety. No throat cutting. It's nice to work in that kind of atmosphere." (Walker 1952, 76–77)

Less information is available for the remaining cases included in this section. The tubing-mill workers of Case 28 coordinate their work during mill changes by verbal and object communication. They also engage in "shop talk" during intervals between "running" and "setup" times. (Walker 1950, 82) The workers in subteams linked by necessary cooperation talk relatively frequently and constantly with all other members of the team. (Walker 1952, 76) "Kidding" is mentioned among the colliers of Case 10. (Dennis, 45) We might argue that the characteristics of communication are similar in Cases 4 (Docks) and 26b and 29b (Mill Changes), where the same technical conditions exist. But whatever technically permitted communication takes place among the coal-face workers of Cases 10 and 11a, the darkness would exclude at least gestures and face-work from among the criteria of sufficiency. Attention requirements are more demanding for the ore feeders of Case 6b and the off-line auto assemblers of Case 21. Their visual attention is more sharply focused and is regulated by the time requirements of the operation. With a very short cycle, the conditions of Case 6b would limit gestures and facework to the short interval between cycles, but permitting perhaps some talking during the work.

The cases of this section include all of the cases of Level A of the previous chapter. The location of workers is open, and more extended distances between workers are overcome by the possibility of walking near any current location of other workers. But most of the time, workers are already within talking distance. The exceptions of the behavioral and technical uniformities observed in, or imputed to, these cases are the two coal-mining situations of Cases 10 and 11a, where darkness limits communication, and Case 6b where both attention requirements and work locations impose somewhat greater restrictions on technically permitted communication.

In the face of scarce data for this section, the argument remains speculative. These are cases with a technology of Types I, II, and III; attention requirements are low; distances between operators are short or can be overcome in the absence of fixed work locations; there is no work flow; and tasks are functionally interdependent. Under these conditions, workers are most likely to engage in both technically required and technically permitted communication. The frequency of communication is comparatively high but distributed irregularly over time. Simultaneous cooperation is facilitated through communication by objects and words in technically required communication. Workers are connected by multidirectional linkages in pairs or larger teams through communication mediated by objects. Communication by words through unidirectional linkages is likely to constitute a stopgap for faults in object communication. With few exceptions, the full range of items of culturally defined sufficiency of permitted communication is available.

The range of permitted communication is reduced in cases where a hand-work technology is built into a higher-level technology; where surface or detailed attention is demanded; and where work locations are fixed. As a result, technically permitted communication has a narrower range of sufficiency.

2. Level B—Hand Work: Constrained Nontechnical Communication

We will now deal with cases of a technology ranging from Type I to Type V in which no communication, or only a minimal amount, is technically required. This condition corresponds to the absence of technically required cooperation discussed in the second section of the preceding chapter, and we are here dealing with the same set of cases. While there is no technically required communication in these cases, technically permitted communication is widespread. However, the distribution of communications over time and the structure of communication linkages vary within this set of cases. Temporal distribution depends on attention requirements and operation cycles, and structure depends primarily on level of technology.

In almost all of the cases included in this section, we find specific statements that no communication, or "interaction," is technically necessary. In some cases, in fact, we find statements that interactions are explicitly forbidden. The work descriptions of these cases also indicate that the technically designed independence of work performance is such that resources need not be shared. Only in the bank-wiring operation of Case 14, the equipment-assembly shop of Case 15, and the weaving shed of Case 20, do we find the occasional necessity of verbal communication for technical reasons. But these requirements either do not appear very compelling or are very widely spaced in time. They are related to the minor or temporally rare aspects of these operations in which operators otherwise unconnected are related by limited work flow and functional dependence.

The absence of technically required communication can be explained in the same way as the absence of technically required cooperation was explained in the first section of this chapter. Cases 3a, 5, 13 to 18, and 20 have work-place technologies of Types I, II, and III, but are distinguished by the absence of functional dependence from the cases of the first section with the same range of types of technology. Cases 19, 11b, and 22 to 25, are distinguished from other cases by their technology of Types IV and V.

The material for Cases 3a and 5 provides no indications about technically permitted communication except summary statements that in these situations all manner of association is likely to occur. (Popitz 1957a, 182–183) But we should notice that in both of these cases workers are spatially separated for a large part of their working time, in distances not immediately overcome by verbal communication. In both cases, work locations are open, and workers are both allowed and required to meet at certain times. Whatever conversations might take place among the ore handlers of Case 5 are likely to be short and rare, limited by the requirements of short operation cycles and of distances to be covered during the cycles. In contrast, the smelting workers of Case 3a work separately on their runners, but come together to help each other, and then take a break together before the tap begins. The long cycles of these operations impose little restriction on the possibilities of technically permitted communication. Distances can be overcome readily since workers can leave their work temporarily at any time. The comments made for these two cases also apply to the weaving shed of Case 20. Here we also have no record of technically permitted communication. Distances between operators are extended during much of the time, but can and must be overcome by sporadic meetings during which conversation is possible.

The source records for the following seven cases are replete with descriptions of what, here, is called technically permitted communication and what, there, is usually put in the framework of so-called informal interactions. In the relay-assembly operation of Case 13 "seven or more persons sat in the room each day, and an average of at least one person was continuously talking." (Whitehead I, 106) In the bank-wiring room of Case 14 "there is no doubt that the members of this group were boisterous." (Roethlisberger, 407) Roy speaks of the stream of communication which he initially observed, and eventually participated in, among the clicking-room operators of Case 18. (Roy, 161) The entire analysis of interaction counts among the workers in the shoe-bottoming room of Case 19 was predicated on the occurrence of relatively constant verbal exchanges. The example in the report indicates that, for every minute of a 15-minute sample period, verbal communication took place among the workers of one of the four lines alone. (Horsfall, 19) Although this report makes no distinction among kinds of content in communication, we can plausibly argue that no communication is technically required between workers in any given section, and that therefore almost all of the recorded communications are of the kind we have called technically permitted.

In all of these four cases, surface attention is technically required. During their work, operators must focus visually on the work before them, but the remainder of their attention is free for conversation with their fellow workers. Conversations are almost continuous but not technically required. As visual attention is focused on the work, gestures and facework are not part of communication. Thus, in these cases, the sufficiency of technically permitted communication is reduced to three of the five items proposed as a measure. Attention is not regulated by machine time, and workers can occasionally interrupt their work and engage in communication encompassing a fuller range of sufficiency.

In one of the two assembly sections of Case 15, "the nature of their assembly assignment enabled [the workers] to work and talk at the same time, and they took full advantage of this opportunity." (Zaleznik 1958, 112) In a cluster of three workers in the other section, we find that "verbal interchanges were frequent"; in another cluster in that section, "on the whole these verbal interactions were not frequent." (Zaleznik 1958, 110) We will, then, include Case 15 with the preceding four cases, as involving surface-attention requirements, sufficiency of communication reduced to three items, and communication which is continuous or continuously possible.

Technically permitted communication varies in the machine shop of Case 16 among different subgroups of the two machine-shop sections. For some of the workers—engaged in the same tasks as the others—very frequent interactions were recorded, but much less frequent for other workers. This difference in frequency is of interest to our concern with the range of choices allowed by different technical settings. The cases just discussed would indicate the previously proposed tendency for people to elaborate their behavior patterns beyond the necessary, to fill the "space" provided by the environment. The behavior of workers in Case 16 suggests that the environment does in fact offer a choice about the extent to which one becomes engaged in technically permitted communication. Much of the report indicates that these choices are in turn regulated by rules which are a product of the nontechnical social system. (Zaleznik 1958, 113–116)

In the two machine-shop cases, 16 and 17, detailed attention requirements were recorded. At certain times, workers must focus their attention intensively on their work, and this kind of attention requires more than a merely visual involvement. At the same time, attention of this kind is required only intermittently. The intermittency is scheduled, as it were, by the characteristics of operation cycles.

Taking work on a multipurpose lathe as an example, we note that a work piece must be clamped into place, the cutting tool moved into position, and at least the beginning of the cut observed. For the remainder of one cut, little or no attention is required. Once the cut is completed, the beginning of the new cycle is under the control of the operator, thus providing for regular breaks. Although we have no direct evidence, reported communication is likely to be intermittent, is likely to take place during the breaks provided by operation cycles, and then exhibits the full range of the list of items of communication sufficiency.

In addition, we find that in Cases 13, 14, 15, 18, and 19, operators' work locations are relatively fixed but in very close proximity. In Cases 16 and 17, work locations are open, and workers are required to move between different machines which must be used to complete a work assignment. In the first five cases, surface attention is required. Communication is constant and verbal, but of restricted sufficiency. In the last two cases, detailed attention is required, and verbal communication is intermittent. In all of these cases, technically permitted communication links a relatively unchanging number of participants, involving linkages of varying frequency of communication, the greatest frequency and the most stable linkage being found in pairs of workers. A detailed analysis of the pair as the basic unit of these systems is found throughout Whitehead's report.

We are now turning to the five cases with an Assembly Line technology of Type V, involving conversion operations by hand and transfer operations by machine beyond the control of operators. Although a work flow is present in all of these cases, there are variations in functional dependency between tasks and variations in the extent to which work speed is set by the continuously moving conveyor. Colliers, automobile assemblers, and chocolate wrappers of Cases 11b, 22, and 23 are functionally independent, while the tasks of operators on the equipment-assembly line of Case 24 and on the garment-sewing line of Case 25 are functionally dependent. In contrast, speed of work is determinately set by the automobile-assembly line of Case 22 and the equipment-assembly line of Case 24. Operators' work speed is partly line-determined in the chocolate-wrapping work of Case 23 and on the garment line of Case 25, and not line-determined for the colliers of Case 11b. Attention requirements in Case 11b are low, and surface attention is required in the remaining cases. In all of these five cases, communication among operators is not technically required, and this fact is again related to the absence of any technically required cooperation. Technically permitted communication is verbal in all these cases. It is continuous or continuously possible in Cases 23, 24, and 25, where the characteristics of communication are the same as those in Cases 13, 14, 15, 18, and 19. There is little information on technically permitted communication among the coal fillers of Case 11b. We can only speculate that it is intermittent because workers are often too far apart to communicate and additionally separated by the noise of the conveyor. But they occasionally come near one another, or can interrupt their work at any time to talk with their neighbors. In addition to its intermittency, communication is restricted in sufficiency because in the darkness the accompaniment of talking by gestures and facework is scarcely possible. Among the workers on the automobile-assembly line, communication is further restricted, in addition to the surface attention requirements, by the fact that along many parts of the line workers move for a short stretch with the line and then return to the beginning of their stretch. Since one's conversation partner is not likely to start and finish his work on the same assembly simultaneously, communicative encounters not only are intermittent but also do not allow the completion of a unit of discourse. In addition, the noise on many sections along the line often allows only brief and shouted verbal exchanges. Thus, sufficiency of communication is radically reduced, precluding to a large extent that words be accompanied by gestures and facework. Subjectively felt units of conversations probably cannot be completed, and the literacy of communication is in many places restricted to brief shouts. The choice of a communication partner is restricted in the sense that one might continue telling a story to a man who has already disappeared unnoticed and his place has been taken by another. (Walker 1952, 69, 71–74; Walker 1956, 97, 131–132; Jasinski, 26–27)

The example of Case 22 suggests a further characteristic of technically permitted communication. In the five assembly-line cases, communication systems are "floating." Each individual worker is linked with a partly different communication network in each of which some members found in the first one are lost in the second one, and new ones are added (see Figure 27). Whether we speak of a floating or a stable linkage system depends in part also on the size of the unit. If, as in the shoe-bottoming room of Case 19, the whole line comprises all the people proximate enough to reach each other through communication by words, we would not speak of a floating network. But on a line where workers are placed only on one side, the number of persons included in a given network is presumably half as large and may, when we focus on a given worker, consist of only two pairs with one member in common.

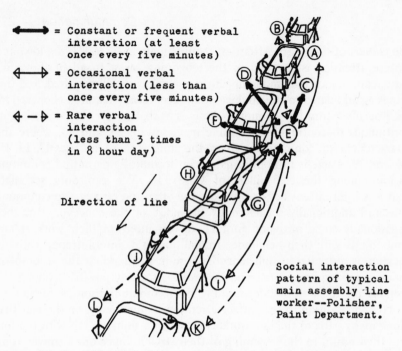

FIGURE 27. **Case 22—Main-Line Automobile Assembly** (Reprinted by permission of the publishers from C. R. Walker and R. H. Guest, *The Man on the Assembly Line*, Cambridge, Mass.: Harvard University Press, Copyright, 1952, by the President and Fellows of Harvard College, p. 71. Redrawn for this book.)

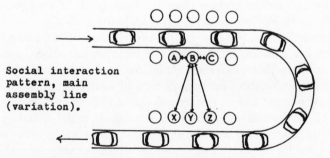

FIGURE 28. **Case 22—Main-Line Automobile Assembly** (Reprinted by permission of the publishers from C. R. Walker and R. H. Guest, *The Man on the Assembly Line*, Cambridge, Mass.: Harvard University Press, Copyright, 1952, by the President and Fellows of Harvard College, p. 74. Redrawn for this book.)

In these five cases, as in those preceding them, we observe the absence of technically required communication and technically permitted communication with reduced sufficiency. In constrast, networks are floating rather than confined to shared membership. These characteristics are found in situations of an Assembly Line technology of Type V; surface attention requirements (with the exception of Case 11b); and short distances between operators. (For additional evidence of the behavioral characteristics of these cases, see Treinen, 74; Zaleznik 1951, 97, 120–121; Wyatt, 34.)

3. Level C—Machine Line: Technical Communication without Words

In the cases of the second section, we found no technically required communication but variously ordered forms of technically permitted communication. In the cases of this section, we find a distinct range of kinds of technically required communication, but we can argue that in most of these cases technically permitted communication is impossible. Where it is possible and in fact takes place, it is further reduced in degree of elaboration in comparison to the cases of the preceding section.

The operation of hot-wire rolling of Case 26a constitutes the only instance where operators probably communicate with each other entirely through objects, while occupying their positions along the line of roll stands during their half-hour turns. They communicate by means of the hot wire which they transfer from one roll stand to the next, and this object communication is a compelling technical necessity. During the half-hour periods of rolling work, no technically permitted communication is possible. But during the off-time half hour, workers can and do become engaged in conversations which may or may not be related to their work. Their object communication has a persistent and highly repetitive regularity, controlled by operation cycles not regulated by operators. Object communication links men in successively shifting pairs with every wire that moves down through the line. Here we have something equivalent to the floating communication linkages of technically permitted cooperation on assembly lines. But this time the linkage involves technically required communication with a distinct frequency and regularity linking at any one time pairs of adjacent operators, and at the next time moving these pair relationships by one step down the line, and so on.

The crane operator of Case 8 sits in the cabin attached to the traveling bridge crane high above the ongoing operations in the mill. No technically permitted communication is possible between him and other workers below and on other cranes. But when picking up or setting down work pieces, the crane operator coordinates his regulation of the crane with the men on the floor by a combination of object and sign communication. He observes the work piece and the pickup mechanism of the crane, and so do the workers below who then communicate with the crane operator by way of work pieces and equipment parts. They also give hand signals to instruct the crane operator directly. The occurrence of this communication is less frequent than in the preceding case, but is still repeated regularly on every trip the crane operator makes while delivering ingots to the rolling mill. The system of links between operators is the same as in the last case, except that fewer operators are involved and that they are connected in less rapid succession. At one time the crane operator communicates with workers at the pickup point, and later with others at the delivery end of his transportation line.

Technically required communication among the blooming-mill operators of Case 27 is almost entirely mediated by objects, that is, by the bloom being rolled and by moving equipment parts. Communication is occasionally supplemented by signs which are given with a whistle by a lead hand or foreman. We are not told whether there is technically permitted communication between the two of the three operators who share the same operating platform. One might assume, however, that the persistently required and externally focused attention demanded by this operation leaves no possibility for direct verbal communication between the two men while a bloom is being rolled, but perhaps there is verbal communication during the short break in-between. In this case, three operators are linked in an object-communication network where sometimes two and sometimes all three are induced to frequent and persistently repeated reacting to cues transmitted through the work piece.

We will now look at the tube-mill operators of Case 28a with a focus on the relationship between operators of successive machines, rather than on the groups of men clustered around any one machine. More specifically, we will be concerned with the men who actually regulate the five major pieces of equipment. These men communicate with each other both through shared observation of the work pieces which move rapidly down the line, and by way of hand and whistle signs. Only during the very short breaks between runs can a man turn around and yell a word or phrase to another man. Thus, when the mill is running, technically permitted communication is reduced to this bare minimum and is in fact impossible during any given run and operation cycle itself. (Walker 1950, 66, 78, 80, 82)

Cases 26a has a Hand and Machine Line technology of Type VI and detailed attention requirements. In contrast to the machine-shop cases dealt with before, the detailed attention requirements are here required not intermittently but continuously. Operators are within shouting distance of one another, but the rapid pace and attention requirements of the operation permit no communication other than technically required communication by objects. Cases 8, 27, and 28a have a Remote Controls technology of Type VII, they require externally focused attention, and operators are within seeing distance of one another. Here we find technically required communication by both objects and signs. There is either no technically permitted communication, or a bare minimum possible only during the short intervals between operation cycles. Technically required communication is frequent and regularly repeated in connection with operation cycles and subcycles.

In the tube-rolling operation of Case 29a, two operators regulate machinery of a Remote Control technology of Type VII, and all operators sometimes revert to that type of technology when switching to "manual" operation. But transfer operations throughout the mill and at all times still display a self-regulating technology. Attention requirements in this case involve externally focused attention and watching. Operators are largely beyond seeing distance of one another. They communicate with one another by object, that is, by the work piece they share in succession during each run. Object communication is here supplemented through communication by words transmitted not directly but through a public-address system. Technically permitted communication takes place through this public-address system but is restricted by attention requirements and the short cycles to shouted joking expressions. Most of the items of sufficiency of technically permitted communication are precluded, since a message cannot be explicitly directed to a chosen partner and is heard and can be responded to by all the operators connected to the public-address system. (Walker 1957, 40–46, 119)

Communication between the soaking-pit operator of Case 32 and others with whom he is connected by technically required cooperation is by objects and signals. His work is coordinated with that of the men who move ingots into and out of the soaking pit, by observation of work pieces and of the remotely controlled furnace doors. Both he and the crane operator can observe these and, through the movement of the work pieces and doors, these men receive the cues required to perform their tasks. Presumably no technically permitted communication is possible among these operators. But the soaking-pit operator is connected with other work stations, like that of the dispatcher, by signals transmitted through electric impulses, and also by telephone. Whether technically permitted communication takes place through the telephone, we are not told in the report. On regular mill runs, telephone communication would be possible only during intervals between operation cycles. It is restricted by the attention requirements of the operation, involving both externally focused attention while regulating machinery, and watching.

Finally, we turn to three cases in which there is technically required communication only by signals, and no technically permitted communication is possible between work stations. Communication among operators at different stations in the blast-furnace feeding operations of both Cases 6a and 7 is mediated through signal lights and moving indicators. It involves messages sent directly through electric impulses, and messages which are first transmitted to the machinery itself and then relayed to operators by other indicators. Communication among operators at the four work locations on the coking battery of Case 9 is by electrically operated lights and horns. These three cases have a Remote Control technology of Type VII, externally focused attention requirements, and work stations beyond seeing distance of one another. In contrast to the purely linelike communication linkages of rapidly shifting pair relationships, we here find different linkages between operators during different parts of the operation cycle. Communication is frequent and regularly repeated in connection with operation cycles. Each cycle demands the sending of messages through signals of different meanings, and only after messages are received or exchanged can subsequent steps in the cycle be performed. (For a reference to the absence of technically permitted communication in these cases and in Case 27, see Popitz 1957a, 185.)

4. Level D—Automation: Close and Remote Communicative Relations

Communication by signals is the characteristic of technically required communication in the four cases of this section. A continuous stream of messages is received by operators, and the major part of their task consists only of observing this stream of communication as it comes to them on their dials. But messages by means of signals are never sent directly by the operators, but rather by monitoring devices reporting events in the technical process. Messages are sent by the operators only when they manipulate one of their controls and an impulse is transmitted to the process in which it creates changes. These changes in turn are picked up by the monitoring devices and reported back to the operators. We know from the petroleum refinery of Case 34 and the power plant of Case 35 that this communication by signals is rare and irregular. It is supplemented through communication either by words between operators who are within talking distance of one another or by telephone between work stations which are far removed from one another. The brief descriptions of the work of the operator of blast air control of Case 33 suggests that he receives instructions from a number of presumably quite remote places. Perhaps telephones are used for this form of technically necessary communication. While work stations in all of these cases are separated by large distances and, with the exception of Case 31, separated by walls or whole buildings, several operators are located at the same work station in the last two cases. It seems that in all four cases communication by signals is supplemented through communication by words, but only in these last two cases is part of the technically required communication by words in the form of direct face-to-face talking from operator to operator.

We are here returning to a combination of behaviors similar to that of the first section. Technically required communication is mediated by technical resources but also requires supplementation through direct verbal communication. With the available data, some technically permitted communication is difficult to distinguish from technically required communication. The material on Case 33 indicates that the blast air-control operator is isolated from the rest of the plant. Yet other workers visit him and he is a center of plant gossip. (Popitz 1957a, 170) Faunce reports that 46 per cent of the workers on transfer machines in Case 31 say that they are able to "interact often" with one another, as against 81 per cent on nonautomated engine lines. (Faunce, 126) Workers from the automated power plant of Case 35 emphasize their reliance on the technical advice of their colleagues. (Mann, 62, 89) The number of men involved in technically permitted communication, at least in the last two cases, is very small, predominantly linking only pairs of workers. Technical communication links all operators in a large part of a plant all the time. Technically permitted communication encompasses all five items of sufficiency.

In the presence of an Automation technology of Type VIII, we find watching as the attention requirement, large distances between work stations, fixed work locations, and only indirect connections by work flow and functional dependency. Infrequently and irregularly, there is technically required communication by signals and words, and permitted communication is continuously possible. Technically permitted and required communication by words predominantly links stable pairs, while technically required communication by signal links all workers connected with a given integrated technical process.

5. Communication and Technology

The development of production technology is paralleled by the increasing remoteness of workers—first from the work piece, and then from control over the operations performed on work pieces—to the point where workers are monitoring processes which largely take care of themselves. But this sequence, as we see it here comparatively, is not followed by the increasing separation of workers from one another in a simple linear relationship to technical development. Between the point at which workers perform all of the operating components and the point at which they merely monitor technical monitoring devices, workers function in different ways as stopgaps for the feedback of observation, information, and control required for continued production. To the extent that workers are fitted into the operation in place of feedback devices, their chances change of having a choice over contact with fellow workers beyond the technically necessary.

Under the conditions of Level A, necessary communication and permitted communication are intermingled and link workers held together by technical objects to which they are in close contact and over which they jointly have complete control. At Level B, hand work is the means of conversion or transfer, and communication is not technically required. Workers at Level A produce a social product made possible by the generation of feedback internal to the unit of organization. Both muscle and control are jointly supplied by workers, but possibly only where attention requirements are low. At Level B, the feedback required to integrate functionally related operations takes place external to our unit of organization and lies either in the larger authority structure or in the transfer machinery. Here, the intense application of a narrow part of workers' attention is demanded in combination with the use of muscles. Supplying only the muscles and a part of their attention—required either on the surface or intermittently—and having relegated feedback functions to authority or technology, workers have a choice of communicating with their fellows. But the quality of their communication and the range of others which it encompasses are limited by the technical setting and its demands and boundaries.

Where transfer operations are performed by hand, and conversion operations by hand or machine, workers' locations might be fixed and close together, but required surface attention prevents workers from looking at each other when they talk and thus keeps communication incomplete. The technical situation does not prevent conversation from being continuous but makes it necessary to choose one's conversation partners from immediate neighbors. Under similar conditions of technology, detailed but intermittent attention might be technically necessary, and then workers are likely to be near each other and often also required or free to move around. These workers can both talk and look at each other in their conversations, but they can do so only part of the time—when operation cycles do not demand the detailed attention which then prevents communication altogether. The choice of conversation partners is not confined to a fixed set of spatial neighbors.

Where transfer operations are performed by a continuously moving belt, surface attention is required which is now tied to operation cycles, keeping workers more insistently from looking at each other while they talk. In the two kinds of situations described first, technical boundaries confine within themselves a small enough number of workers to be encompassed by stable conversation networks within which they can make their choice of partners. But now these boundaries are lost, and conversation networks are different for every man. The workers in this situation do not have the wider choice possessed by workers of whom detailed but intermittent attention is required and who can move around. They also do not have the predictability of a contained network of communication relationships. Added to this in some cases is the noise of transfer machinery and hand tools and sometimes even the spatial shifting of work locations on the belt, thus reducing further the predictability of who is a part of one's conversation circle.

When we now move to work-place technologies where transfer operations are performed by machines and conversion operations are also, in part or in whole, performed by machines, workers become the crucial feedback links which keep an integrated operation in motion. At Level B, we found variously delimited communication which is technically permitted, but no technically required communication. We now find a compelling necessity for communication at Level C, in order to attain technically designed ends, but no communication contacts between workers beyond the technically necessary during the time the production operation is in process. Where continuous transfer operations are performed by machine, and conversion operations by both hand and machine, as on the wire mill of Case 26a, workers are likely to be in fixed locations and, although relatively close to one another, separated by machine noise. Detailed attention is required of them continuously, and thus the technically necessary communication between them is entirely confined to communication mediated by observation of, and reaction to, the movements of work pieces and equipment parts.

But once the hand-work component disappears, workers primarily perform the feedback functions required for the maintenance of continuous operations. When workers in fixed locations are separated by extended distances, but can still see one another and the equipment and work pieces they control, they are likely to communicate by way of technical objects, and to supplement this object-mediated communication by directly transmitted *signs*. But if they can no longer see one another and the work process, their communication is confined to the use of specifically installed technical media for transmitting short *signals* quickly.

With the Automation technology at Level D, we have gone the full circle of communication requirements and possibilities, but a circle whose ends do not meet. Conversion and transfer operations and, at least in part, feedback functions are performed by equipment. Operators are more loosely fitted into the technical process and again have a choice of communication with their fellows beyond the technically necessary. While these conditions may seem similar to those of the "low-level" technology discussed at the beginning of this chapter, operators are still likely to be separated by distances which prevent them from seeing one another. But now they are probably connected by technical means of communication which allow contact not by brief and abstract signals but by words, or they will have fellow workers near them with whom they are jointly separated from other distant workers.

Where operations are only partially self-regulating, spatially remote operators in fixed locations will communicate both by means of the technical objects which they can see and by communications installations supplementing object-mediated communication through words or signals. The same technical installations which allow communication by words may provide opportunities for technically permitted communication. But at the same time, these processes require continuous watching and externally focused attention. They permit only very brief "messages" and preclude the possibility of workers looking at each other while talking. They also prevent a choice of conversation partners since who is connected to the communication network is technically predetermined. In cases where self-regulating devices play a much greater part, some workers are likely to be close to one another while separated by large distances from others. Technically required communication among them is infrequent. At any time, and independently from operation cycles, verbal supplementation of communication is possible. It is mediated not by distinct technical objects but by whole, ongoing, and integrated processes. While there is no technically permitted communication among workers remote from one another, workers at the same location have a choice of communication partners within a contained conversation network.

At Level A, the system of social relationships encompasses conduct within its boundaries which combines technically necessary and permitted behaviors. The same men are connected by simultaneous cooperation and relationships of reversible influence and by direct communication which reaches all participants. They communicate in the language of shared objects and through verbal directions for the attainment of joint technical ends. Networks of technically permitted communication continue throughout the time during which these men work at this first level of technical conditions.

This interconnectedness of components of conduct disappears at Level B, when workers are technically required neither to cooperate nor to communicate with one another. Here the technology permits behavior elaborations beyond the technically necessary in varying degrees. Workers become connected in relationships of influence, cooperation, and communication on nontechnical grounds, but these relationships are still delimited by the technical environment.

The division of components of conduct reaches an extreme at Level C, where workers are separated from one another but must communicate and cooperate by means of the technical objects they share. They can supplement these technically mediated relationships only by communication through abstract cues. The technology and its demands prevent behavior elaboration beyond the technically necessary while the operation is in process. The technological demands also bind men in the compelling relationship of irreversible influence, which permits little choice. This does not mean that these men are entirely precluded from coming into contact with one another. But these contacts can only take place outside work time or during periods of setup operations when in fact they move to Level A.

At Level B, social relationships are confined to an area external to the technical framework. At Level C, social relationships are confined to within the technical framework. At Level A, the technical setting encompasses both of these components of conduct. At Level D, both components are again present; yet they are at least in part differentiated in the sense that different sets of men are connected by different kinds of cooperation, influence, and communication.

The proposed relationships between levels of technical conditions and variation of kinds of communication are summarized in the following tables. In these tables we refer to Levels A, B, C, and D, constructed in the preceding chapter. For the sake of clarity, the detailed criteria which distinguish these levels by types of technology and connections between work stations are not repeated. With regard to technically required communication at Level C and technically permitted communication at Level B, the simplicity of presentation conceals further variation within these levels. Gross distinctions are therefore shown in Tables 35 and 37, and subdistinctions for these two levels are given in Tables 36 and 38. When relations among behavioral dimensions are presented in Table 41, only the gross distinctions are provided.

Table 35 shows that certain combinations of means of technically required communication are characteristic of each level of technical condition. Communication is not technically necessary at Level B. At Level A, there is a combination of communication by objects and words; and at Level D, by signals and words. A greater variety of means by which required communication is transmitted and perceived is available at Level C. The likelihood of each set of means in the presence of additional technical demands is shown in Table 36. Communication solely through shared objects occurs where *continuous* detailed attention is required and where work stations are separated by shouting distance. Operators within seeing distance of one another and working under the requirements of externally focused attention, communicate by sign language and through shared objects. Signals are the only means of communication between workers who are beyond seeing distance of one another and who are subject to the requirement of external focus of attention. When watching is added to the attention requirements of external focus for workers beyond seeing distance, workers are likely to communicate through shared objects and by way of technical installations permitting verbal contact. In Chapter II signals were defined as being transmitted by technical installations for communication. The use of a public-address system is a special instance of this category. In the case of a combination of external focus and watching as attention requirements, where some workers are within seeing distance and others are beyond seeing distance, communication between different sets of operators takes place through shared objects, by signals, and verbally by telephone.

Tables 37, 38, and 39 are equivalent to Tables 35 and 36, and deal with technically permitted communication. The categories at the top of Table

TABLE 35. TECHNOLOGY AND REQUIRED COMMUNICATION

	Required Communication			
Technology and Constraints	Absent	Objects and Words	Objects, Signs, and Signals	Signals and Words
Level A		I: 1,2,3b,4, 6b,26b, 28b,29b II: 10,21 III: 11a		
Level B	I: 3a,5 II: 13,14, 15 III: 16,17, 18,20 IV: 19 V: 11b,22, 23,24,25			
Level C			VI: 26a VII: 6a,7,8, 9,27,28a, 29a,32	
Level D				VIII: 31,33, 34,35

37 are combinations of two sets of distinctions proposed in Chapter II, which suggested that *culturally defined sufficiency* of permitted communication would be measured by a count of the number of items available. We now call permitted communication "complete" when at least four of the five items occur, and "incomplete" when less than four items occur. The absence of technically permitted communication is noted separately. The term "continuous" refers to conditions where communication is not governed by operation cycles, while technical time regulates the incidence of "intermittent" communication. Complete sufficiency does not mean that workers have the choice of persistent access to all five items (gestures, facework, literacy, completion of unit of discourse, choice of partners), but that they have such a choice at almost any given time, and that at these chosen times there is "completeness."

Table 37 indicates opportunities for continuous and complete permitted

TABLE 36. REQUIRED COMMUNICATION - LEVEL C

Tech-nology Type	Required Attention	Distance	Objects	Objects and Signs	Signals	Objects and Signals
			Required Communication			
VI	continuous detailed	shouting	26a			
VII	external focus	seeing		8,27, 28a		
VII	external focus	beyond seeing			6a,7,9	
VII	external focus and watching	beyond seeing and seeing				29a,32[a]

[a]Here communication by signals includes the special case of public-address systems or telephone, where words are conveyed by a technical transmitter.

communication at Levels A and D. For the cases of Level C, no technically permitted communication is reported. The exception is Case 29a with its fun over the public-address system, and this case constitutes a transition to Level D, through the components of a self-regulating technology it contains. At Level B, technically permitted communication is either intermittent or incomplete, or both. The technical characteristics associated with this internal difference are given in Table 38.

In Table 39 an attempt is made to relate levels of technical conditions to varying restriction of choices of communication partners. We use the term "closed" to refer to the situation in which operators can choose partners only from within their organizational or technical unit, for communication of the same level of continuity and completeness. When outsiders to such a unit are chosen, we use the term "open." When we say that the choice is unrestricted, we mean that workers choose anyone within their unit for conversation at the same level of continuity and completeness. Choice is "restricted" by conditions of proximity. A communication network is "floating" when its boundaries differ systematically for each individual.

In Table 40, variations of required and permitted communication are

TABLE 37. TECHNOLOGY AND PERMITTED COMMUNICATION

Technology and Constraints	Permitted Communication		
	Continuous and Complete	Intermittent and/or Incomplete	Absent
Level A	I: 1,3b,4,6b, 26b,28b,29b II: 10,21 III: 11a		
Level B		I: 3a,5 II: 13,14,15 III: 16,17, 18,20 IV: 19 V: 11b,22,23, 24,25	
Level C		VII: 29a	VI: 26a VII: 6a,7,8,9, 27,28a,32
Level D	VIII: 34,35		

related. At Levels A and D, both classes of behavior occur. There is no technically required communication at Level B, and no technically permitted communication at Level C.

In Table 41, relationships stated in the preceding chapter are combined with those given in this chapter. There would be little value in repeating the full number of possible combinations. This table shows only those categories that do occur in a set of relationships. Thus, both the information in the marginals and in the cells together describes relations among characteristics of cooperation, influence, and communication at the four gross levels of technical conditions.

TABLE 38. PERMITTED COMMUNICATION - LEVEL B

Technology Type	Required Attention	Distance	Operator Location	Permitted Communication		
				Continuous Incomplete	Intermittent Complete	Intermittent Incomplete
I	low	shouting	open		3a,5	
III	detailed	talking or shouting	open		16,17, 20	
II, III, IV, V	surface	talking	confined	II: 13, 14,15 III: 18 IV: 19 V: 23, 24,25		
V	surface	shouting	confined			11b,22

TABLE 39. TECHNOLOGY AND SYSTEMS OF PERMITTED COMMUNICATION

Technology and Constraints	Restricted Choice of Partners		Unrestricted Choice of Partners	
	Floating Boundaries	Closed Boundaries	Open Boundaries	Closed Boundaries
Level A				I: 1,3b, 4,6b, 26b, 28b, 29b II: 10, 21 III:11a

Level B

Technology Type	Required Attention	Operator Location	Floating Boundaries	Closed Boundaries	Open Boundaries
I,III	low or detailed	open			I: 3a,5 III: 16, 17,20
II,III, IV	surface	confined		II: 13, 14,15 III: 18 IV: 19	
V	surface	confined	V: 22, 23,24, 25		

Level D	VIII: 34,35	

TABLE 40. REQUIRED AND PERMITTED COMMUNICATION

Required Communication	Permitted Communication				
	Continuous Complete	Continuous Incomplete	Intermittent Complete	Intermittent Incomplete	Absent
Objects and Words	**Level A** I: 1,3b, 4,6b, 26b, 28b, 29b II: 10, 21 III: 11a				
Absent		**Level B** II: 13,14, 15 III: 18 IV: 19 V: 23,24, 25	I: 3a,5 III: 16, 17,20	V: 11b,22	
Objects					**Level C** VI: 26a
Objects and Signs					VII: 8, 27,28a
Signals					VII: 6a,7,9
Objects and Signals				VII: 29a	VII: 32
Signals and Words	**Level D** VIII: 34,35				

TABLE 41. COOPERATION, INFLUENCE, AND COMMUNICATION

			Required Communication			
			Objects and Words	Absent	Objects, Signs, and Signals	Signals and Words
			Permitted Communication			
Required Cooperation	Permitted Cooperation	Influence	Continuous Complete	Intermittent or Incomplete	Absent	Continuous Complete
Simultaneous	Present	Reversible	Level A			
Absent	Absent or Present	Nontechnical		Level B		
Sequential	Absent	Irreversible			Level C	
Sporadic-Symbolic	Present	Irreversible				Level D

234

Chapter XIII

INDUSTRIAL TECHNOLOGY:
Its Dimensions, Constraints, and Consequences

A study of this kind has a visible beginning and end. Some of the choices of its contents are made before the overt beginning, and have their sources in the dispositions and preferences of the author. These dispositions and preferences find their way into questions looking for answers. What kinds of answers are sought and what conduct is displayed in seeking them are limited by·upbringing, necessity, and resources. When all is said and done, not only are the hoped-for answers different from what they were expected to be, but also the questions that led to them have changed—and perhaps even the dispositions and preferences from which it all started. In the process a mountain is likely to build up which at best will bring forth only a mouse. To produce a mouse which is at least alive is a rare trick, since "most mountains, when they go in for this sort of thing, produce nothing better than lava, steam, and hot air."[1]

This study has been an attempt to create the belief in the living presence of the mouse. If the attempt has met with success, the mountain's progeniture will be left behind in the continuing search, and its life expectancy will be short. What, then, have we discovered, and where does it fit with what we already know?

1. Summary: Technology and Its Constraints

At the beginning, we asked: What is the nature of industrial technology? Can the design of production operations be ordered analytically to distinguish stages of technical development? The answer lay in the construction of a two-dimensional classification of industrial technology. For both the conversion and the movement of work pieces, successively more

---

[1] Crane Brinton, *The Anatomy of Revolution* (New York: Prentice-Hall, 1952), p. 27.

components of work performance are built into machines. For each "higher level" of technology, the number of components performed by machines is greater. We have defined the criteria and demonstrated the assignment of case-study data to the types of technology contained in the two-dimensional classification.

Our next question was: What are the demands which industrial technology makes on the performance of its users? What do production workers have to do in order to make technical designs work? We answered these questions by defining the dimensions of a number of technical constraints, by marshaling evidence to show the descriptive utility of these dimensions, and by showing that each of the main sets of constraints is systematically associated with segments from the range of technological differences.

The customary term for describing the characteristics of temporal and perceptual constraints on work performance has been *attention requirements*. We constructed a typology composed of the habituation of hand movements, the length and repetitiveness of operation cycles, the degree of cognitive involvement necessary, and the location of visual focus. Examination of the data suggested five types of attention requirements. With one major exception, we found that low, surface, detailed, externally focused attention, and watching were necessary in that order as the number of work components performed by machines increased, that is, as we moved up the scale of technology. Also, near both extremes, temporal conditions were relatively more open, in cases without effective operation cycles or with long cycles.

Certain elements of technical constraints have appeared centrally in past research. Studies of machine-feeding work and its effects on fatigue and feelings of monotony have been concerned with attention requirements. Walker and Guest have specifically related the condition of "surface mental attention" to job satisfaction among auto assemblers. Popitz has imaginatively described variations in the perceptual and temporal structure of work in steel mills.[2] However, the composition of the demands on workers' attention has not been fully analyzed for more than a few selected job types. The distribution of these requirements over a full range of technology has so far been unknown.

In the same technological sequence, we have found first production units without work flow and then work stations connected by work-piece

---

[2] S. Wyatt and H. N. Langdon, *The Machine and the Worker: A Study of Machine Feeding Processes* (Great Britain, Medical Research Council, Industrial Health Research Board, Report No. 82. London: HMSO, 1938); Max Weber, "Zur Psychophysik der industriellen Arbeit (1908–09)," in his *Gesammelte Aufsätze zur Soziologie und Sozialpolitik* (Tübingen: Mohr, 1924), pp. 61–255; C. R. Walker and R. H. Guest, *The Man on the Assembly Line* (Cambridge: Harvard University Press, 1952), pp. 12–14; H. Popitz et al., *Technik und Industriearbeit* (Tübingen: Mohr, 1957), pp. 154–172, 194–203.

flow. Within each of these two classes, the first began with cases of functional dependence between working positions, and then shifted to separate, functionally independent tasks. As machine-performed work components increased, a man could do his job without another man near him having done his. In the second half of the range of technologies, the order was reversed. In a few cases of conveyor-bound production units, work stations were connected by work flow and yet tasks were performed independently. In the last, upper segment of the technological dimension, we returned to the condition proverbially common to modern industry: a work flow in the production sequence, and dependent tasks. Jobs were also more differentiated at this level.

The systematic and technically directed flow of work in a sequence of production operations is one of the most obvious conditions of many industrial work places, but small attention has been given to work flow in research. Similarly, interdependence of tasks is a clear concomitant of the division of labor—one of the oldest interests of the discipline of sociology —but this interest has rarely found its way into the analysis of what men actually do when they work. Job satisfaction and work-team effectiveness have been associated with work-flow characteristics in only a few reports.[3] In each report the coincidence of work flow and functional dependence of tasks was taken for granted, and thus we have no description of the structure of relations among tasks where, for instance, there is dependence and no work flow in contrast to their conjunction, and under what conditions they are likely to occur.

Perceptually defined distances between working positions tended to increase from the lower to the higher levels of technology, and there was confinement to fixed work positions in the upper half. Spatial mobility could be the condition for overcoming the constraints of extended distance and yet freedom from spatial confinement was more frequent as distances were shorter.

The spatial order of social interaction is largely unexplored territory in sociology. There have been attempts to assess preferences for relative position and distance for comfortable conversation within and across cultures.[4] These studies were entirely concerned with circumstances where

---

[3] W. F. Whyte, "The Social Structure of the Restaurant," *American Journal of Sociology*, 54 (1949), 302–310; F. L. W. Richardson and C. R. Walker, *Human Relations in an Expanding Company* (New Haven: Labor and Management Center, Yale University, 1948); E. W. Bakke, *Bonds of Organization* (New York: Harper, 1950), pp. 10–48, 222–233; E. L. Trist and K. W. Bamforth, "Some Social and Psychological Consequences of the Longwall Method of Coal-Getting," *Human Relations*, 4 (1951), 3–38.

[4] R. Sommer, "Studies in Personal Space," *Sociometry*, 22 (1959), 247–260; R. Sommer, "Leadership and Group Geography," *Sociometry*, 24 (1961), 99–110; R. Sommer, "The Distance for Comfortable Conversation," *Sociometry*, 25 (1962), 111–116; E. T. Hall, *The Silent Language* (Garden City, N.Y.: Doubleday, 1959).

spatial choice existed. In the expectation that distance and spatial confinement make a difference for interaction, we have here considered the production process as a source of spatial constraint.

2. Summary: Cooperation, Influence, and Communication

The third set of questions asked at the beginning was: Where does the social behavior of workers adapt to the constraints of technology and its demands? In particular, what differences can be observed under varying technical conditions in the characteristics of cooperation, influence, and communication among factory workers? Let us look at the findings of this study and highlight the major effects of the technical dimensions of production on the behavior of workers. Subsequently we will compare our findings with the dimensions and findings of a number of other studies in which technology is a major concern.

We have combined certain categories of technology with the dimensions of technical constraints into four over-all levels of technical conditions. Level A was team work in heavy manual *hauling*. It included those cases of technology Type I (Handling), Type II (Hand Work), and Type III (Machine Work), where task relations were characterized by interdependence, no work flow, and little differentiation. These were all cases where the work consisted either exclusively or primarily of manually moving heavy materials or equipment.

Level B contained a wide variety of conditions of individual *hand work*. It included the remainder of the cases of technology Types I, II, and III, all of which were distinguishable by independence of tasks. It also covered all cases of technology Type IV (Machine-Work Sequence) and Type V (Assembly Line). These cases differed from the "heavy haul" of Level A by comparatively lighter work where either work-piece movement or work-piece conversion, or both, were done by hand, and not in teams with mutually dependent tasks. Mechanization at this level was limited to no more than either transfer or conversion.

The cases of Level C described heavily mechanized sequences of conversion and transfer operations remotely controlled by the operators. At this level of the *machine line*, tasks were highly connected by work flow, functional dependence, and differentiation.

Automation described the characteristics of Level D, where tasks were dependent by way of signal flow and connectedness to an integrated process. The production process was to a large extent self-regulating and demanded active intervention only in its nonroutine components.

These four levels of technical conditions became sharply identified when we looked at the difference they made for the social organization of the behavior of workers. We asked whether a certain class of behavior was required by way of technical necessity, or permitted within the technological constraints. We applied this distinction to both cooperation and communication among workers while they were actually working.

We discovered that, generally, the behavioral characteristics at the level of Hauling (Level A) and Automation (Level D) were quite similar. At these levels, cooperation and communication were both required and permitted. In fact, permitted cooperation was incorporated in the technical requirements, thus making "voluntary" behavior "necessary." At both levels, permitted communication was continuous, and complete in the range of communicative means available. These were also the two levels at which there was technically necessary communication *and* it included verbal communication. Altogether, work at the technically undeveloped, almost preindustrial level *and* at the most advanced and perhaps postindustrial level (automation) appeared to permit the widest range of choices when it came to the integration of voluntary and necessary cooperative and communicative acts. It should be made clear that these conditions, by themselves, do not necessarily indicate greater chances for pleasure or commitment in work. The Hauling level of work is backbreaking and perhaps more open to control by a driving boss. Work at the Automation level is a potential source of worry and is subject to the unpredictable vagaries of a complex process. And yet, at both levels the regulation of the technical process is predicated by the nontechnical social process.

Between the labor of hauling and the jobs of skilled watchmen in automation lie the more centrally industrial, manufacturing operations with their varying degrees of mechanization of physical work. While nearly all the work at Level A was performed by men, and nearly all the work at Level D by machines, we found in-between a man-machine mixture, and in that sense incomplete states in technical advance. The result of this incompleteness was that workers performed partial operations as stopgaps, as it were, to an imperfect technical design. The characteristics of social behavior were correspondingly lacking in one aspect or other. At the Hand Work level (B), there was no required cooperation or communication; and at the Machine Line level (C), virtually no permitted cooperation or communication. At all levels except automation, confinement to work station meant no permitted cooperation, and thus we found a number of Hand Work cases with altogether no cooperative behavior. They were also uniformly limited in the range of communicative opportunities. Not surprisingly, perhaps, these conditions applied to all the cases one would readily identify as being monotonous and containing the most repetitive routines.

We have so far summarized the location of work places in the conjunction of a few gross dimensions: levels of technical conditions and the incidence of cooperation and communication as technical necessity or collective "choice" within technical bounds. The more specific structure of cooperative action, its association with influence relations, and the nature of communication need to be reexamined now.

The exercise of influence rests on the use of resources. In the circumstances of industrial production, the technical means of production constitute an important resource. Where there was no required cooperation, there was no use of technical resources in influence relations, as at the Hand Work level (B). At the level of Automation, necessary cooperation was sporadic and mediated by symbols of an inaccessible process, rather than by events in the process itself. Although the temporal dimensions of the workers' involvement in the process were not sharply defined, influence was irreversible in direction within any sequence of changes performed on the controls. At the Machine Line level (C), and the Hauling level (A) of technical conditions, the repeated distribution of work operations over time constituted a boundary to the expression of influence relations. At the Hauling level, within the bounds of an operation cycle, influence relations were reversible and the acts of required cooperation simultaneous. At the Machine Line level, cooperative acts occurred in sequence, and influence was irreversible.

When we think of interaction in voluntaristic groups, we pay attention to the content of verbal communication, that is, speech. In technically circumscribed behavior systems, however, what are the available communicative means, and how does access to different means vary with the technical circumstances? Workers, like everyone else, do not rely only on speech, but speech seems central to much ordinary interaction. Contacts among workers actually working often rest equally or more often on other media by which cues are transmitted. At the two extremes of our levels of technical conditions, required verbal communication was commonly coupled with one other dominant mode. At the Automation level, direct communication by words was observed together with the mediated communication through signals, that is, the sending of messages through technical transmitters. At the Hauling level, objects (work pieces, tools, equipment parts) constituted an important resource for communication, together with words. At the Hand Work level (B), there was no required communication, and the often proliferate permitted communication would be principally verbal. In sharp contrast, there was almost only required communication at the Machine Line level, and it seemed to preclude speech almost entirely. At this level, workers had to rely on signs (that is, characteristic movements of parts of the body directly perceived by the recipient), objects, and signals, in varying combinations and with different amounts of paucity.

It now remains to summarize the properties of technically permitted communication, the dimensions of the "informal social interaction" on which so much industrial sociology has rested in the past. In the analysis, we have been concerned with two elements: (1) the continuity and "completeness" of communicative opportunities, and (2) the structure of communication systems described by the relative closure of boundaries and restrictions on choice of participants. As there was virtually no permitted communication in the technical conditions of the Machine Line, we are now describing only three levels.

Permitted communication was continuous and complete at the extreme levels, Hauling and Automation. It was either intermittent or incomplete, or both, at the Hand Work level. Conversations were necessarily discontinuous when the demands of getting work done included changed attention requirements in the course of an operation cycle. They were incomplete to the extent that the technical environment reduced the number of commonly expected properties of conversational encounters: by preventing choice over the finishing of a joke, a story, or some other utterance; by reducing control over who was listening in; by cutting down literacy of expression when only shouting was possible; or by creating barriers to the joint use of gesture, facial expression, and speech. It was shown that the incidence of continuity and completeness was associated with combinations of distance and spatial mobility.

Within a conversation network, one may or may not have a choice of participants. Also, the boundaries of the network may be more or less confining. At the Hauling level of technical conditions, the boundaries were relatively closed: participants in conversations were most predominantly the members of a given work team. At the same time, a worker could choose whom to talk to and thus control the particular character of the conversational relationship. From the limited amount of information available for the level of Automation, it would be concluded that choice of partners was restricted. There were commonly other workers with whom a man was regularly linked through their joint relation to the production process, but to whom he could not address conversational expressions. For those with whom conversation was possible, the boundaries were relatively closed, containing a known small number of participants and limiting contact with "outsiders."

The structure of networks of permitted communication at the Hand Work level (B) was more variable and was weakly associated with both attention requirements and spatial mobility in three different ways. In two sets of cases the choice of conversation partners was restricted by proximity. The constraints in force were spatial confinement and surface attention requirements. These cases were further distinguishable by the boundaries of communication networks. An assembly-line technology commonly made for "floating" boundaries. As one moved up or down the line, the network had a successively different composition for each participant (or sometimes pair of participants), excluding one or two on one end and including one or two at the other end. In the remaining cases with spatial confinement and surface attention, boundaries were relatively closed, that is, including a set of participants common to all members and keeping communication with outsiders proportionately much lower. In a third set of cases at the Hand Work level, we found low or detailed attention requirements and spatial mobility. In these cases the choice of partners was unrestricted by proximity of fixed locations. The network boundaries were open: participants were as likely to talk with members of the immediate work group as with others.

We return now to the properties of industrial technology and examine several pieces of research which take off from technology as a central interest. A review of these studies will permit us to compare our measures of the technical conditions of work with others and to attempt to show where and to what extent they correspond. In the process, we will see what other dimensions of production organizations are associated with technology, and thus locate the present undertaking in the context of previous research of similar scope.

3. Production Process and Management Structure (Woodward)

In a study of one hundred industrial firms in Britain, Joan Woodward pursued the question: What kinds of management organization are conducive to the commercial success of a firm?[5] She argued that the objectives of a firm are expressed in its products and in the nature of the production process. Characteristics of the product and production process describe the technology of the firm. Control is the purpose of management organization, and it becomes apparent in the structure of authority relations. The findings suggested that certain forms of authority structure are more appropriate to particular technologies than to others. Appropriateness is defined by the central tendency in the distribution of cases. The median cases on a given dimension of authority structure are most appropriate in a distribution of cases for a particular level of technology. These are the cases most likely to display commercial success.

What is the meaning of *technology* employed in the study? Woodward suggested two levels at which the term can be used: "the 'tool' and the 'control' level."[6] To the extent that she was concerned with control through the authority structure, her dimensions of technology were located at the control level. Our usage rested on the distribution of performance components in man-machine relations, and thus lay at the tool level. In Woodward's study, control was the property which linked technology with authority relations.

---

[5] J. Woodward, *Management and Technology* (London: HMSO, 1958); J. Woodward, *Industrial Organization: Theory and Practice* (London: Oxford University Press, 1965).

[6] Woodward, *Industrial Organization*, p. 36.

Two empirical referents indicated levels of technology in Woodward's data, in sequence. First, the product was identified as either "integral" (ordinarily produced in manufacturing and measured enumeratively) or "dimensional" (made in process industries and measured by weight, capacity, or volume).[7] The size (or uniqueness) and continuity (or intermittency) of the production order were characterized by the terms "single unit," "small batch," "large batch," and "mass." In the analysis, we found a combination of these dimensions to three major categories: "unit and small batch production" and "large batch and mass production" for integral products, and "process production" for dimensional products.[8]

Having given an order to the data by this two-step classification device, Woodward imputed to the order two further properties: (1) sequence of development, and (2) increasing complexity. "Moving along the scale . . . it becomes increasingly possible to exercise control over manufacturing operations, the physical limitations of production becoming better known and understood."[9] If complexity becomes greater, why should it become easier to control the operations? The reported data showed a proportionately greater managerial and supervisory staff with advancing production technology, a declining ratio of direct workers to indirect workers, and a greater number of levels of authority.[10] Dubin argued that with advancing technology the necessary control over machines and *their* output became so critical that surveillance shifted from workers to management. In unit and small-batch production, much of the control was exercised by the worker.[11] Was Woodward suggesting that it is easier to control machines than workers, even if it takes an expanded management structure to do it?

In contrast, our data indicated that the workers' discretion, so far as it was determined by the technology of man-machine relations and their

---

[7] *Ibid.*, p. 38.

[8] *Ibid.*, p. 39.

[9] *Ibid.*, p. 40. The historical, developmental dimension was common to a number of analyses, including our own and Woodward's. Touraine's argument was historical, but was applied to concurrent characteristics observed in automobile manufacture. In its conception it rested on Marx's brilliant analysis of technical change in industry. Blauner ordered the four industries of his study in an over-all developmental sequence. Historical direction is implied even in terms like "advanced forms," in an otherwise non-historical classification of levels of mechanization by Bright, and "traditional methods," in Hammer's distinctions among types of machinery in European auto production. See A. Touraine, *L'Évolution du travail ouvrier aux Usines Renault* (Paris: Centre National de la Recherche Scientifique, 1955), p. 48; Karl Marx, *Das Kapital* (1867) (Berlin: Dietz, 1947), Vol. I, pp. 352–532; R. Blauner, *Alienation and Freedom: The Factory Worker and His Industry* (Chicago: University of Chicago Press, 1964), p. 8; J. R. Bright, *Automation and Management* (Boston: Harvard Business School, 1958), p. 41; M. Hammer, *Vergleichende Morphologie der Arbeit in der europäischen Automobilindustrie* (Tübingen: Mohr, 1959), p. 5.

[10] Woodward, *Industrial Organization*, pp. 52–59.

[11] Robert Dubin, "Supervision and Productivity," in Dubin *et al.*, *Leadership and Productivity* (San Francisco: Chandler Publishing Company, 1965), p. 15.

constraints, was greater at both extremes of the scale. Blauner proposed a similar curvilinear relation of work organization and its alienating effects. He also said that "the case of the continuous process industries . . . shows that automation increases the worker's control over his work process."[12] This apparent discrepancy in the interpretation of findings may have two sources. Let us first assume that the technological dimension is similar in these several studies, and look for possible reasons for the difference in outcomes. We can then ask how well the orderings of types of technology map into each other.

Both Woodward and Dubin were concerned with the managerial control structure, and Woodward particularly with control over the production process rather than the performance of workers. Blauner's and our study have focused on the conditions affecting workers' feelings and behavior, respectively. The link between these two concerns would seem to be the character of first-line supervision. We find in Woodward's report that first-line supervisors had authority over fewer workers at both extremes of the technological dimension than they had in mass production.[13] Dubin suggested that supervisors' activities became more directed to machines and paper work with advancing technology, and less to the supervision of people.[14]

The apparent differences in findings, then, may lie in the focus of the control exercised by workers, foremen, and management. Still assuming comparability in the technological dimensions of these inquiries, we can say that workers control the details of their work performance at the lower levels of technology, either individually or in teams. Tools or machines, if there are any, are simple and controlled by the worker. In the middle range of the technological scale, there is a man-machine mixture, and the performance of workers is extensively programed to machine demands. At the upper levels, workers monitor processes from which they are quite removed. Their performance is not controlled by the routine events in the process, and neither do they control the process extensively.

Let us assume the following control problems of foremen. At the lower levels of technology, their task would be the maintenance and coordination of the performances of workers and worker teams. At the middle levels, foremen would be heavily concerned with coordination between technical units and with the performance of machines. At the upper levels, a foreman would pay attention to product change-overs, emergencies, schedules, and quality control, that is, paper work and contacts with engineers and maintenance men.

The problems of workers and foremen are largely confined to their units

[12] Blauner, *Alienation and Freedom*, p. 182.
[13] Woodward, *Industrial Organization*, pp. 60–62.
[14] Dubin, "Supervision and Productivity," pp. 15, 24, 49.

of the production organization. Each of these units has specific technological characteristics and demands. Management's control problems lie in the coordination of these units and other nonproduction units in the technological context of the whole organization. Woodward indicated that managerial attention goes to development in unit production, to production itself in mass production, and to marketing in process production.[15]

It seems clear that constraints on workers' conduct are more severe and have primarily technical sources in the middle range of technology, that is, Woodward's mass-production systems; Blauner's machine-tending and assembly-line technologies of textiles and auto assembly; and our Machine Line level and parts of the Hand Work level. Because there is a substantial man-machine mixture at these levels, control of production performance is most tenuous. Workers are constrained by machine demands, but both machine performance and the fit of worker performance to machine requirements is imperfect, thus necessitating primary attention from foremen. There is also greater differentiation and interdependence of production units, demanding more coordinative attention from management.

We could, then, reconcile the variations in control: Workers, supervisors, and management each exercise control at varying points. These points coincide at the middle levels of technology, making for greatest pressure on workers and least independence. However, workers perform more autonomously at the lower levels, having control over the detailed technical process. At the upper levels, control over the production process is built into the integrated operation which is "merely" being watched by workers. Over the three sets of technological levels, the attention of higher-ups is directed to the product, the production operation, and the plant, respectively.[16] Workers are thus more independent at the low and high levels of technology, where supervisors and managers look elsewhere. The successively greater demands on management are related to the requirements of integrating increasingly more differentiated and interdependent production units.

Effects of technology are typically curvilinear at the "tool" and worker level, including the span of control of first-line supervisors reported by Woodward. At the "control" level, that is, the level of management structure, they are continuous. The consequences of technology for the nature of supervision lie perhaps in-between. However, here we find ourselves in a region of nearly complete ignorance, and the conjectures tried out on the preceding pages are just that.

This speculative attempt to reconcile findings was made on the assump-

---

[15] Woodward, *Management and Technology*, p. 25.
[16] Such a sequence, concerning the relations of supervisors and their men under changing technical circumstances, was described by J. H. Goldthorpe, "Technical Organization as a Factor in Supervisor-Worker Conflict: Some Preliminary Observations on a Study Made in the Mining Industry," *British Journal of Sociology*, 10 (1959), 213–230.

tion that the dimensions of technology are comparable. Having pointed to the difference between the tool and the control level of technology, it is important to ask now how well the different classifications of technology match. An inspection of our cases suggests the following joint listing of categories:

Man-Machine Relation (Meissner)		Product and Production Order (Woodward)
Type I	Handling	Large Batch
II	Hand Work	Mass/Small Batch
III	Machine Work	Mass/Small Batch
IV	Machine-Work Sequence	Mass
V	Assembly Line	Mass
VI	Hand and Machine Line	Large Batch
VII	Remote Controls	Large Batch
VIII	Automation	Process/Mass/Large Batch

Quite clearly the match is rather imperfect. The case studies used in our analysis contained no unit-production systems; both mass production and small-batch production could be found in two of our categories; and automation at the man-machine level of description did not necessarily coincide with continuous-process production. This indeterminacy in the relation between the two classifications points to other difficulties. Where, in Woodward's account, would an integrated steel plant fit? Production measurement in the steel industry is commonly "dimensional," that is, by the ton, and the production sequence is only continuous in short segments. Weaving, as Dubin pointed out, is continuous only over the short time span.[17] In relevant parts of our analysis it appeared that weaving shared other partial features of an automation technology.

Our comparison so far would suggest that no clear inferences can be drawn from these studies about the relations of management structure to workers' behavior systems in different technical environments. To begin with, attention will have to be paid to the technological constraints of supervisors' jobs, and a small beginning has been made.[18] The empirical and theoretical link between the dimensions of technology at the man-machine level and the organizational level would require investigation.

4. Industry and Alienation (Blauner)

Let us now turn to an inquiry which has attempted to account for variations in the alienation of factory workers and which rests on differ-

---

[17] Dubin, "Supervision and Productivity," p. 41.
[18] K. E. Thurley and A. C. Hamblin, *The Supervisor and His Job* (London: HMSO, 1963).

ences in technology for much of its explanatory value.[19] Blauner has conducted a secondary analysis of varied sources of information, including American government statistics on various industry characteristics, a few case-study reports, a 1947 Roper survey of worker satisfaction, and some inquiries of his own. The unit of concern was an industry, and Blauner selected four industries for close inspection: he argued that the printing, textile, automobile, and chemical industries were ordered in that sequence by degree of mechanization and by standardization of the work process.[20] However, no direct measures of these two dimensions were used. Instead, the analysis referred to three indicators of mechanization: (1) capital investment per production worker, (2) value added by manufacturing per production worker, and (3) proportion of maintenance costs of total payroll. These indicators were also given for the entire range of industries in separate tables.[21] The ranking of the four industries on these indicators was as follows:

	Capital Investment	Value Added	Maintenance Costs
Printing (craft)	3	3	4
Textiles (machine tending)	4	4	2
Automobile (assembly line)	2	2	3
Chemical (continuous process)	1	1	1

There is some indeterminacy in the technological ordering of industries. It is reflected in Blauner's comment that mechanization is quite high in the automobile industry as a whole, but less advanced than in textiles when it is compared with work on the auto-assembly line—his main focus of attention.

The ordering by standardization of the production process is similarly difficult. Constant changes in the mix of models, and variations in line speed, demand quite frequent redistributions of the job segments comprising auto assemblers' jobs. In comparison, the variety (low in any event) in the job of a loom attendant appears smaller when we consider that it consists almost entirely of discovering that a loom has stopped (in a group of looms), tying a broken thread, and restarting the loom.[22] Even in printing, standardization is high for at least one numerically quite large class of jobs. I have worked near a Linotype operator who spent a whole

---

[19] Blauner, *Alienation and Freedom.*

[20] *Ibid.,* pp. 7, 37, 58, 90, 95, 125.

[21] *Ibid.,* pp. 36, 95, 125, 191–192.

[22] C. R. Walker, R. H. Guest, and A. N. Turner, *The Foreman on the Assembly Line* (Cambridge: Harvard University Press, 1956), pp. 7–8, 68–72; A. K. Rice, "Productivity and Social Organization in an Indian Weaving Shed," *Human Relations,* 6 (1953), 297–329.

year producing the type for an edition of Shakespeare's works. His comment, that he immensely enjoyed the opportunity of "reading" his material, does not change the fact that his work was technically highly standardized.[23]

It is possible to show the relation between our and Blauner's classification of technology by locating those of our cases which belong or are very similar to Blauner's industries:

Industry (Blauner)	Man-Machine Relation (Meissner)	
Printing (craft)	Type II	Hand Work (hand compositors)
	III	Machine Work (Linotype, press)
Textiles (machine tending)	III	Machine Work
Automobile (assembly line)	V	Assembly Line
Chemicals (continuous process)	VIII	Automation

The case studies reanalyzed in our study were concerned predominantly with those kinds of work which were central to the production process. It is this fact which contributes to the consistency in the two orderings of categories. However, these case studies and other reports give clear support to Blauner's warning that "no industry has a completely homogeneous technology."[24] The difficulty in matching dimensions between different reports is not helped much by the proposition that "most industries have their characteristic forms of production" and that "the four compared in this [Blauner's] study have distinctive technological arrangements."[25]

The problem appears similar to that contained in the comparison with Woodward's classification. Our categories were at the level of man-machine relations in order to deal with variations in the behavior of workers. Woodward's dimensions described technical characteristics of production systems which accounted for variations in their organizational counterparts. Blauner described the technological arrangements of whole industries, but in order to account for the responses of individual workers to their work.

If the relation is one between "characteristic" forms of technology and "characteristic" responses of workers, there is no problem. A correspondence between the apparently similar dimensions applied in other studies

---

[23] For a description of the Linotype operator's job, see Blauner, *Alienation and Freedom*, p. 41. According to his figures, more than 23 per cent of the printing craftsmen in the United States in 1958 were Linotype operators.

[24] *Ibid.*, p. 7. (See also Touraine, *L'Évolution du travail ouvrier aux Usines Renault*, p. 49, a study to which Blauner refers in this context, and others cited in Chapter II of the present report.)

[25] *Ibid.*

and the "characteristic" components of Blauner's account cannot be established because there are no assignment rules. If the relation should bring together properties of the larger unit (industry) with distributions of the properties of component elements (worker responses), we have an equivalent to the "ecological fallacy." Such would be the case if one attempted to associate, for instance, "capital investment per production worker," as an indicator of level of mechanization, and "proportion of factory workers who feel their jobs make them work too fast," as an indicator of alienation as a feeling of powerlessness to control one's work pace.[26]

These problems were inherent in our analysis on a smaller scale. The unit of description was the collection of workers and their work stations that happened to have been of interest in the original case study. When the technical characteristics of a case were clearly heterogeneous, the unit was divided accordingly. This procedure still left a residue of cases where the properties of the "dominant" or "most central" components were assigned to the whole case. The same was true of workers' relations, and these were in some cases obtained from distributions of individual behaviors. Yet, if these problems were found with relatively small units, they must be more severe with a unit as inclusive as an industry.

In comparison to our analysis, an interesting assignment of meanings could be found in Blauner's work when it came to identifying the conditions and characteristics of "alienation." We have been concerned here with spatial and temporal constraints as contingencies through which man-machine relations took their effect on social behavior. For Blauner, control over work pace (or freedom to control the quantity of production) and freedom of physical movement became elements of powerlessness, which in turn was a dimension of alienation.[27] One can easily recognize that these are the same sets of characteristics: variation and variability in spatial mobility and work pace. A difficulty arises from a fundamental difference in the meaning of alienation in Blauner's two major sources, Marx and Seeman—a difference recognized by both Seeman and Blauner.[28] Marx was interested only in "objective conditions," and these are exemplified in industry by technically determined pace and mobility. Seeman's concern was limited to the feelings of individuals, and these found reference in Blauner's analysis when he used work-satisfaction questions from an opinion poll. Work pace as measured by an observer and a worker's expression that his job makes him work too fast are two different things. Neither of them is a strong measure of the feeling of powerlessness.

---

[26] *Ibid.*, pp. 191 and 200 (Tables 18 and 33). The main industry characteristics are for 1954, 1956, and 1958, while worker responses were obtained in a Roper poll of 1947.

[27] *Ibid.*, pp. 20–21.

[28] M. Seeman, "On the Meaning of Alienation," *American Sociological Review*, 24 (1959), 784; Blauner, *Alienation and Freedom*, pp. 1 and 31.

Let us consider the responses to two questions from the Roper survey used by Blauner. Among the four industries compared by Blauner, printing contained the highest proportion of workers who felt their jobs were not essential, and the lowest proportion who said their jobs made them work too fast, and who said they could not leave their jobs for 30 minutes without replacement. Printers' tasks were presumably those least connected by work flow or direct functional dependence, and that characteristic may account for both sets of responses. A job that is technically connected with others is more likely to be machine-paced or spatially confined, or both. Technical connection is also a more likely condition for feeling that the job is essential. Unfortunately, the remaining data do not fit these expectations or, for that matter, the direction of Blauner's argument. The proportions of both auto and chemical workers who said they could not leave their work for 30 minutes without replacement, and who did not feel that their jobs were essential, were nearly the same. However, their technical environments were markedly different.

We have attempted to show that the gross dimensions of technical work conditions seemed to order data similarly and that similarities in effect were crudely visible. Closer fits could not be demonstrated because classification criteria were not sufficiently comparable and because the assumptions on which classifications seemed to rest were not explicit. One might expect that a system of relations of man-machine levels, technical constraints, and worker behavior would be associated with a system of relations of the technical and organizational properties of the plants of an industry and the attitudinal responses of its workers. Such demonstration would require discarding the uniqueness of a few industries in favor of generalized relations among properties relevant to workers' responses. In this context, Blauner's elements of "meaninglessness" (another dimension of alienation) suggest a possible source. Blauner listed the uniqueness and scope of the product and the span of responsibility for the production process. These were characteristics discoverable in Woodward's study.

5. Task Attributes and Satisfaction (Turner and Lawrence)

Another study, concerned with the technical features of industrial jobs and the dispositions of their holders, has been reported by Turner and Lawrence.[29] The job characteristic of interest to them was "complexity." They argued that the greater the complexity of jobs, the better the attendance records and job satisfaction of workers. It seems, however, that complexity was an afterthought (put into quotation marks and mentioned only a few times) to something called "Requisite Task Attributes." A complex index was constructed by combining 18 scored observations into

---

[29] A. N. Turner and P. R. Lawrence, *Industrial Jobs and the Worker: An Investigation of Response to Task Attributes* (Boston: Harvard Business School, 1965).

several more inclusive categories which were then entered into the over-all index after differential weighting. The index contained three major elements divided into prescribed and discretionary components: activity (variety and autonomy), interaction (required and optional), and mental states (time to learn the job and responsibility). Prescribed and discretionary interaction were combined in the analysis. Under variety and autonomy, we found such (by now familiar) dimensions as work pace and choice of work location.[30]

In addition, a number of "Associated Task Attributes" were identified which were not regarded as requisite for job performance but still closely associated with the nature of the job. These included pay and physical working conditions, several elements of identifiability of task and product, cycle time, capital investment per worker, and level of mechanization. The ranking of jobs by mechanization was "guided" by the detailed classification of Bright, who distinguished variations in source of power and control, and type of machine response.[31]

The data for Requisite and Associated Task Attributes were obtained by making a half-hour observation of each of 47 jobs and by spending another half hour in getting additional information from supervisors, in 11 companies. By assignment rules not mentioned in the report, the attributes of the 47 jobs were then apparently assigned to 470 workers who had answered a questionnaire with questions on satisfaction, task perception, and a host of other items borrowed from a variety of attitude surveys.[32]

Turner and Lawrence argued that their task attributes were to a large extent technologically determined.[33] Yet, the rank correlation of level of mechanization and the Requisite Task Index was weak and negative (−.13). We saw previously that Blauner referred to capital investment per worker as an indicator of mechanization, and Turner and Lawrence showed a similarly inconclusive association (−.27). Another indicator of interest to Blauner, namely, "value added" per worker in production, was confounded with capital investment by Turner and Lawrence when they vaguely included both in one of the Associated Task Attribute measures of "task identity."[34]

Turner and Lawrence's classification by level of mechanization seemed to be similar to the one applied in our analysis. As amplified by certain technical constraints, these levels were shown in our report to be associated with differences in the distribution of required and discretionary interaction. The latter were salient components of Turner and Lawrence's Task Attribute Index. Why, then, was there no apparent relation in their case between mechanization and task attributes?

---

[30] *Ibid.*, pp. 20–26.
[31] *Ibid.*, pp. 24–27; Bright, *Automation and Management*, pp. 41–46.
[32] Turner and Lawrence, *Industrial Jobs and the Worker*, pp. 9, 133–147, 149.
[33] *Ibid.*, pp. 2, 49.
[34] *Ibid.*, pp. 157, 168.

The answer lay predominantly in Turner and Lawrence's construction of a summative index. Of the large number of ordinal measures contained in the index, some have been shown in our description to vary independently with certain technical conditions. The important example is social interaction. We have demonstrated that required and "optional" interaction occur in conjunction at some technological levels, and separately at others. By feeding observation scores of the dimensions of interaction into their composite index, Turner and Lawrence treated these as mutually substitutable and additive. There is good reason to believe that they are neither. In addition, it appears that their scoring recognized only verbal communication as interaction.[35] The relation of amount of verbal communication with levels of mechanization is curvilinear; that is, one would expect more talking at either end of the mechanization scale. The same is probably true for some other elements of their index—job-learning time, for instance. These relations would account for the *low* rank correlation reported by Turner and Lawrence.

Control over work pace is part of the classification by levels of mechanization, in the sense that Bright spoke of the source of initiating control, and the same applies to other measures of variety and autonomy used. The more such control a worker has, the higher the score becomes on the Requisite Task Index, and the lower the score for mechanization. This inverse relation of the same component in two different measures would account for the *negative* rank correlation between mechanization and task attributes.

The preceding review suggests that the construction of a complex index hid determinate relations between index components and their relations with other dimensions. Many of the specific characteristics identified by Turner and Lawrence have obvious similarity with those dealt with in other studies. Several of these have already been mentioned. Span of responsibility for the production process was an element of alienation ("meaninglessness") for Blauner. Several elements of responsibility (for example, time span of discretion) were parts of Turner and Lawrence's technologically determined task attributes. In the same context, Blauner listed uniqueness and scope of product, while Turner and Lawrence located similar properties as parts of "task identity" in their Associated Task Attributes. Uniqueness of product was also a part of Woodward's classification of the technology of production processes. Complexity was a property assigned to technological dimensions by Woodward and by Turner and Lawrence.

Considering the characteristics of the Task Attribute Index, it is perhaps not surprising that Turner and Lawrence did not find the index associated with expressions of job satisfaction. A questionnaire-derived index of Per-

---

[35] Interaction and interdependence were also not differentiated: *ibid.*, p. 22.

ceived Task characteristics was associated with the Requisite Task Index. Attendance was associated with the Requisite Task Index but not with the Perceived Task Index.[36] No reason was given why one should expect "complexity," or a composite of many varied task characteristics, to make a difference for either attendance or job satisfaction. There are a number of more promising possibilities (suggested both by our and Blauner's studies) for an analysis of the internal relations among many of the dimensions identified by Turner and Lawrence.

6. Task Relations and Grievance Action (Sayles)

Unlike our study and the research by Woodward, Blauner, and Turner and Lawrence, a study by Sayles did not employ an over-all scale of technology or mechanization. Yet Sayles' report began with the following specification: "The technology and organization of the plant are the architects of the work group, constructing with the materials of human interaction a variety of types of groups."[37] Sayles referred to several technical characteristics which have been recognized in this review and in the preceding analysis: task differentiation, work flow and dependence, machine pacing, and required interaction. The incidence of these characteristics was used, albeit inconsistently, to account for differences in the strategies of worker groups in management-worker relations in the production plant. The analysis proceeded backward, as it were, from the classification of work-group strategies to the description of the technical and organizational properties which may account for different types of strategy. Four types of groups were called apathetic, erratic, strategic, and conservative, to indicate the amount, consistency, concertedness, and intensity of protest activities. Distinguishing between relatively high and low concerted activity, a number of relations with technical constraints were indicated.

According to Sayles, a relatively lower level of concerted activity in the grievance process was associated with the following conditions: (1) interdependence of tasks in a work flow; (2) high task differentiation, identified in work groups with few identical tasks, or spatial separation of workers with similar tasks; and (3) predominantly machine-paced jobs. In addition, groups were distinguished by performing work individually, in crews, and on short or long assembly lines. Crews with differentiated tasks and workers on long assembly lines were apathetic. Workers with similar tasks in crews or on short assembly lines were erratic. Individual, technically independent operations were also characteristic of apathetic groups, *and* of strategic and conservative groups.[38]

---

[36] *Ibid.*, pp. 36–43, 50–51, 56–57.
[37] L. R. Sayles, *Behavior of Industrial Work Groups* (New York: Wiley, 1958), p. 3.
[38] *Ibid.*, pp. 69–72.

For the 300 cases from 30 plants on which Sayles' analysis relied, no actual distribution of cases by the various characteristics was provided. Most of the data were obtained from metal-processing operations, and one-third alone from the automobile industry. In the analysis, some technical characteristics were indicated only for some groups and not for others. Without data distributions, a limited range of industries, and inconsistent use of descriptive dimensions, it is not possible to seek correspondence with the findings of other studies. However, we can examine certain apparently similar characteristics and their analytical uses.

Interdependence, for Sayles, was found in the flow of work (and is interdependence of workers rather than tasks).[39] Also, interdependence meant interaction. "By definition, jobs in crews and assembly lines require constant interaction." These are then immediately referred to as "interdependent work situations."[40] Our previous analysis would suggest that it is useful to regard the three dimensions—work flow, dependence of tasks, and interaction—as independent in order to recognize the conditions for their coincidence. By what "definition" work on assembly lines required constant interaction is not clear. By observation, assembly lines do *not* require interaction for many workers. Sayles cited two studies in which such observations were reported.[41] The crews to which Sayles referred were presumably the simultaneously cooperative teams of our description. They were characterized by interdependence of tasks and relatively high interaction, but no work-flow connection of tasks.

The constraints of work flow and of dependence and differentiation of tasks were indeed dimensions on which much of our analysis relied, and they appeared in certain combinations at different levels of technology. Variations in interaction (cooperation, influence, and communication) were accounted for by the conjunction of levels of man-machine relations and technical constraints. Sayles' study has made the fascinating promise of explaining differences in trade-union action at the plant level by reference to the sociotechnical organization of production. Perhaps the promise could be fulfilled when the arguments generated in this report are linked with the dimensions of protest strategies offered by Sayles.

7. The Organization of Production: Technical and Social

This report and the studies just reviewed constitute the entire complement of empirical work which is comparative and deals with a relatively

---

[39] *Ibid.*, pp. 71, 93.

[40] *Ibid.*, p. 76.

[41] Walker and Guest, *The Man on the Assembly Line*, p. 79: "The largest number of men, including most of those on the main conveyor line, were related to each other through proximity and not through interdependent function." A. Zaleznik, *Worker Satisfaction and Development* (Boston: Harvard Business School, 1956), p. 120: ". . . on this mechanized assembly line . . . the job required absolutely no interaction between workers."

full range of technological variation in industry.[42] Together with most of the supporting case studies, all of this work has been done within the past ten or fifteen years. It constitutes a collective renewal of an earlier interest in the central role of the means of production, most clearly expressed in the work of Karl Marx and Max Weber. However, the more recent work differs from the earlier confinement to the objective conditions of technical and organizational structure. Modern research has incorporated dimensions brought to the fore in the intervening period: When people come together in order to get work done, they respond to the constraints of technology and organization, so it was recognized, in behavior, evaluations, and dispositions.

At the beginning of this study, two apparently divergent approaches to social research in industry were pointed out: one focusing on interaction and evaluation in groups of workers; the other, on the technical organization of tasks and their composition. The bulk of this study has been an attempt to demonstrate the usefulness of combining the specific interests of these approaches. Casting more widely, the several studies in the field now suggest a convergence in the direction of inquiry, although not in theoretical integration beyond the taxonomic level.

What conclusions can be drawn? The authors of many reports have yielded to the temptation of giving advice to the participants on the industrial scene, and particularly to managers, from interpretations of their findings. Both the power and the precision of the research accounts are so low that it would be better advice not to listen—yet. What kind of action could be taken from the better understanding of the character of industrial work provided by research? Let us take as an example the claim that many kinds of industrial work are meaningless for workers. Insofar as a technical system can be said to reveal a rational design, as we have assumed, it does not make sense to regard it as meaningless if in fact workers are capable of fitting their performance to its demands. Its meaning may be miserable, but the situation is quite clearly defined. The argument, well demonstrated in this report, may then be made that some forms of technical design restrict the opportunities for expressive behavior. If work can be meaningful only when full expression is possible, the technically more constrained forms of work are meaningless. The conclusion has been drawn, by the researchers of the Tavistock Institute for instance, that work may be made more meaningful either by changing the task distribution or by offering opportunities for participation in production decisions.[43] In either case, the

---

[42] Nonindustrial production is treated in S. H. Udy, *Organization of Work: A Comparative Analysis of Production Among Non-Industrial Peoples* (New Haven: HRAF Press, 1959).

[43] E. Jaques, *The Changing Culture of a Factory* (London: Tavistock Publications, 1951); A. K. Rice, *Productivity and Social Organization, the Ahmedabad Experiment* (London: Tavistock Publications, 1958); E. L. Trist *et al., Organizational Choice* (London: Tavistock Publications, 1963).

assumption seems to have been made that the zest of expressive behavior in primary groups can be put to the use of better attainment of organizational ends. Yet, a reading of the accounts of the Hawthorne studies or of Donald Roy's clicking room suggests that the expressive conduct of these primary groups is an end in itself, a respite from the instrumental demands of production. Attempts to give organizational direction to expressive conduct, rather than putting exuberance to good uses, would likely mean the end of exuberance.

Our research has indicated that behavior is most constrained when technical design is "incomplete," in the sense that human performance is a partial stopgap in the man-machine mixture. An example is the piercer plugger in an extensively automated tubing mill, who must regularly lift hot and heavy plugs between piercer rolls and water trough,[44] at a rate more relentless than in a technically less advanced operation. Under such circumstances, the effects of the devices of "human relations" appear trivial in comparison to those of further technological change. As Blauner has attentively observed, it is at the automation level of technology that workers can heat a can of soup on the job.

Over a decade ago, Robert Dubin had argued that work was a "necessary" and not a "voluntary" form of action—"that the worker behaves as he does while performing his work because of the technologies with which he works."[45] He discovered, indeed, that large proportions of workers respond to their work with affective indifference.[46] For men who thus "only work for a living," the can of soup on the job is not a trivial matter.

In order to make improvements in industrial life, it would seem more important to work on the sources of technical necessity, rather than on the better adaptation of workers to circumstances which allow them little choice. For workers this means having a say-so, not so much in how to cope with necessity, but in how to modify it in the design and change of production processes.

We have here described the empirical meaning of technical necessity and its relation to the balance between necessary and voluntary behavior, between choice and constraint, in the organization of production. Such information can be used and abused: A photo-finishing plant was described to me recently in which machinery and layout were deliberately designed to limit contacts between operators, because talking was thought to be bad for production.

---

[44] C. R. Walker, *Toward the Automatic Factory* (New Haven: Yale University Press, 1957), p. 14.

[45] R. Dubin, "Industrial Research and the Discipline of Sociology," *Proceedings of the 11th Annual Meeting, Industrial Relations Research Association*, 1958, p. 153.

[46] R. Dubin, "Industrial Workers' Worlds: A Study of the Central Life Interests of Industrial Workers," *Social Problems*, 3 (1956), 131–142.

APPENDIX: Data Sources by Case Number

CASE 1—STEEL-PLANT MAINTENANCE
(Walker 1922) Walker, C. R. *Steel: The Diary of a Furnace Worker.* Boston: Atlantic Monthly Press, 1922.

CASE 2—DEPARTMENT STORE (case omitted)
(Bradney) Bradney, P. "The Joking Relationship in Industry," *Human Relations,* 10 (1957), 179–187.

CASE 3—SMELTING
(Popitz 1957a) Popitz, H., H. P. Bahrdt, E. A. Jüres, and H. Kesting. *Technik und Industriearbeit: Soziologische Untersuchungen in der Hüttenindustrie.* Tübingen: Mohr, 1957.

CASE 4—DOCKS
(Liverpool) Liverpool University Department of Social Science. *The Dock Worker: An Analysis of Conditions of Employment in the Port of Manchester.* Liverpool, England: Liverpool University Press, 1954.

CASE 5—BLAST-FURNACE BATCHING I
(Popitz 1957a) See Case 3.
(Popitz 1957b) Popitz, H., H. P. Bahrdt, E. A. Jüres, and H. Kesting. *Das Gesellschaftsbild des Arbeiters: Soziologische Untersuchungen in der Hüttenindustrie.* Tübingen: Mohr, 1957.

CASE 6—BLAST-FURNACE FEEDING I
(Popitz 1957a) See Case 3.
(Popitz 1957b) See Case 5.

CASE 7—BLAST-FURNACE BATCHING AND FEEDING II
(Popitz 1957a) See Case 3.
(Popitz 1957b) See Case 5.

CASE 8—BRIDGE CRANE
(Popitz 1957a) See Case 3.
(Popitz 1957b) See Case 5.

CASE 9—COKING BATTERY
(Popitz 1957a) See Case 3.

CASE 10—COAL MINING I
(Dennis) Dennis, N., F. Henriques, and C. Slaughter. *Coal Is Our Life: An*

257

Analysis of a Yorkshire Mining Community. London: Eyre and Spottıs-woode, 1956.

(Goldthorpe) Goldthorpe, J. H. "Technical Organization as a Factor in Supervisor-Worker Conflict: Some Preliminary Observations on a Study Made in the Mining Industry," *British Journal of Sociology,* 10 (1959), 213–230.

(Jantke) Jantke, C. *Bergmann und Zeche: Die Sozialen Arbeitsverhältnisse einer Schachtanlage des nördlichen Ruhrgebietes in der Sicht der Bergleute.* Tübingen: Mohr, 1953.

(Trist) Trist, E. L., and K. W. Bamforth. "Some Social and Psychological Consequences of the Longwall Method of Coal-Getting: An Examination of the Psychological Situation and Defenses of a Work Group in Relation to the Social Structure and Technological Content of the Work System," *Human Relations,* 4 (1951), 3–38.

CASE 11—COAL MINING II
(Dennis) (Goldthorpe) (Jantke) (Trist) See Case 10.

CASE 12—COAL MINING III (case omitted)
(Goldthorpe) See Case 10.

CASE 13—RELAY ASSEMBLY
(Whitehead) Whitehead, T. N. *The Industrial Worker: A Statistical Study of Human Relations in a Group of Manual Workers.* 2 vols. Cambridge: Harvard University Press, 1938.

CASE 14—BANK WIRING
(Roethlisberger) Roethlisberger, F. J., and W. J. Dickson. *Management and the Worker.* Cambridge: Harvard University Press, 1939.

CASE 15—EQUIPMENT-ASSEMBLY SHOP
(Zaleznik 1958) Zaleznik, A., C. R. Christensen, and F. J. Roethlisberger. *The Motivation, Productivity, and Satisfaction of Workers: A Prediction Study.* Boston: Division of Research, Graduate School of Business Administration, Harvard University, 1958.

CASE 16—MACHINE SHOP
(Zaleznik 1958) See Case 15.

CASE 17—MACHINE SHOP
(Zaleznik 1956) Zaleznik, A. *Worker Satisfaction and Development: A Case Study of Work and Social Behavior in a Factory Group.* Boston: Division of Research, Graduate School of Business Administration, Harvard University, 1956.

CASE 18—CLICKING ROOM
(Roy) Roy, D. F. " 'Banana Time': Job Satisfaction and Informal Interaction," *Human Organization,* 18, No. 4 (Winter 1959–1960), 159–168.

CASE 19—SHOE BOTTOMING
(Horsfall) Horsfall, A. B., and C. M. Arensberg. "Teamwork and Productivity in a Shoe Factory," *Human Organization,* 8, No. 1 (Winter 1949), 13–25.

CASE 20—WEAVING
(Rice 1953) Rice, A. K. "Productivity and Social Organization in an Indian

Weaving Shed: An Examination of Some Aspects of the Socio-Technical System of an Experimental Automatic Loom Shed," *Human Relations,* 6 (1953), 297–329.

(Rice 1955a) Rice, A. K. "The Experimental Reorganization of Non-Automatic Weaving in an Indian Mill: A Further Study of Productivity and Social Organization," *Human Relations,* 8 (1955), 199–249.

(Rice 1955b) Rice, A. K. "Productivity and Social Organization in an Indian Weaving Mill II: A Follow-Up Study of an Experimental Reorganization of Automatic Weaving," *Human Relations,* 8 (1955), 399–428.

(Rice 1958) Rice, A. K. *Productivity and Social Organization, the Ahmedabad Experiment: Technical Innovation, Work Organization and Management.* London: Tavistock Publications, 1958.

(Nash) Nash, M. *Machine Age Maya: The Industrialization of a Guatemalan Community.* Glencoe, Ill.: Free Press, 1958.

CASE 21—AUTO ASSEMBLY I
(Walker 1952) Walker, C. R., and R. H. Guest. *The Man on the Assembly Line.* Cambridge: Harvard University Press, 1952.

CASE 22—AUTO ASSEMBLY II
(Guest) Guest, R. H. "Men and Machines: An Assembly-Line Worker Looks at His Job," *Personnel,* 31 (1954–1955), 496–503.

(Jasinski) Jasinski, F. J. "Technological Delimitation of Reciprocal Relationships: A Study of Interaction Patterns in Industry," *Human Organization,* 15, No. 2 (Summer 1956), 24–28.

(Walker 1952) See Case 21.

(Walker 1956) Walker, C. R., R. H. Guest, and A. N. Turner. *The Foreman on the Assembly Line.* Cambridge: Harvard University Press, 1956.

CASE 23—CANDY WRAPPING
(Wyatt) Wyatt, S., and H. N. Langdon. *The Machine and the Worker: A Study of Machine Feeding Processes.* Great Britain Medical Research Council, Industrial Health Research Board, Report No. 82. London: HMSO, 1938.

CASE 24—EQUIPMENT-ASSEMBLY LINE
(Zaleznik 1951) Zaleznik, A. *Foreman Training in a Growing Enterprise.* Boston: Division of Research, Graduate School of Business Administration, Harvard University, 1951.

CASE 25—GARMENT LINE
(Treinen) Treinen, H. "Eine Arbeitsgruppe am Fliessband: Sozialstruktur und Formen der Beaufsichtigung," *Kölner Zeitschrift für Soziologie und Sozialpsychologie,* 8 (1956), 73–83.

CASE 26—WIRE ROLLING
(Popitz 1957a) See Case 3.
(Popitz 1957b) See Case 5.

CASE 27—BLOOM ROLLING
(Popitz 1957a) See Case 3.
(Popitz 1957b) See Case 5.

CASE 28—TUBE ROLLING I
(Walker 1950) Walker, C. R. *Steeltown: An Industrial Case History of the Conflict Between Progress and Security.* New York: Harper, 1950.

CASE 29—TUBE ROLLING II
(Walker 1957) Walker, C. R. *Toward the Automatic Factory: A Case Study of Men and Machines.* New Haven: Yale University Press, 1957.

CASE 30—TUBE ROLLING (case omitted)
(Stieber) Stieber, H. W. "Interaktionen: Ausdruck der sozialen Organisation einer Arbeitsgruppe," *Kölner Zeitschrift für Soziologie und Sozialpsychologie,* 8 (1956), 83–89.

CASE 31—AUTO ENGINES
(Faunce) Faunce, W. A. *Automation in the Automobile Industry: Some Consequences for In-Plant and Union-Management Relationships.* Microfilmed Ph.D. dissertation. Detroit: Wayne State University, 1957.

CASE 32—SOAKING PIT
(Popitz 1957b) See Case 5.

CASE 33—BLAST-FURNACE AIR CONTROL
(Popitz 1957a) See Case 3.

CASE 34—PETROLEUM REFINERY
(Whyte) Whyte, W. F. "Engineers and Workers: A Case Study," *Human Organization,* 14, No. 4 (Winter 1956), 3–12.

CASE 35—POWER PLANT
(Mann 1956) Mann, F. C., and L. R. Hoffman. "Individual and Organizational Correlates of Automation," *Journal of Social Issues,* 12, No. 2 (1956), 7–17.
(Mann 1960) Mann, F. C., and L. R. Hoffman. *Automation and the Worker: A Study of Social Change in Power Plants.* New York: Holt, 1960.

INDEX